Biology and Classification of
DWARF MISTLETOES (*Arceuthobium*)

by

Frank G. Hawksworth

Rocky Mountain Forest and Range Experiment Station
Fort Collins, Colorado

and

Delbert Wiens

Department of Biology
University of Utah
Salt Lake City, Utah

Agriculture Handbook No. 401

Library of Congress Catalog Card Number 72-609841

Forest Service
United States Department of Agriculture

February 1972

Washington, D.C.

CONTENTS

DEDICATION

This work is dedicated to the memory of Dr. Lake S. Gill (1900–1969), Forest Pathologist with the U.S. Department of Agriculture from 1923 to 1960. Dr. Gill's classic paper *"Arceuthobium* in the United States" (1935) was the first comprehensive treatment of the North American dwarf mistletoes, and since its appearance has been the authoritative publication on the genus.

Through his continued research and missionary zeal, Dr. Gill, more than any other man, was responsible for the present awareness of *Arceuthobium* as economically important forest pathogens. He demonstrated that dwarf mistletoes were not merely curiosities, but caused significant mortality and reduction of growth rates in western conifers.

Dr. Gill followed our work with interest and encouraged our efforts. We discussed many aspects of the study with him, but his death on July 5, 1969 precluded his seeing the final manuscript. His enthusiasm and interest was a constant source of encouragement for those with whom he worked.

ACKNOWLEDGMENTS

We want to thank the curators of the many herbaria in North America and Europe who allowed us to examine dwarf mistletoe specimens; and the many colleagues who have collected the specimens, reviewed the manuscript, supplied photographs or drawings, assisted with numerical analyses and chromatographic work, and performed innumerable other courtesies.

Canada

Joe A. Baranyay
Jan M. Bonga
Job Kuijt
Michael J. Larsen
John G. Laut
John A. Muir
Richard B. Smith

Honduras

Robert Armour
Antonio Molina R.

Mexico

Rudolfo Salinas Quinard
José de Jesus Valdivia Sanchez
Francisco Muños Sandoval

Netherlands

John Gremmen

United States

John W. Andresen
  Southern Illinois University
Lyman Benson
  Pomona College
Charles M. Drew
  U. S. Navy, China Lake, Calif.
George F. Estabrook
  University of Colorado
Ari Ferro
  University of Utah
Henry S. Fleming
  University of Colorado
David W. French
  University of Minnesota
Robert L. Gilbertson
  University of Arizona
Sharon Harris
  University of Utah
John H. Hart
  Michigan State University
Hugh H. Iltis
  University of Wisconsin

Lee W. Lenz
  Rancho Santa Ana Botanic Garden
Estella B. Leopold
  U. S. Geological Survey, Denver
C. V. Morton
  U. S. National Museum
J. R. Parmenter, Jr.
  University of California
David J. Rogers
  University of Colorado
Lewis F. Roth
  Oregon State University
Richard Snyder
  University of Utah
Frank H. Tainter
  University of Minnesota
R. K. Vickery, Jr.
  University of Utah
Edward G. Voss
  University of Michigan
William A. Weber
  University of Colorado

Personnel of The U.S. Department of Agriculture—Forest Service

Gerald W. Anderson
Ralph L. Anderson
Stuart R. Andrews
Wilmer F. Bailey
Donald H. Brown
T. W. Childs
Oscar Dooling

David A. Graham
Donald P. Graham
Thomas E. Hinds
Bohun B. Kinloch
Donald M. Knutson
Richard G. Krebill
Thomas H. Laurent

Paul C. Lightle
Elbert L. Little, Jr.
Douglas R. Miller
Roger S. Peterson
Robert F. Scharpf
Keith R. Shea

James L. Stewart
John H. Thompson
Harvey V. Toko
Willis W. Wagener
Melvyn J. Weiss
Ed F. Wicker

ABSTRACT

Arceuthobium (dwarf mistletoes), a distinctive genus of the family Viscaceae, is parasitic on conifers of the Pinaceae in the Old and New Worlds and on Cupressaceae in the Old World. Although conifer forests in many parts of the Northern Hemisphere are infected with dwarf mistletoes, those most seriously damaged are in North America.

In this taxonomic revision, the 32 recognized taxa comprise 28 species, 5 subspecies, and 2 *formae speciales*. Four taxa are known in the Old World; 28 in the New. In North America, *Arceuthobium* ranges from central Canada and southeastern Alaska to Honduras and Hispaniola, but most species are found in western United States and Mexico. Only *A. pusillum*, a parasite of *Picea*, occurs in eastern North America.

Taxonomic characteristics presented for each of the 32 taxa include: morphology and color of shoots, fruits, and flowers; pollen features; phenology of flowering and seed dispersal; hosts and host reactions; chromosomal features; and chromatography of shoot pigments.

The classification system is based on extensive field studies of all known New World dwarf mistletoes in their natural state, examination of specimens at the major herbaria in North America and Europe, and computer analyses of all taxonomic data collected.

The system, the first below-genus classification of *Arceuthobium*, divides the genus into subgenera *Arceuthobium* and *Vaginata*. Subgenus *Arceuthobium* comprises all four Old World species (*A. chinense*, *A. minutissimum*, *A. oxycedri*, and *A. pini*), and three New World species, but is not formally subdivided into sections. Subgenus *Vaginata*, exclusively New World, contains three sections: *Vaginata*, 6 taxa; *Campylopoda*, 17 taxa; and *Minuta*, 2 taxa. Section *Campylopoda* contains three series: *Rubra*, 3 taxa; *Campylopoda*, 13 taxa; and *Stricta*, 1 taxon. Identification keys, artificial and natural, are provided.

The detailed botanical description of each dwarf mistletoe includes its distinctive taxonomic features, hosts, a colored photograph, and a map of its geographic distribution.

Biology and Classification of Dwarf Mistletoes (*Arceuthobium*)

by Frank G. Hawksworth[1] and Delbert Wiens[2]

INTRODUCTION

The dwarf mistletoes (*Arceuthobium*) are a highly specialized and clearly defined genus of aerial dicotyledonous parasites that occur on Pinaceae or Cupressaceae. These mistletoes are small, leafless, glabrous, and are characterized by a number of unusual features: explosive, bicolored fruits; ringlike archesporium; chlorophyllous endosperm; germinating radicle that contains stomata; and stems that have no central vascular cylinder or sieve tube elements.

Arceuthobium has been classically included in the subfamily Viscoideae of the Loranthaceae. Tieghem (1895) considered *Arceuthobium* so distinct from related genera that he proposed its classification as a separate family placed between the Viscaceae and the Santalaceae; his proposal has never been followed. Dixit (1962) and Barlow (1964) suggest that the subfamilies Loranthoideae and Viscoideae warrant family status. The two families differ in many features of floral morphology, floral anatomy and embryology. Previously supposed similarities between the two groups are apparently the result of convergence rather than common phyletic origin. We accept full family status for the two groups as formally proposed by Barlow (1964) and retained by Thorne (1968). This treatment places *Arceuthobium* in the Viscaceae.

Engler and Krause (1935) classified *Arceuthobium* as a monogeneric tribe in the Viscoideae. They placed *Dendrophthora*, *Phoradendron*, and *Korthalsella* in the tribe *Phoradendreae*; with *Korthalsella* in subtribe *Korthalsellinae*, and *Dendrophthora* and *Phoradendron* in subtribe *Phoradendrinae*. Regardless of its relationship to other Viscaceae, *Arceuthobium* has clearly defined limits, and its generic status has never been questioned. No formal subgeneric treatment of *Arceuthobium* has been published, although Kuijt (1970) suggests that the genus is separable into two natural groups on the basis of branching habit.

Arceuthobium is the only genus of the Viscaceae or Loranthaceae that is clearly represented in both the Old and New Worlds. Of four Old World species discussed here, three have been described previously —*A. chinense* in southwestern China, *A. minutissimum* in the Himalayas, and *A. oxycedri*, which ranges from the Azores to the Himalayas and south to Kenya; the fourth species is recorded in this paper—*A. pini* of southwestern China and Tibet. In the New World, 24 species (28 taxa) are distributed from central Canada and southeastern Alaska to Honduras and Hispaniola.

The greatest species diversity is in northwestern Mexico and the western United States, where 24 of the 28 New World taxa occur. The four New World species outside this area are *A. bicarinatum* of Hispaniola in the Caribbean, *A. hondurense* and *A. guatemalense* in Central America, and *A. pusillum* in southeastern Canada, the Lake States, and the northeastern United States. Fourteen taxa occur in Mexico, six of which are found in the western United States. Of the 17 dwarf mistletoes found in the United States, 5 are also common to Canada. One species, *A. douglasii*, ranges from southern British Columbia to southern Durango Mexico.

Objectives and Scope

With the increasing recognition of *Arceuthobium* as destructive parasites on commercially important forest trees, and the expanding interest in the biology of the genus, the need for additional systematic work on the group became apparent. For example, control of dwarf mistletoes in some areas is hampered by inadequate knowledge of the identity of the parasite involved.

[1] Principal Plant Pathologist, Rocky Mountain Forest and Range Experiment Station, Forest Service, U.S. Department of Agriculture, with central headquarters maintained at Fort Collins in cooperation with Colorado State University.

[2] Associate Professor of Biology, Department of Biology, University of Utah, Salt Lake City.

Our initial concern in these studies was to clarify the confusion surrounding the *A. campylopodum* complex (see Hitchcock and Cronquist 1964), which centered primarily around Gill's (1935) designation of host forms in this group. When we discovered, however, the relatively rich dwarf mistletoe flora in Mexico (Hawksworth and Wiens 1965; Hawksworth, Lightle, and Scharpf 1968), we expanded our investigations to include comprehensive treatment of the entire genus.

We have studied all known North American taxa, plus the Himalayan species, *A. minutissimum*, in their natural state. Since 1962 our field studies of *Arceuthobium* have taken us by foot, hoof, wheel, and wing over 100,000 miles throughout western North America, Mexico, Central America, the Caribbean, and the Himalayas. Over 1,500 dwarf mistletoe specimens that we collected in our field work, plus many early U.S. Department of Agriculture collections by J. R. Weir, G. G. Hedgcock, J. S. Boyce, and L. S. Gill, are filed in the U.S. Forest Service Mistletoe Herbarium at Fort Collins, Colorado. Duplicates of our collections are deposited in many North American herbaria, particularly the University of Colorado, Missouri Botanical Garden, U.S. National Museum, University of Utah, and the Instituto de Biología, Mexico City. In addition to our own collections, we have studied dwarf mistletoes at the major herbaria in North America and Europe (see appendix, p. 186).

Our objectives in this study have been to develop a useful, yet natural, system of classification for *Arceuthobium*. Although the New World species have been emphasized, the literature on the Old World taxa has been reviewed, and results of our field studies on one Old World species, *A. minutissimum*, are included.

This handbook is divided in 10 main sections: (1) general life cycles, (2) biogeography, (3) host relationships, (4) mechanisms and trends in evolution, (5) systematics of the genus, (6) classificatory criteria, (7) numerical analyses, (8) formal taxonomic treatment, (9) major conclusions, and (10) suggestions for further research. The appendix contains the list of specimens that are cited for each taxon in the taxonomic section, a glossary of some of the less familiar terms used in the paper, and a list of the trees mentioned in the text.

Taxonomic History

The first dwarf mistletoe described, *Arceuthobium oxycedri*, was originally included in *Viscum*, but was later segregated by Hoffman (1808) under the name *Razoumofskya*. The name *Arceuthobium*, proposed by Marschall von Bieberstein (1819), was generally used until the early 1900's. The Vienna Botanical Congress in 1905 conserved *Arceuthobium* over *Razoumofskya*, but because the American Code emphasized strict priority, most botanists in the United States continued to use *Razoumofskya*. *Arceuthobium* finally displaced *Razoumofskya* as a result of the 1930 Cambridge Botanical Congress and Gill's publication (1935).

Humboldt and Bonpland's collection of a dwarf mistletoe on Cofre de Perote, Veracruz, Mexico, in 1804 was apparently the first in the New World. This specimen was the type of *Arceuthobium* (as *Viscum*) *vaginatum* that Willdenow described in 1806. David Douglas, who explored the Pacific Northwest from 1823 to 1827, discovered two dwarf mistletoes in 1826. Although his journals were not published until 1914, the plants he discussed seem certain to be *A. campylopodum* (on *Pinus ponderosa*)[3] and *A. americanum* (on *Pinus contorta*). Hooker (1840), who first discussed the taxonomy of *Arceuthobium* in North America (north of Mexico), compared Douglas' specimens and another by Drummond (*A. americanum*) with the European *A. oxycedri*, but detected no specific differences except some inconsistent color variations. Engelmann was the first to publish (Gray 1850) a formal description of a dwarf mistletoe found in the United States, *A. americanum*. As the taxonomic architect of the genus in North America, Engelmann named most of the American species of *Arceuthobium* during the latter half of the 19th century (Gray 1850, Watson 1880).

Between 1910 and 1920, George G. Hedgcock and James R. Weir of the United States Department of Agriculture each initiated studies to clarify the taxonomy of *Arceuthobium* in the United States. Although both scientists published several articles on dwarf mistletoes, their main taxonomic works were left unpublished, and are on file with the U.S. Forest Service at Fort Collins, Colorado, and at Moscow, Idaho.

Hedgcock completed a series of manuscripts in 1914 on the taxonomy of the dwarf mistletoes, but for unknown reasons this work was never published. This is unfortunate because Hedgcock had a keen understanding of the genus. For example, he first recognized that the dwarf mistletoe (our *A. californicum*) on *Pinus lambertiana* was distinct from *A. cyanocarpum*, and that *A. campylopodum* was distinct from *A. occidentale*. Hedgcock (1915) published a host list of the United States dwarf mistletoes and later (Hedgcock and Hunt 1917) reported on some new hosts of *A. campylopodum* and *A. occidentale* based on artificial inoculations. The only one of Weir's published papers that

---

[3] A list of scientific names, authorities, and available common names of the trees mentioned is given in the appendix, p. 184.

includes major taxonomic implications is a report of a series of studies in which he artificially inoculated several species of Northwestern dwarf mistletoes on various hosts under field and greenhouse conditions (Weir 1918a). A taxonomic treatise on Amreican dwarf mistletoes that he began to write was never completed. Weir did, however, publish observations of hosts associated with several Northwestern dwarf mistletoes.[4]

Nelson described two new dwarf mistletoes (Coulter and Nelson 1909, Nelson 1913), and Tubeuf (1919) published a review of the genus. Tubeuf's work was based mainly on the literature, his extensive knowledge of the European *Arceuthobium oxycedri,* and results of a brief trip to the western United States in 1913. His paper was a good summary of the available literature, but it did little to clarify the taxonomic relationships of the genus.

Following Nelson's and Tubeuf's work, taxonomic understanding of the genus did not advance significantly until Gill's (1935) revision of the United States species. Gill reevaluated Engelmann's works, discovered flowering periods as an important taxonomic character, and reduced the rank of several closely related species to host forms of *A. campylopodum.* Although Gill's paper clearly established a taxonomic framework for the genus, he considered his work to be provisionary "pending a complete revision of the genus based on further field and experimental evidence."

Kuijt[5] rejected Gill's treatment of *A. campylopodum* and *A. vaginatum* as being composed of host forms. He adopted an even more conservative philosophy than Gill for *A. campylopodum* and *A. vaginatum,* in which he preferred to consider each taxon as only a single variable species. In his earliest work, Kuijt (1955) even questioned the distinctness of *A. vaginatum* from *A. campylopodum,* and stated that they were separated "only by a two- or- three months difference in flowering time, no consistent morphological differences having been discovered." Furthermore he suggested, as did Gill (1935), that *A. campylopodum* should include *A. bicarinatum* from Hispaniola.

Hawksworth and Graham (1963) discussed the difficulties of applying Gill's host-form concept to the dwarf mistletoes that parasitize western spruces. They also reported that Gill's forms in the *A. campylopodum* complex can be distinguished morphologically. We (Hawksworth and Wiens 1964, 1965, 1970a, 1970b) have reported additional taxonomic studies of the genus.

GENERALIZED LIFE CYCLE

Because we interpret discontinuities between life cycles as the basis for taxonomic distinction, we place considerable emphasis on life cycles in this paper (see p. 40).

Shoots, flowers, and fruits of *Arceuthobium* are illustrated in figures 1–3. Some important aspects of the life cycle of one species (*A. americanum*) are shown in figure 4. Taxa whose life cycles have been studied in some detail are: *A. abietinum* (Scharpf and Parmeter 1967), *A. americanum* (Hawksworth 1965b), *A. vaginatum* subsp. *cryptopodum* (Hawksworth 1961a, 1965b), *A. campylopodum* (Roth 1959, Wagener 1962), *A. douglasii* (Wicker 1965, 1967a), *A. laricis* (Smith 1966a; Wicker 1965, 1967a), *A. tsugense* (Smith 1966a) and *A. oxycedri* (Heinricher 1915a, 1915b, 1924).

Although the dwarf mistletoes are typically aerial parasites on branches or main stems of coniferous trees, there are a few reports of their occurrence on roots. Scharpf (in Kuijt 1969) noted parasitism of roots of *Pinus sabiniana* by *Arceuthobium occidentale* in California; also root parasitism has been found on pines infected by *A. globosum* near Mexico City,[6] and on Volcán Tajumalco, Guatemala (Steyermark specimen *36940* at the University of Michigan). These are certainly abnormal situations, however, and are presumably due to vegetative spread into roots from infections on the main stem near the groundline. Thus, the rare root parasitism by *Arceuthobium* is not comparable to that in the typical terrestrial members of the Loranthaceae (*Gaiadendron, Nuytsia*) where *initial* infection takes place through the roots.

Our discussion of dwarf mistletoe life cycles begins with seeds. The normal *Arceuthobium* fruit contains a single seed with one embryo, but rarely fruits may contain two seeds or seeds with two embryos (Hawksworth 1961b). Seed dispersal takes place from midsummer to late fall depending on the taxon involved. Seeds are explosively expelled from the fruits at initial velocities of about 90 feet per second for distances up to 50 feet, although the average distance is considerably less (Hinds, Hawksworth, and McGinnies 1963; Hinds and Hawksworth 1965; Hawksworth 1961a). Birds may be involved in

---

[4] Weir 1915a, 1915b, 1916c, 1917, 1918b.
[5] Kuijt 1955, 1960a, 1960b, 1963, 1964.

[6] Personal communication, Rudolfo Salinas Q., Instituto Nacional de Investigaciones Forestales, Mexico D. F., 1966.

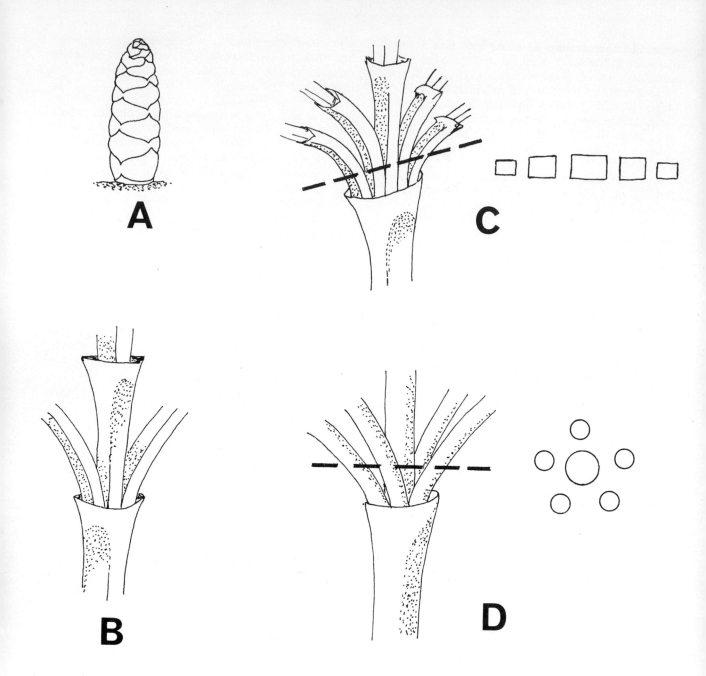

Figure 1.—Shoots of dwarf mistletoe: *A*, Young shoot showing the decussate arrangement of the internodes; *B*, Older shoot showing elongated internodes and typical decussate branching; *C*, Typical flabellate branching pattern with cross section through dashed area; *D*, Typical verticillate or whorled type of branching with cross section through the dashed area. All taxa show the type of primary branching (*B*), but in most instances a secondary type of branching also develops which may be either flabellate (*C*) or verticillate (*D*).

long-distance dispersal (see p. 9). The seeds are viscous coated, and readily adhere to objects they strike. Needles of coniferous trees are particularly effective in intercepting the seeds in flight (Roth 1959, Hawksworth 1965b). Seeds that have been intercepted usually remain on the needles until the first rain lubricates the viscous coating, and causes the seeds to slide down the needles. Although many fall from the needles to the ground, some seeds become attached to the twigs by their viscous coating.

Growth of dwarf mistletoe radicles is limited, so only those seeds that germinate on or very near the twigs can cause infection. The time of germination

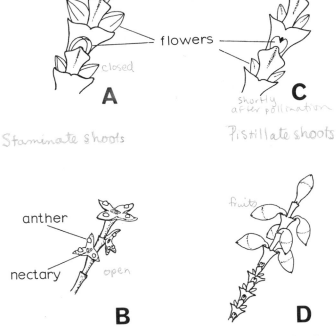

flowers

closed

A

Staminate shoots

anther

nectary

open

B

flowers

shortly after pollination

C

Pistillate shoots

fruits

D

Figure 2.—Flowers and fruits of *Arceuthobium*: *A* and *B*, Staminate shoots; *C* and *D*, Pistillate shoots. *A*, Terminal part of staminate shoot showing flowers prior to opening; *B*, Terminal part of staminate shoot showing open 3- and 4-merous flowers; *C*, Terminal portion of pistillate shoot showing flowers shortly after pollination; *D*, Terminal portion of pistillate shoot showing two crops of fruit, the terminal internodes with nearly mature fruits, and the lower internodes with fruit 1 year younger than the terminal fruit.

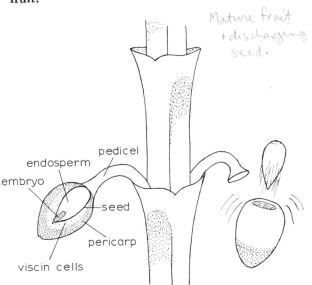

Mature fruit + discharging seed.

endosperm

embryo

pedicel

seed

pericarp

viscin cells

Figure 3.—Mature fruit and seed dispersal in *Arceuthobium*: *A*, Diagrammatic cross-section of mature fruit and seed (left) and fruit just discharging its seed (right); *B*, Photograph of seed in flight immediately after discharge from fruit (lower right). Photograph taken at 5 millionths of a second (Hinds, Hawksworth, and McGinnies 1963).

is poorly known for most taxa, but most species investigated germinate in late winter or spring. The known exceptions are *A. vaginatum* subsp. *cryptopodum* and *A. guatemalense* which germinate in the fall immediately after seed dispersal. Seeds of the other Mexican and Central American species probably also germinate soon after dispersal. The germinating radicle forms a holdfast when it contacts an obstruction on the host branch, such as the base of a needle (Bonga 1969b). The holdfast develops a penetrating wedge of tissue into the host (Scharpf and Parmeter 1967), and thus initiates the infection process.

For most host-parasite combinations that have been investigated infection can take place only through the most recent tissues, usually segments[7] less than 5 years old. An exception is *A. americanum*, which can become established on segments at

---

[7] We refer to the single year's growth length of a conifer branch or stem, sometimes incorrectly called an "internode," as a *segment*. The area of branchlet emergence or bud scales, sometimes incorrectly called a "node," is termed a *girdle* (see Thoday and Johnson 1930, Kuijt 1960b).

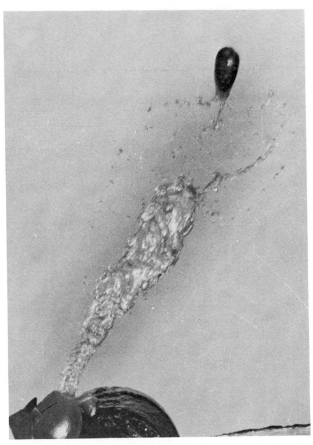

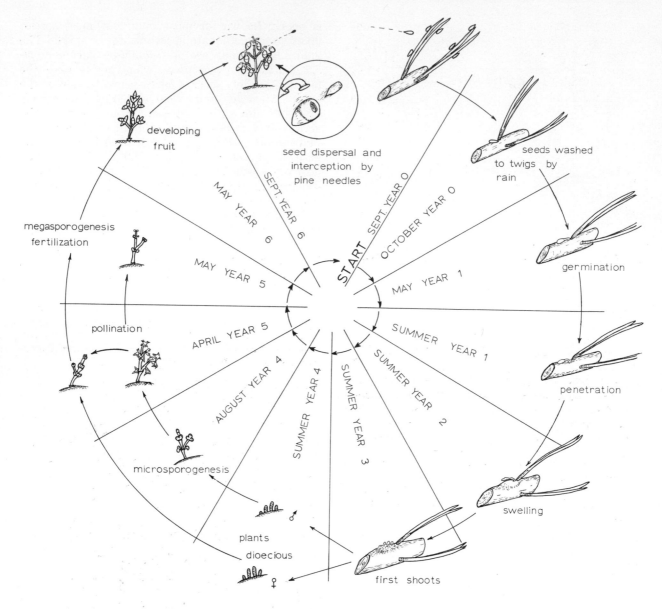

Figure 4.—Generalized life cycle of a dwarf mistletoe as exemplified by *Arceuthobium americanum* on lodgepole pine.

least 60 years old (Hawksworth 1954). Once the penetrating wedge has entered the cortex, an endophytic (or rootlike) system ramifies throughout the bark. Some parts of the endophytic system (the "sinkers") become embedded in successive layers of xylem.[8] Once infection is established, an incubation period of usually 2 to 5 years elapses before aerial shoot formation begins. A swelling at the point of infection often precedes shoot production

by a year or more, but this varies with the mistletoe, the host, and other factors. Usually 1 to 2 years pass after initial shoot appearance before flowering begins.

Meiosis may immediately precede flower production or it may occur approximately 5 to 8 months previously (Wiens 1968). Flowering may occur as early as February and March (*A. globosum*) or as late as November and December (*A. occidentale*). For a given taxon and locality, flowering usually lasts 4 to 6 weeks, but most pollen is dispersed within a 2- to 3-week period (Hawksworth, unpublished data).

[8] The endophytic systems of various species of *Arceuthobium* have been intensively studied by Heinricher 1924; Heil 1923; Thoday and Johnson 1930; Cohen 1954, 1963; Kuijt 1960b; Srivastava and Esau 1961.

The dwarf mistletoes have features characteristic of insect-rather than wind-pollinated plants (Whitehead 1969): they bear a relatively limited amount of spined pollen that is shed in clusters, produce nectar, and emit odors from both staminate and pistillate flowers. Experimental work on dwarf mistletoe pollination is in progress (Gregor and Wiens, unpublished data). Thrips seem to be involved in the pollination of *A. vaginatum* subsp. *cryptopodum* (Hawksworth 1961a), but different types of insects are apparently more important in other species (Stevens and Hawksworth 1970). Some wind pollination may be effected, at least at very close distances. The staminate flowers and the terminal parts of the shoots are usually shed a few weeks after anthesis. In species such as *A. verticilliflorum*, the entire flowering spikes are deciduous after anthesis. In species other than *A. pusillum*, individual shoots may produce crops of flowers over several successive years.

The time required for fruits to mature varies considerably; it is only about 5 months for *A. pusillum*, a year or more in other taxa, and as long as 18 to 19 months in *A. gillii* subsp. *gillii*. The minimum time from infection to initial seed production averages 6 years in *A. americanum* and 7 to 8 years in *A. vaginatum* subsp. *cryptopodum*. There have been reports (Peirce 1905, Korstian and Long 1922) that the shoots die after the fruits mature, but this is certainly not the normal situation. We have observed individual shoots of *A. americanum* and *A. vaginatum* subsp. *cryptopodum* that have produced successive crops of fruits for 5 years and are still living. Also, Kuijt (1970) reports that several taxa have relatively long-lived shoots. With seed production, our discussion of the life cycle is completed.

All dwarf mistletoes are dioecious; the pistillate and staminate plants occur in approximately equal numbers in the taxa that have been investigated: *A. vaginatum* subsp. *cryptopodum* (Hawksworth 1961), *A. campylopodum* (Wicker 1967b), and *A. americanum* (Hawksworth, unpublished data).

Several biotic and abiotic factors affect the shoots, fruits, and seeds of the dwarf mistletoes. A number of fungi attack these plants and, although they are damaging and abundant in some areas in certain years, they seem to exert relatively little biological control (Wicker and Shaw 1968, Wilson 1969). Little information is available on the effects of the many insects associated with the dwarf mistletoes (Gill and Hawksworth 1961, Stevens and Hawksworth 1970). Squirrels, porcupines, birds, and other animals eat dwarf mistletoe shoots, but their effects seem to be rather minor. Various climatic factors such as temperature extremes and winter drying affect dwarf mistletoe shoots, but no data on the importance of these factors on populations are available.

BIOGEOGRAPHY

Paleobotany

The fossil record of *Arceuthobium* is meager. The oldest known fossil pollen is from the middle Eocene[9] in East Germany. Identified as *Spinulaepollis arceuthobiodes* (Krutzsch 1962), it was found at more than 60 East Germany stations. Most grains were in upper Eocene to Miocene strata, with extremes from middle Eocene to the Pliocene. Stuchlik (1964), working in Polish Miocene deposits, considered the pollen similar to, if not identical with, the living *Arceuthobium oxycedri*. He also found a rarer, larger type of pollen described as a new subspecies: *Spinulaepollis arceuthobioides* subsp. *major*.

The fossil subspecies had pollen grains 24 to 30μ in diameter compared with 20 to 24μ for the species. Possibly swelling due to fossilization or to laboratory preparation procedures could have affected pollen size. The *A. oxycedri* pollen that we have examined has a diameter of 18 to 20μ. From our pollen studies a range from 20 to 30μ is unusual within a taxon; therefore the larger grained type may represent an extinct species. The northern limits of *A. oxycedri* are now about 500 miles south of the East German and Polish fossil pollen sites.

The fossil genus *Patzea* (Caspary 1872), which was considered by Engler and Krause (1935) to be synonymous with *Arceuthobium*, was described from Oligocene amber formations on the Baltic Coast. However, judging by the drawings of *Patzea* published by Conwentz (1886), we believe that *Patzea* is not congeneric with *Arceuthobium*.

[9] The Cenozoic era, or approximately the last 65 million years of geologic history, is divided by the U.S. Geological Survey as follows: (data provided by Dr. Estella B. Leopold, 1970).

Period	Series or epoch	Years before present
Quaternary	Holocene	10,000
	Pleistocene	3 million
Tertiary	Pliocene	3–12 million
	Miocene	12–26 million
	Oligocene	26–38 million
	Eocene	38–53 million
	Paleocene	53–65 million

Leopold[10] noted two Miocene *Arceuthobium* pollen records from North America: (1) early or middle Miocene pollen from the north flank of the Alaska range, associated with *Pinus* and *Picea* pollen (Wahrhaftig, Wolfe, Leopold, and others 1969), and (2) pollen in the middle Miocene Troublesome formation in north-central Colorado; with associated coniferous pollen, predominantly *Picea* and *Pinus*, and some *Abies* (Weber 1965).

Leopold[10] also found *Arceuthobium* pollen in sediment dated from 5,000 to 10,000 years before present (B.P.) in cores from near the center of Searles Lake in the Mojave Desert in California. The species of *Arceuthobium* has not been determined, but it is probably *A. divaricatum* which occurs today in the same area on *Pinus monophylla*.

Adam (1967) reported the occurrence of *Arceuthobium* pollen over the last 10,000 years at four sites in the central Sierra Nevada of California. He noted irregular distribution of *Arceuthobium* pollen during this period and found that the peaks occurred when pines were declining. *Arceuthobium* was perhaps more abundant during drier periods because dwarf mistletoe, at least on *Pinus ponderosa*, now seems to be more abundant in the drier regions of California. Data published by Janssen (1968) show a similar trend for *A. pusillum* on spruce in Minnesota; that is, peaks in *Arceuthobium* pollen occurred when spruce was declining.

Baker (1969) found *Arceuthobium* pollen in sediments near Lake Yellowstone, Wyoming, that dated to about 11,000 years B.P. The species was presumed to be *A. americanum* because this is the only species now common in the region and the pollen grains were associated with fossilized needles of *Pinus contorta*, the principal host of this dwarf mistletoe.

Pleistocene *Arceuthobium* pollen (presumably *A. pusillum*), has been found in the southeastern United States about 300 miles south of the present southern limits of *A. pusillum*. Fossil pollen (radiocarbon dated at 38,000 years B.P.) has been found in North Carolina and South Carolina (Whitehead 1963, 1964; Whitehead and Barghoorn 1962; Whitehead and Doyle 1969) and in northwestern Georgia (radiocarbon dated at about 15,000 to 23,000 years B.P.) (Watts 1970). Whitehead and Barghoorn (1962) consider the possibility that the *Arceuthobium* pollen represents a species from the western United States or an extinct species. However, since the dwarf mistletoe pollen is associated with spruce pollen and needles, and *A. pusillum* is the only eastern species, it seems almost certain to be this taxon. Also, *A. pusillum* is the only species now

occurring within about 1,200 miles of the fossil sites.

Fossil pollen of *Arceuthobium pusillum* has also been found within the present range of the species in Minnesota. McAndrews (1966) reported it at Lake Itasca, Clearwater County (radiocarbon dated at about 5,000 B.P.) and Janssen (1968) found it at Myrtle Lake, Koochiching County (radiocarbon age from present to 9,000 years B.P.).

The only reported macrofossils of *Arceuthobium* are those from Pleistocene formations of Coastal California (Chaney and Mason 1930, 1933; Mason 1934). Axelrod (1966) dated the sites as late Pleistocene, and obtained radiocarbon dates of 30,000 to 40,000 years B.P. These fossils, found at Carpenteria and Santa Cruz Island in Santa Barbara County, and at Tomales Bay, Marin County, were abundant at the latter two localities. The dwarf mistletoe was associated with *Pinus radiata* and *P. muricata*, and was reported to be indistinguishable from modern *A. occidentale* (as "*A. campylopodum*"), which presently parasitizes these pines. This mistletoe does not now occur at the fossil sites in Santa Barbara County, although *P. muricata* is still present on Santa Cruz Island. The closest modern mistletoe population on these pines is about 100 miles north near Cambria on *P. radiata*. In Marin County, *A. occidentale* is still present on *P. muricata* on Inverness Ridge adjacent to Tomales Bay. Chaney and Mason (1933) note that the fossil plant had primarily 4-merous staminate flowers. This character is quite variable, however, and the 4-merous condition is predominant in many modern *A. occidentale* populations.

Paleogeography

The occurrence of *Arceuthobium pusillum* on eastern spruces is perplexing, because dwarf mistletoes have not colonized the eastern and southern pines. *Arceuthobium pusillum* may have evolved somewhere outside the present range of the parasite, perhaps in northwestern North America. According to Mirov (1967), the pines in eastern and western North America have been essentially isolated since the Pliocene; hence, the dwarf mistletoes may not have had an opportunity to colonize the eastern pines.

Presumably the Pleistocene glaciations eliminated *A. pusillum* from the northern and western parts of the range of spruce. The dwarf mistletoe was pushed southward into spruce refugia in the Appalachians (as witnessed by Pleistocene *Arceuthobium* pollen in the Carolinas), and possibly on the Gaspé Peninsula in Ontario. Since the glacial period, *A. pusillum* has again moved northward, but its spread has been slower than that of its hosts. Both *Picea mariana* and *P. glauca* now occur as far northwestward as

---

[10] Personal communication, Dr. Estella B. Leopold, U.S. Geological Survey, 1969.

Alaska, but *A. pusillum* just enters eastern Saskatchewan. Possibly the mistletoe is still migrating northward and westward in Canada.

Picea apparently arrived in North America in two or more migration waves (Gordon 1968, Wright 1955). The available information on dwarf mistletoe parasitism of *Picea* tends to confirm this. The species that arrived in the Cretaceous or earlier (relatives of *Picea breweriana*, *P. chihuahuana*, and possibly *P. sitchensis*) do not have principal dwarf mistletoes associated with them. However, spruces that evolved later (early Tertiary?) such as forms related to *P. pungens*, *P. engelmannii*, *P. mariana*, and *P. glauca*, are now severely parasitized. These data indicate that *Arceuthobium* may have arrived in the New World in the early Tertiary.

Three species of *Arceuthobium* (*A. americanum*, *A. pusillum*, and *A. tsugense*) now have far northern distributions. Their northward migration since the last Wisconsin glaciation is difficult to explain. Current migration rates of dwarf mistletoes through host stands are reported to average only about 1 to 2 feet per year (Hawksworth 1958, 1961a). If, during Wisconsin glaciation, the parasites were pushed to the presumed northern forest limits as mapped by Dillon (1956), it indicates that all three dwarf mistletoes have migrated 1,000 miles or more in the last 10,000 to 12,000 years. This equals a rate of spread (on the order of 0.1 mile per year) many times greater than that recorded in present stands, and suggests different means of dispersal. Spread data in present stands are based only on spread due to the explosive fruits, and do not account for possible long distance vectors such as birds. Perhaps birds were primarily responsible for this northward migration, but the explosive mechanism enabled the plants to intensify locally once they became established in new areas. No definitive studies have been made on the importance of birds as dispersal agents of the dwarf mistletoes,[11] but these characteristics should be kept in mind: (1) dwarf mistletoes are dioecious, so at least two seeds must germinate, cause infection, flower, and fruit before a new population can be established, and (2) these plants mature their seeds in the fall, so bird migration patterns would presumably tend to disseminate seeds southward.

The occurrence of *A. bicarinatum* on the Island of Hispaniola in the Caribbean is of unusual biogeographic interest. This species occurs only on the relatively high-altitude species, *Pinus occidentalis*. Probably this parasite reached this area during Miocene time when land connections may have existed between islands of the Caribbean and Central America (Mirov 1967). The recent discovery

of *A. hondurense* in the uplands of Honduras is possibly of paleogeographic significance in this regard. *Arceuthobium bicarinatum* and *A. hondurense*, which are now separated by about 1,000 miles, may represent remnants of what was once a common stock in Miocene time.

The lack of dwarf mistletoe on the low-elevation Caribbean pines is difficult to explain because these trees were undoubtedly exposed to infection during the migration of *A. bicarinatum* to Hispaniola. *Pinus caribaea* is a host of *A. globosum* in the uplands of British Honduras but the dwarf mistletoe apparently does not occur on the more extensive low-elevation stands of this species elsewhere in the Caribbean. Perhaps the *Arceuthobium* type of seed dispersal is not adaptable to low, moist, tropical climates, although *A. tsugense* is abundant in the cool, very wet climate of the northwestern coast of North America.

Extant Distribution

Ranges of the Genus and Species

In the Old World *Arceuthobium* is represented by four known species: *A. oxycedri* on *Juniperus*, *A. minutissimum* on *Pinus griffithii*, *A. chinense* on *Abies* and *Keteleeria*, and *A. pini* on *P. tabulaeformis*.

Arceuthobium oxycedri, the only member of the genus exclusively parasitic on Cupressaceae, ranges from the Himalayas, throughout the Mediterranean region, to the Azores, and south to Kenya. This extreme range is perhaps explained because its main distribution is east-west and in regions relatively unaffected by Pleistocene glaciation.

Arceuthobium minutissimum is a markedly reduced species that is known only on *Pinus griffithii* in the western Himalayas. In size, systemic habit, and high specificity it resembles *A. pusillum* and *A. douglasii* of the New World. However, the similarity is probably due to convergence rather than close phyletic relationship.

The dwarf mistletoe known as *A. chinense* consists of two taxa: *A. chinense sensu stricto* on *Abies* and *Keteleeria* and the newly described *A. pini* on *Pinus tabulaeformis* (Hawksworth and Wiens 1970b). *Arceuthobium chinense* has some verticillate branching (Kuijt 1970). Although the branching type has not been determined for *A. pini*, specimens we have seen showed no secondary branching. Both species are poorly known, but they deserve intensive study because they occur near the presumed area of origin of the genus.

In the New World, *Arceuthobium* is widely distributed and is represented by 28 taxa. The known range of *Arceuthobium* in North America (fig. 5) indi-

---

[11] Gill 1935; Hawksworth 1961a, 1967; Kuijt 1955; Zavarin, Critchfield and Snajberk 1969.

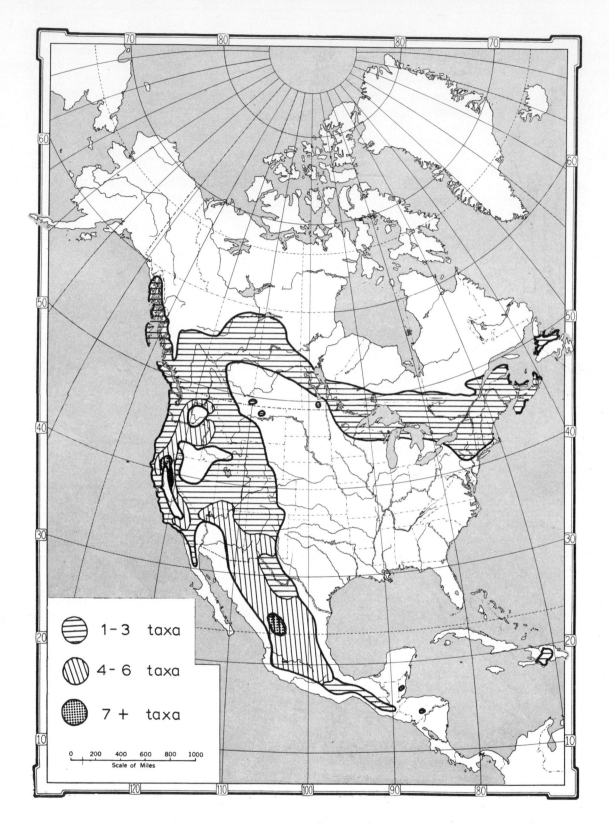

Figure 5.—Distribution of *Arceuthobium* in North America. The number of taxa in various areas is indicated. Two areas of highest concentration of taxa are in Durango, Mexico, and in the vicinity of Mount Shasta in northern California. Outline map copyrighted by Denoyer-Geppert Co., Chicago (used by permission).

cates that the genus is concentrated mainly in Mexico and the western United States. Also indicated in figure 5 is the number of taxa within various parts of the range of the genus. For example, although five taxa occur in Colorado, no more than three are found within a local area. Two North American regions have high numbers of taxa. In western Durango, Mexico, nine taxa are found: *A. blumeri*, *A. douglasii*, *A. gillii* subsp. *nigrum*, *A. globosum*, *A. vaginatum* subsp. *vaginatum* and *durangense*, *A. verticilliflorum*, *A. rubrum* and *A. strictum*; the latter four are endemic to this region. The second area where *Arceuthobium* is highly concentrated is in northern California where these nine taxa occur: *A. abietinum* (both *formae speciales*), *A. cyanocarpum*, *A. californicum*, *A. douglasii*, *A. americanum*, *A. campylopodum*, *A. occidentale*, and *A. tsugense*.

Of the 17 taxa in the United States, all but one are western, and six are endemic to the western United States (table 1); 10 are found in California, 9 in Arizona, and 8 in Oregon. The only eastern species, *A. pusillum*, is found in Maine, Vermont, New Hampshire, Massachusetts, Rhode Island, Connecticut, New York, New Jersey, Pennsylvania, Michigan, Wisconsin, and Minnesota.

Five of the species found in the United States also occur in Canada:

A. americanum—Ontario, Manitoba, Saskatchewan, Alberta, British Columbia
A. douglasii—British Columbia
A. laricis—British Columbia
A. pusillum—Newfoundland, Prince Edward Island, Nova Scotia, New Brunswick, Quebec, Ontario, Manitoba, Saskatchewan
A. tsugense—British Columbia.

Of the 15 taxa found in Mexico (table 2), 7 range into the western United States. Dwarf mistletoes are reported from 20 of the 32 States or territories in Mexico, but information is lacking on the distribution of many Mexican taxa. Two species are found in Guatemala, and one each in Honduras, British Honduras, and Hispaniola.

Extension of Dwarf Mistletoe Ranges

No intercontinental transfer of dwarf mistletoes, such as the accidental introduction of the European *Viscum album* into California (Howell 1966), has been reported. Occasionally, dwarf mistletoes have become established outside their natural ranges, when infected trees have been transplanted. Most such introductions have been for relatively short distances, but some from 100 to 300 miles have

TABLE 1.—*Distribution of* Arceuthobium *in the western United States*

Taxon	Alaska	Washington	Oregon	California	Nevada	Idaho	Montana	Wyoming	Utah	Colorado	Arizona	New Mexico	Texas
A. abietinum f. sp. concoloris		X	X	X	X				X		X		
A. abietinum f. sp. magnificae			X	X									
A. americanum		X	X	X	1	X	X	X	X	X			
A. apachecum											X	X	
A. blumeri											X		
A. californicum			X	X									
A. campylopodum		X	X	X	X	X							
A. cyanocarpum			1	X	X	X	X	X	X	X	X		
A. divaricatum				X					X	X	X	X	X
A. douglasii		X	X	X	X	X	X	X	X	X	X	X	
A. gillii subsp. gillii											X	2	
A. laricis		X	X			X	X						
A. microcarpum											X	X	
A. occidentale				X									
A. tsugense	X	X	X	X									
A. vaginatum subsp. cryptopodum									X	X	X	X	X
Number of taxa	1	6	8	10	5	5	4	3	6	5	9	5	2

Note: Data marked by leaders (--) not known in State.
[1] Reported in State but locality unknown.
[2] Probably occurs within State.

TABLE 2.—*Known distribution of* Arceuthobium *in Mexico (dwarf mistletoe records are available for only 20 of the 32 States)*

Estado	*A. abietis-religiosae*	*A. apachecum*	*A. blumeri*	*A. campylopodum*	*A. divaricatum*	*A. douglasii*	*A. gillii* subsp. *gillii*	*A. gillii* subsp. *nigrum*	*A. globosum*	*A. rubrum*	*A. strictum*	*A. vaginatum* subsp. *vaginatum*	*A. vaginatum* subsp. *cryptopodum*	*A. vaginatum* subsp. *durangense*	*A. verticilliflorum*
Baja California N.				X	X										
Chiapis									X						
Chihuahua					X			X	X			X	X		
Coahuila		X				X						X	X		
D. F.	X								X			X	X		
Durango					X	X	X		X	X	X	X		X	X
Hidalgo	X								X			X			
Jalisco	X								X			X			
Mexico	X								X			X			
Michoacán									X						
Nayarit															
Nuevo León	X		X			X						X			
Oaxaca							X	X				X			
Puebla												X			
Sinaloa									X		X	X		X	
Sonora													X		
Tamaulipas												X			
Tlaxcala												X			
Veracruz							X	X				X			
Zacatecas												X			

Note: Data marked by leaders (__) not known in State.

been reported. Examples of such transfer include *Arceuthobium occidentale* on *Pinus radiata* at Stanford University and North Berkeley, California (Peirce 1905, Offord 1946b), and our observations of *A. divaricatum* on *P. edulis* in Albuquerque, New Mexico; *A. vaginatum* subsp. *cryptopodum* on *P. ponderosa* in Denver, Colorado; and *A. microcarpum* on *Picea pungens* in Alpine, Arizona. Thomas (1954) found *A. pusillum* in planted windbreak and ornamental *Picea glauca* in an area in southern Manitoba where the closest natural infection is about 6 miles away.[12] In all these instances, the dwarf mistletoes matured fruit in the new areas, and in most cases had spread to nearby planted trees of the same species.

Boyce (1961) emphasized that dwarf mistletoes should be eradicated from the vicinity of conifer nurseries to eliminate the possibility of introducing these parasites into new areas on planting stock. Because the holding period is longer, the danger seems greater in nurseries where trees are grown as ornamentals than in those for forest plantings. Weir (1916b) found a dwarf mistletoe-infected *Pinus*

ponderosa in a denuded planting site near Wallace, Idaho, and assumed that the tree was infected at the nursery near Boulder, Montana. The only dwarf mistletoe that occurs in this area of Montana is the lodgepole pine dwarf mistletoe, *A. americanum*, which sometimes occurs on *Pinus ponderosa*. The longest range extension reported to date[13] is a small dwarf mistletoe-infected *Picea pungens* found in a nursery near Riverside, California. The parasite, not yet definitely identified, appears to be *Arceuthobium tsugense*. The tree was presumably infected in a nursery near Portland, Oregon.

Relation of Parasite to Host Distribution

The distribution of a dwarf mistletoe is generally centered within the range of its principal host or hosts. Probably climatic history is primarily involved in the four exceptions to this "central distribution" rule:

ARCEUTHOBIUM PUSILLUM ON PICEA MARIANA and *P.* GLAUCA.—Possibly this spruce dwarf mistletoe

[12] Personal communication, J. G. Laut, Canada Dep. Fisheries and Forestry, 1969.

[13] Personal communication, Dr. L. J. Farmer, California Department of Agriculture, 1969.

was centrally distributed within the range of its hosts prior to the Wisconsin glaciations, but now only the southern ranges of spruce range are infected. *Picea glauca* and *P. mariana* migrated northward after the glacial period faster than the dwarf mistletoe, and vast areas in the northern parts of the ranges of these spruces are now free of *A. pusillum*. Whether the mistletoe has reached its northern climatic limit or is still migrating northward is not known.

ARCEUTHOBIUM MICROCARPUM on PICEA ENGELMANNII and P. PUNGENS.—This western spruce dwarf mistletoe occurs in western montane coniferous forests near the southern limits of its hosts' ranges. *A. microcarpum* is confined to four general regions in Southwestern United States: (1) the north rim of the Grand Canyon, (2) the San Francisco peaks, (3) the Graham mountains, and (4) the eastern Mogollon Rim. The distribution of this dwarf mistletoe appears relictual on spruces in the Southwest. Perhaps *A. microcarpum* once had a more northern distribution, but for unknown reasons did not survive in the higher latitudes where the two spruces are now most abundant. The phyletic affinities of *A. microcarpum* are anomalous, but since it does not seem to be closely related to the other dwarf mistletoes now in the Southwest, the spruce dwarf mistletoe probably did not evolve from extant species presently in the region. *Arceuthobium microcarpum* probably evolved in another area, migrated southward, and eventually became isolated in the southern parts of its hosts' ranges.

ARCEUTHOBIUM AMERICANUM on PINUS BANKSIANA.—The range of *A. americanum* coincides closely with that of *Pinus contorta* which is its major host. However, the parasite is also common on *Pinus banksiana*, but only in the western parts of this tree's range. Jack pine extends for about 1,500 miles east from the known limits of the mistletoe to western Ontario. Presumably, *A. americanum* evolved as a principal parasite of *Pinus contorta* and spread relatively recently to *P. banksiana* through central Alberta where the two trees occur together and frequently hybridize. Possibly *A. americanum* is still spreading eastward on *P. banksiana*. This situation is discussed in more detail in the Formal Taxonomy section.

ARCEUTHOBIUM ABIETINUM f. sp. CONCOLORIS on ABIES CONCOLOR.—The main distribution of *A. abietinum* f. sp. *concoloris* is in California where *Abies concolor* obtains its maximum development. However, the host extends for about 500 miles beyond the known eastern limits of the parasite in Grand Canyon, Arizona, and in southern Utah. Possibly the scattered distribution of *Abies concolor* in the Great Basin and Southern Rockies has prevented the spread of *A. abietinum* into these areas.

Sympatry

We consider sympatry (the occurrence of two taxa together) to be important in the taxonomic understanding of *Arceuthobium*. If two taxa are sympatric and if their flowering periods overlap, hybridization of the two taxa should occur if they are genetically compatible and have mutual pollinators. However, as will be discussed later, no evidence of hybridization exists in *Arceuthobium*.

Dwarf mistletoes observed within 100 feet of each other are arbitrarily considered to be sympatric (fig. 6) because interspecific pollinations should be possible within such limits. However, observations of other taxa within ¼ mile are also shown in the figure. Little is known of the effective distance of pollen transfer in *Arceuthobium*, but the limited data available suggest that the 100-foot distance may be conservative. Potter and Rowley (1960) found a single *Arceuthobium* pollen grain at a station in the treeless San Augustin Plains of New Mexico. Judging by the locality and time of year when the grain was caught, we estimate that the closest dwarf mistletoe populations are at least 3 miles away. Also Leopold[14] discovered *Arceuthobium* pollen in 8 of 11 pollen traps in a transect across Searles Lake in the Mojave Desert in California. The closest *Arceuthobium* has not been determined but the closest probable host in this region, *Pinus monophylla*, occurs on Argus Peak, about 10 miles north of Searles Lake.

Most North American taxa are known to be sympatric with at least one other member of the genus except *A. hondurense*, *A. bicarinatum*, and *A. guatemalense*, although the latter may occur with *A. globosum* in Guatemala. Nothing is known of sympatry in the Old World species but *A. minutissimum* and *A. oxycedri* possibly occur together in the Indian Himalayas where their elevational ranges overlap (Brandis 1907). Also, *A. chinense* and *A. pini* may be sympatric in southwestern China.

We observed several instances where three species of *Arceuthobium* occur sympatrically, and one case where four species were involved (table 3).

An interesting aspect of dwarf mistletoe parasitism is the occurrence of two species on an individual host tree (table 4). This phenomenon is rare, perhaps because of an exclusion principle in which infection of a tree by a secondary parasite is rare if the principal parasite is present (see p. 25).

[14] Personal communication, Dr. Estella B. Leopold, U.S. Geological Survey, 1970.

SYMPATRY

● Within 100 feet
▲ Within 1/4 mile

Column key (left to right):
1. A. verticilliflorum
2. A. vaginatum subsp. durangense
3. A. vaginatum subsp. cryptopodum
4. A. vaginatum subsp. vaginatum
5. A. tsugensis
6. A. strictum
7. A. rubrum
8. A. pusillum
9. A. occidentale
10. A. microcarpum
11. A. laricis
12. A. globosum
13. A. gillii subsp. nigrum
14. A. gillii subsp. gillii
15. A. douglasii
16. A. divaricatum
17. A. cyanocarpum
18. A. campylopodum
19. A. californicum
20. A. blumeri
21. A. apachecum
22. A. americanum
23. A. abietis - religiosae
24. A. abietinum f. magnificae
25. A. abietinum f. sp. concoloris

(▓ = diagonal / self cell)

	1	2	3	4	5	6	7	8	9	10	11	12	13	14	15	16	17	18	19	20	21	22	23	24	25
A. abietinum f. sp. concoloris			●		▲				▲						●	▲		●	●					●	▓
A. abietinum f. sp. magnificae																					▲		●	▓	●
A. abietis - religiosae			●												●						●		▓		
A. americanum			●		●			●		●					●		●	●				▓			
A. apachecum			●							●					●	▲					▓				
A. blumeri			●	●								●		●	●					▓			●		
A. californicum																▲		●	▓					▲	●
A. campylopodum									●		●				●		▲	▓				●			●
A. cyanocarpum			●												●		▓	▲				●			
A. divaricatum			●												●	▓					▲				▲
A. douglasii			●	▲					●	●					▓	●	●	●	●	▲	●	●	●	●	●
A. gillii subsp. gillii			●	●										▓						●					
A. gillii subsp. nigrum												●	▓												
A. globosum			●									▓	●							●					
A. laricis											▓				●			●				●			
A. microcarpum			●							▓					●										
A. occidentale					▲				▓									●							▲
A. pusillum								▓														●			
A. rubrum		●					▓																		
A. strictum	●					▓																			
A. tsugense					▓				▲													●			▲
A. vaginatum subsp. vaginatum		●		▓						●			●	▲					●				●		
A. vaginatum subsp. cryptopodum			▓	●					●				●	●			●	●			●	●	●		●
A. vaginatum subsp. durangense		▓		●																					
A. verticilliflorum	▓				●																				

Figure 6.—Sympatry of the North American dwarf mistletoes.

14

TABLE 3.—*Instances of observed sympatry of three or four species of* Arceuthobium *(occurrence within 100 feet)*

Dwarf mistletoes	Hosts	Locality
THREE SPECIES:		
A. abietinum f. sp. concoloris	Abies concolor	Grand Canyon, Arizona
A. douglasii	Pseudotsuga menziesii	
A. vaginatum subsp. cryptopodum	Pinus ponderosa var. scopulorum	
A. cyanocarpum	Pinus flexilis	Bryce Canyon, Utah
A. douglasii	Pseudotsuga menziesii	
A. vaginatum subsp. cryptopodum	Pinus ponderosa var. scopulorum	
A. apachecum	Pinus strobiformis	Mogollon, New Mexico
A. douglasii	Pseudotsuga menziesii	
A. vaginatum subsp. cryptopodum	Pinus ponderosa var. scopulorum	
A. apachecum	Pinus strobiformis	Alpine, Arizona
A. douglasii	Pseudotsuga menziesii	
A. microcarpum	Picea pungens	
A. americanum	Pinus contorta var. latifolia	Tieton Lake, Washington[1]
A. douglasii	Pseudotsuga menziesii	
A. laricis	Larix occidentalis	
A. abietis-religiosae	Abies vejarii	Cerro Potosí, Nuevo León, Mexico
A. blumeri	Pinus strobiformis	
A. vaginatum subsp. vaginatum	Pinus ponderosa var. arizonica	
A. blumeri	Pinus strobiformis	El Salto, Durango, Mexico
A. globosum	Pinus cooperi	
A. vaginatum subsp. vaginatum	Pinus cooperi	
A. blumeri	Pinus strobiformis	La Junta, Chihuahua, Mexico
A. gillii subsp. gillii	Pinus leiophylla	
A. vaginatum subsp. vaginatum	Pinus ponderosa var. arizonica	
FOUR SPECIES:		
A. apachecum	Pinus strobiformis	Big Lake, Arizona
A. douglasii	Pseudotsuga menziesii	
A. microcarpum	Picea pungens	
A. vaginatum subsp. cryptopodum	Pinus ponderosa var. scopulorum	

[1] Also observed near Growden, Washington by Ed F. Wicker, personal communication, 1969.

TABLE 4.—*Known instances of dual parasitism in* Arceuthobium *and* Arceuthobium *with other mistletoes*

Mistletoes	Host	Locality	Reference
ARCEUTHOBIUM:			
A. americanum & A. campylopodum	Pinus ponderosa	Idaho	Weir 1916a
Do.	Pinus contorta	do.	Do.
A. americanum & A. laricis	do.	British Columbia	Kuijt 1954
Do.	do.	Washington	Wicker[1]
Do.	do.	Montana	Hawksworth and Wicker[2]
Do.	Pinus sylvestris	Washington	Graham and Leaphart 1961
A. americanum & A. vaginatum subsp. cryptopodum	Pinus ponderosa	Colorado	Hawksworth and Peterson 1959
Do.	Pinus contorta	do.	[2]
A. cyanocarpum & A. vaginatum subsp. cryptopodum	Pinus ponderosa	do.	[2]
A. globosum & A. vaginatum subsp. vaginatum	Pinus spp.	Mexico	Hawksworth and Wiens 1965
A. rubrum & A. vaginatum subsp. durangense	Pinus herrerai	Durango, Mexico	[2]

[1] Personal communication, Ed F. Wicker, 1969.
[2] First reported in this paper.

15

Mistletoes	Host	Locality	Reference
ARCEUTHOBIUM AND OTHER MISTLETOES:			
A. abietinum f. sp. concoloris & Phoraden- dron bolleanum subsp. pauciflorum	Abies concolor	California	Gill 1935 and our observations
A. bicarinatum & Dendropemon pycnophyllus	Pinus occidentalis	Dominican Republic	[2]

[1] Personal communication, Ed F. Wicker, 1969.

[2] First reported in this paper.

HOST RELATIONSHIPS

Natural Hosts

A summary of the principal host groups of the 32 dwarf mistletoes (fig. 7) includes the four Old World species. Each species is restricted to a certain host group, with the exceptions of *A. occidentale* (on pines of sections *Insignes, Oocarpae,* and *Sabinianae*), *A. globosum* (on pines of sections *Australes, Oocarpae,* and *Ponderosae*) and the poorly known *A. chinense* (on *Abies* and *Keteleeria*).

Although previous dwarf mistletoe literature has mentioned the susceptibility of trees in terms of common, principal, uncommon, and rare hosts, these classifications have not been specifically defined.

The susceptibility classes that we devised are based on the determination of an "infection factor" or the percentage of trees of the species in question that are infected within 20 feet of heavily infected[15] principal, or main, hosts of a dwarf mistletoe. Infection-factor determinations should be made only in stands older than 20 to 30 years.

This classification, based entirely on natural *susceptibility,* may not necessarily reflect the *abundance* of a dwarf mistletoe on a particular host. For example, we have classed *Pinus cembroides* as a principal host of *A. divaricatum* (table 5). This tree

---

[15] Heavily infected trees are class 5 or 6 of the 6-class system described by Hawksworth (1961a). For this system the live crown is divided into thirds, and each third is rated as: 0, no mistletoe; 1, light mistletoe (less than one-half of branches infected); and 2, heavy mistletoe (more than one-half of branches infected). The ratings of each third are added to obtain a total for the tree. For example, a tree heavily infected in the lower one-third of the crown, lightly infected in the middle one-third, and not infected in the upper third would be class 3. A tree heavily infected in each third would be class 6.

rarely occurs within the range of the dwarf mistletoe, but it is as susceptible as the other pinyons in the few areas where this host-parasite combination is found.

The five susceptibility classes used here are:

Host class	Infection factor	Remarks
I. Principal	At least 90 percent; usually nearly 100 percent	Uninfected trees are seldom found within the 20-foot zone unless they are small and stunted
II. Secondary	50 to 90 percent	
III. Occasional (or tertiary)	5 to 50 percent	
IV. Rare	More than 0 but less than 5 percent	
V. Immune	0	Potential host trees not infected even where the dwarf mistletoe in question is common

Dwarf mistletoe parasitism is a dynamic process, and some variation is to be expected. A tree species that is heavily infected in one area may sometimes be less severely parasitized in another part of the dwarf mistletoe's range. This could be due to ecotypic variation in the host or parasite or to environmental factors. Also, a tree species may be more frequently infected when it occurs in certain habitats. For example, Daubenmire (1961) found that ponderosa pine was commonly parasitized by *Arceuthobium campylopodum* on habitat types where the tree was associated with xerophytic grasses but not on the more mesic habitat types associated with the shrubs *Physocarpus* and *Symphoricarpos.* In spite of such occasional differences, however, the relatively consistent host relationships of each dwarf mistletoe make overall susceptibility ranking meaningful and useful.

ARCEUTHOBIUM	PINUS (HAPLOXYLON)		PINUS (DIPLOXYLON)							OTHER GENERA						
	White pines	Pinyons	Leiophyllae	Sylvestres	Australes	Ponderosae	Sabinianae	Contortae	Oocarpae	Abies	Larix	Tsuga	Pseudotsuga	Picea	Keteleeria	Juniperus
A. abietinum f. sp. concoloris										●						
A. abietinum f. sp. magnificae										●						
A. abietis – religiosae										●						
A. americanum								●								
A. apachecum	●															
A. bicarinatum					●											
A. blumeri	●															
A. californicum	●															
A. campylopodum						●										
A. chinense										●					●	
A. cyanocarpum	●															
A. divaricatum		●														
A. douglasii													●			
A. gillii subsp. gillii			●													
A. gillii subsp. nigrum			●													
A. globosum					●	●			●							
A. guatemalense	●															
A. hondurense									●							
A. laricis											●					
A. microcarpum														●		
A. minutissimum	●															
A. occidentale								●	●							
A. oxycedri																●
A. pini				●												
A. pusillum														●		
A. rubrum						●										
A. strictum			●													
A. tsugense												●				
A. vaginatum subsp. vaginatum						●										
A. vaginatum subsp. cryptopodum						●										
A. vaginatum subsp. durangense						●										
A. verticilliflorum						●										

Figure 7.—Principal hosts of the New and Old World dwarf mistletoes. (Divisions of *Diploxylon* according to Critchfield and Little 1966.)

TABLE 5.—*Susceptibility of hosts of North American dwarf mistletoes based on natural infection of native trees (a question mark indicates that we have not determined the appropriate susceptibility class or that the reported host-parasite combination has not been confirmed)*

Arceuthobium	Principal host	Secondary host	Occasional host	Rare host	Immune[1]
A. abietis-religiosae	Abies religiosa Abies vejarii				Pinus hartwegii Pinus leiophylla var. leiophylla Pinus montezumae Pinus ponderosa var. arizonica Pseudotsuga menziesii
A. abietinum f. sp. concoloris	Abies concolor Abies grandis	Abies amabilis? Picea breweriana	Abies lasiocarpa var. lasiocarpa	Pinus contorta subsp. murrayana Pinus lambertiana Pinus monticola	Abies magnifica Picea engelmannii Picea pungens Pinus flexilis Pinus monophylla Pinus muricata Pinus ponderosa var. ponderosa Pinus ponderosa var. scopulorum Pinus washoensis Pseudotsuga menziesii Tsuga heterophylla
A. abietinum f. sp. magnificae	Abies magnifica Abies procera?				Abies concolor Abies grandis Tsuga mertensiana
A. americanum	Pinus banksiana Pinus contorta subsp. latifolia Pinus contorta subsp. murrayana	Pinus contorta subsp. contorta? Pinus ponderosa var. scopulorum	Pinus albicaulis Pinus aristata Pinus flexilis Pinus ponderosa var. ponderosa	Picea engelmannii Picea glauca Picea pungens Pinus attenuata Pseudotsuga menziesii	Abies grandis Abies lasiocarpa var. lasiocarpa Abies magnifica Larix occidentalis Tsuga mertensiana
A. apachecum	Pinus strobiformis				Abies concolor Abies lasiocarpa var. arizonica Picea pungens Pinus edulis Pinus engelmannii Pinus ponderosa var. arizonica Pinus ponderosa var. scopulorum Pseudotsuga menziesii

[1] Includes only members of the Pinaceae in a particular stand, but associated Cuppressaceae or Taxodiaceae are likewise not infected.

TABLE 5.—*Susceptibility of hosts of North American dwarf mistletoes based on natural infection of native trees (a question mark indicates that we have not determined the appropriate susceptibility class or that the reported host-parasite combination has not been confirmed)*—Continued

Arceuthobium	Principal host	Secondary host	Occasional host	Rare host	Immune[1]
A. *bicarinatum*	*Pinus occidentalis*				
A. *blumeri*	*Pinus strobiformis*				*Abies vejarii* *Pinus cooperi* *Pinus engelmannii* *Pinus leiophylla* var. *leiophylla* *Pinus ponderosa* var. *arizonica* *Pinus ponderosa* var. *scopulorum* *Pseudotsuga menziesii*
A. *californicum*	*Pinus lambertiana*	*Pinus monticola*	*Picea breweriana*		*Abies concolor* *Pinus attenuata* *Pinus coulteri* *Pinus ponderosa* var. *ponderosa*
A. *campylopodum*	*Pinus ponderosa* var. *ponderosa* *Pinus jeffreyi* *Pinus attenuata*	*Pinus coulteri* *Pinus ponderosa* var. *scopulorum*	*Pinus contorta* subsp. *contorta* *Pinus contorta* subsp. *latifolia* *Pinus contorta* subsp. *murrayana*	*Pinus lambertiana*	*Abies concolor* *Abies grandis* *Pinus monophylla* *Pinus monticola* *Pinus quadrifolia* *Pinus sabiniana* *Pseudotsuga menziesii*
A. *cyanocarpum*	*Pinus flexilis* *Pinus aristata*	*Pinus albicaulis*	*Pinus monticola*	*Picea engelmannii?* *Pinus balfouriana* *Pinus contorta* subsp. *latifolia* *Pinus ponderosa* var. *scopulorum*	*Abies lasiocarpa* var. *lasiocarpa* *Pinus lambertiana* *Pinus strobiformis* *Pseudotsuga menziesii*
A. *divaricatum*	*Pinus edulis* *Pinus monophylla* *Pinus quadrifolia* *Pinus cembroides*				*Pinus jeffreyi* *Pinus ponderosa* var. *scopulorum* *Pseudotsuga menziesii*
A. *douglasii*	*Pseudotsuga menziesii*	*Abies lasiocarpa* var. *arizonica*	*Abies grandis*	*Abies concolor* *Abies lasiocarpa* var. *lasiocarpa* *Picea engelmannii* *Picea pungens* *Pinus flexilis*	*Abies magnifica* *Abies vejarii* *Larix occidentalis* *Pinus edulis* *Pinus ponderosa* var. *ponderosa* *Pinus ponderosa* var. *scopulorum* *Pinus strobiformis*

[1] Includes only members of the Pinaceae in a particular stand, but associated Cuppressaceae or Taxodiaceae are likewise not infected.

TABLE 5.—*Susceptibility of hosts of North American dwarf mistletoes based on natural infection of native trees (a question mark indicates that we have not determined the appropriate susceptibility class or that the reported host-parasite combination has not been confirmed)—Continued*

Arceuthobium	Principal host	Secondary host	Occasional host	Rare host	Immune[1]
A. gillii subsp. *gillii*	*Pinus leiophylla* var. *chihuahuana*	*Pinus leiophylla* var. *leiophylla* *Pinus lumholtzii*		*Pinus ponderosa* var. *arizonica* *Pinus ponderosa* var. *scopulorum*	*Pinus cembroides* *Pinus engelmannii* *Pinus strobiformis*
A. gillii subsp. *nigrum*	*Pinus leiophylla* var. *leiophylla* *Pinus leiophylla* var. *chihuahuana* *Pinus lumholtzii* *Pinus teocote*		*Pinus montezumae*		*Pinus cooperi* *Pinus engelmannii*
A. globosum	*Pinus cooperi* *Pinus douglasiana* *Pinus durangensis* *Pinus engelmannii* *Pinus hartwegii* *Pinus lawsonii* *Pinus michoacana* *Pinus montezumae* *Pinus pringlei* *Pinus pseudostrobus* *Pinus rudis* *Pinus tenuifolia*	*Pinus ponderosa* var. *arizonica*		*Cupressus* sp.? *Pinus teocote*	*Abies guatemalensis* *Abies religiosa* *Pinus leiophylla* var. *leiophylla*
A. guatemalense	*Pinus ayacahuite*				*Abies guatemalensis* *Pinus pseudostrobus*
A. hondurense	*Pinus oocarpa*	*Pinus pseudostrobus?*			
A. laricis	*Larix occidentalis*	*Abies lasiocarpa* var. *lasiocarpa* *Larix lyallii?* *Pinus contorta* subsp. *latifolia* *Tsuga mertensiana*	*Picea engelmannii* *Pinus albicaulis* *Pinus ponderosa* var. *ponderosa*	*Abies grandis* *Pinus monticola*	*Abies concolor* *Pinus contorta* subsp. *murrayana* *Pseudotsuga menziesii* *Tsuga heterophylla*
A. microcarpum	*Picea engelmannii* *Picea pungens*			*Abies lasiocarpa* var. *arizonica*	*Abies concolor* *Abies lasiocarpa* var. *lasiocarpa* *Pinus ponderosa* var. *scopulorum* *Pinus strobiformis* *Pseudotsuga menziesii*
A. occidentale	*Pinus sabiniana* *Pinus radiata* *Pinus muricata*	*Pinus attenuata* *Pinus coulteri*	*Pinus contorta* subsp. *bolanderi*		*Abies grandis* *Pinus ponderosa* var. *ponderosa* *Pseudotsuga menziesii* *Tsuga heterophylla*

[1] Includes only members of the Pinaceae in a particular stand, but associated Cuppressaceae or Taxodiaceae are likewise not infected.

TABLE 5.—*Susceptibility of hosts of North American dwarf mistletoes based on natural infection of native trees (a question mark indicates that we have not determined the appropriate susceptibility class or that the reported host-parasite combination has not been confirmed)*—Continued

Arceuthobium	Principal host	Secondary host	Occasional host	Rare host	Immune[1]
A. pusillum	Picea mariana Picea glauca	Picea rubens	Larix laricina	Pinus strobus Pinus resinosa Pinus banksiana	Abies balsamea
A. rubrum	Pinus cooperi Pinus durangensis Pinus engelmannii Pinus teocote Pinus herrerai				Pinus strobiformis
A. strictum	Pinus leiophylla var. chihuahuana		Pinus teocote	Pinus engelmannii	
A. tsugense	Tsuga heterophylla Tsuga mertensiana	Abies amabilis Abies lasiocarpa var. lasiocarpa Abies procera Pinus albicaulis Pinus contorta subsp. contorta Pinus monticola	Abies grandis Picea breweriana	Picea engelmannii Picea sitchensis	Abies magnifica Larix occidentalis Pinus contorta subsp. murrayana Pinus jeffreyi Pseudotsuga menziesii
A. vaginatum subsp. vaginatum	Pinus durangensis Pinus cooperi Pinus engelmannii Pinus hartwegii Pinus herrerai Pinus montezumae Pinus ponderosa var. arizonica Pinus ponderosa var. scopulorum Pinus rudis Pinus lawsonii			Pinus culminicola	Pinus leiophylla var. chihuahuana Pinus leiophylla var. leiophylla Pinus lumholtzii Pinus strobiformis Pinus teocote Pseudotsuga menziesii
A. vaginatum subsp. crypto- podum	Pinus ponderosa var. scopulorum Pinus ponderosa var. arizonica Pinus engelmannii Pinus arizonica var. stormiae		Pinus contorta subsp. latifolia Pinus aristata	Pinus flexilis Pinus strobiformis	Abies concolor Abies lasiocarpa var. arizonica Picea pungens Pinus cembroides Pinus edulis Pinus leiophylla var. chihuahuana Pseudotsuga menziesii
A. vaginatum subsp. durangense	Pinus montezumae Pinus durangensis	Pinus herrerai?			Pinus leiophylla var. leiophylla Pinus lumholtzii

[1] Includes only members of the Pinaceae in a particular stand, but associated Cuppressaceae or Taxodiaceae are likewise not infected.

TABLE 5.—*Susceptibility of hosts of North American dwarf mistletoes based on natural infection of native trees (a question mark indicates that we have not determined the appropriate susceptibility class or that the reported host-parasite combination has not been confirmed)*—Continued

Arceuthobium	Principal host	Secondary host	Occasional host	Rare host	Immune[1]
A. verticilliflorum	*Pinus cooperi* *Pinus engelmannii*				*Pinus leiophylla* var. *chihuahuana* *Pinus leiophylla* var. *leiophylla* *Pinus teocote*

[1] Includes only members of the Pinaceae in a particular stand, but associated Cuppressaceae or Taxodiaceae are likewise not infected.

Classification of host susceptibility for each North American dwarf mistletoe (table 5) is based primarily on actual infection-factor determinations. In some cases, however, no data are available, and we have placed trees in the susceptibility class which seems most appropriate on the basis of our field experience. No such susceptibility classification is currently possible for the Old World species, because we have not studied all of them in the field.

Also, when we rated the trees by susceptibility classes, we based our decision on the most common condition for a particular tree throughout the range of the dwarf mistletoe in question. This, of course, may not necessarily apply in individual instances. For example, near Snow Valley in the San Bernardino Mountains, California, *Pinus coulteri* is heavily infected by *Arceuthobium campylopodum*, but at lower elevations (where the mistletoe is severe on associated *P. attenuata*), *P. coulteri* is only occasionally attacked. We have placed *P. coulteri* in the "secondary host" category because it is typical of most situations where this host-parasite combination occurs. Variation as extreme as this example is exceptional and most dwarf mistletoe populations readily fall into the susceptibility classes indicated in table 5.

As shown in table 5, some trees are parasitized by several dwarf mistletoes: eight are known on *Pinus ponderosa* (table 6), eight on *Pinus contorta* (table 7), and six on *Pinus engelmannii* in Mexico (Hawksworth and Wiens 1965). Some dwarf mistletoes are quite specific, for example, *A. blumeri* and *A. apachecum*, which are restricted to *Pinus strobiformis*, but occur in different parts of the host range. Others have broad host ranges, such as *A. laricis*, which not only parasitizes *Larix* but also *Abies*, *Pinus*, *Picea*, and *Tsuga*. The principal host of *A. douglasii* is *Pseudotsuga menziesii*, and it is the only dwarf mistletoe that parasitizes *Pseudotsuga*. *Arecuthobium douglasii*, however also grows on *Abies* and *Picea*.

The five dwarf mistletoes that occur principally on the North American white pines (table 8) are: *A. cyanocarpum* on *Pinus flexilis* and *P. aristata*; *A. californicum* on *P. lambertiana*; *A. guatemalense* on *P. ayacahuite*; and *A. blumeri* and *A. apachecum* on *P. strobiformis*. The Central American *Pinus chiapensis* is the only member of this group not known to be parasitized.

Pinus monticola is the only widespread western white pine that is not a *principal* host for any dwarf mistletoe. Although six taxa parasitize this tree, these are mainly crossover situations (table 8). It may be of evolutionary significance that none of the members of the *Pinus chiapensis-strobus-monticola* phylad (Andresen 1966) has been colonized as a principal host by *Arceuthobium*. This may suggest that the phylad originated in an area outside the range of *Arceuthobium*. If this is true, *P. monticola* may not have occupied its present range until after the principal radiation of *Arceuthobium* onto the various conifers of the area had already occurred. This could explain why various dwarf mistletoes sometimes utilize *P. monticola* as a lesser host, and why it is not the principal host of any species.

Dwarf mistletoes parasitize nearly all western firs (*Abies* spp.) (table 9). Only *Arceuthobium abietinum* in the western United States and *A. abietis-religiosae* of Mexico, however, are principal parasites of *Abies*. *Arceuthobium abietis-religiosae* is known only from *Abies religiosa* and *A. vejarii*, but is to be expected on other Mexican true firs.

In addition to the firs listed in table 9, we have examined one collection on the rare bristlecone fir *Abies bracteata*, from the Santa Lucia Mountains of California. We believe that the specimen is a crossover infection of a pine dwarf mistletoe, probably *A. occidentale*. The specimen is in the Weir collection at the University of Illinois, and was obtained by Raymond in 1915. Positive identification is impossible because the specimen is fragmentary and poorly documented.

All North American spruces, except the recently described Mexican species *Picea chihuahuana* and *P. mexicana* (Martínez 1963), are known hosts for *Arceuthobium* (table 10). *Picea sitchensis*, however, is a very rare host. We have a recent collection on this tree from Oregon and this host-parasite combination has been reported from Alaska (Laurent 1966) and British Columbia (Molnar, Harris, Ross, and Ginns 1968).

TABLE 6.—*Susceptibility of members of the* Pinus ponderosa *complex to dwarf mistletoes*[1,2]

Arceuthobium	*Pinus ponderosa* variety			
	ponderosa	*scopulorum*	*arizonica*	*"stormiae"*[3]
A. *americanum*_____	III	II	--	--
A. *cyanocarpum*_____	--	IV	--	--
A. *campylopodum*_____	I	II	--	--
A. *gillii* subsp. *gillii*_____	--	IV	IV	--
A. *globosum*_____	--	--	II	--
A. *laricis*_____	III	--	--	--
A. *vaginatum* subsp. *cryptopodum*_____	--	I	I	I
A. *vaginatum* subsp. *vaginatum*	--	I	I	--

[1] I = Principal host, II = secondary host, III = occasional host, and IV = rare host; "__" dwarf mistletoe not observed within range of the tree.

[2] In addition, Smith and Craig (1968) have artificially infected *Pinus ponderosa* (presumably var. *ponderosa*) with *Arceuthobium tsugense*.

[3] The tree known in northern Mexico as *Pinus arizonica* Engelm. var. *stormiae* Martínez (1948) has not been formally described as a variety of *Pinus ponderosa*, but our field studies in Coahuila indicate that it is quite distinct from the tree known in the United States as *Pinus ponderosa* var. *arizonica*.

TABLE 7.—*Susceptibility of members of the* Pinus contorta *complex to dwarf mistletoes*[1]

Arceuthobium	*Pinus contorta* subspecies			
	contorta	*latifolia*	*murrayana*	*bolanderi*
A. *abietinum* f. sp. *concoloris*__	--	--	IV	--
A. *americanum*_____	[2]	I	I	--
A. *campylopodum*_____	III	III	III	--
A. *cyanocarpum*_____	--	IV	--	--
A. *laricis*_____	--	II	V	--
A. *occidentale*_____	--	--	--	III
A. *tsugense*_____	II	--	--	--
A. *vaginatum* subsp. *cryptopodum*_____	--	III	--	--

[1] I = Principal host, II = secondary host, III = occasional host, IV = rare host, and V = immune; "__" dwarf mistletoe not observed within range of the tree.

[2] Presumably on this subspecies in the Oregon Mountains, southern Josephine County, Oregon (Weir 1917), but this has not been confirmed.

TABLE 8.—*Susceptibility of North American white pines to dwarf mistletoes*[1]

Arceuthobium	Pinus								
	albicaulis	aristata*	ayacahuite	balfouriana	flexilis	lambertiana	monticola	strobiformis	strobus
A. abietinum f. sp. concoloris	--	--	--	--	V	IV	IV	--	--
A. americanum	III	III	--	--	III	--	--	--	--
A. apachecum	--	--	--	--	--	--	--	I	--
A. blumeri	--	--	--	--	--	--	--	I	--
A. californicum	--	--	--	--	--	I	II	--	--
A. campylopodum	--	--	--	--	--	IV	V	--	--
A. cyanocarpum	II	I	--	IV	I	V	III	V	2
A. douglasii	--	--	--	--	V	--	--	V	--
A. guatemalense	--	--	I	--	--	--	--	--	--
A. laricis	III	--	--	--	--	--	IV	--	--
A. pusillum	--	--	--	--	--	--	--	--	IV
A. tsugense	II	--	--	--	--	--	II	--	--
A. vaginatum subsp. cryptopodum	--	III	--	--	IV	--	--	IV	--

[1] I = Principal host, II = secondary host, III = occasional host, IV = rare host, and V = immune; "--" dwarf mistletoe not observed within range of the tree.

[2] Susceptible in greenhouse inoculations at Fort Collins, Colorado.

* Recent studies (Bailey, D. K., Phytogeography and taxonomy of *Pinus* subsection *Balfourianae*, Ann. Mo. Bot. Gard. 57: 210–249, 1970) have shown that *"Pinus aristata"* as formerly understood comprises two species: *Pinus longaeva* D. K. Bailey in the Great Basin (California, Nevada, and Utah) and *Pinus aristata sensu stricto* in the Rocky Mountains (Colorado, New Mexico, and Arizona). *Pinus longaeva* is frequently parasitized by *Arceuthobium cyanocarpum* in southern Utah and Nevada. *Pinus aristata* is an occasional host for *A. americanum* and *A. vaginatum* subsp. *cryptopodum* in Colorado. *Arceuthobium cyanocarpum* is not known on *Pinus aristata* in Colorado or New Mexico but it may be the taxon on this tree in Arizona (see p. 117).

TABLE 9.—*Susceptibility of western North American and Mexican species of true firs (Abies) to dwarf mistletoes*[1]

Arceuthobium	Abies								
	amabilis	concolor	grandis	lasiocarpa var. lasiocarpa	lasiocarpa var. arizonica	magnifica	procera	religiosa	vejarii
A. abietinum f. sp. concoloris	II?	I	I	III	--	V	--	--	--
A. abietinum f. sp. magnificae	--	V	V	--	--	I	I?	--	--
A. abietis-religiosae	--	--	--	--	--	--	--	I	I
A. laricis	--	V	IV	II	--	--	--	--	--
A. microcarpum	--	V	--	V	IV	--	--	--	--
A. tsugense	II	--	III	II	--	V	II	--	--
A. douglasii	--	IV	III	IV	II	V	--	--	V

[1] I = Principal host, II = secondary host, III = occasional host, IV = rare host, and V = immune; "--" dwarf mistletoe not observed within range of the tree.

Arceuthobium	Picea						
	breweriana	engelmannii	glauca	mariana	pungens	rubens	sitchensis
A. abietinum f. sp. concoloris	II	V	--	--	V	--	--
A. americanum	--	IV	IV	--	IV	--	--
A. californicum	III	--	--	--	--	--	--
A. cyanocarpum	--	IV?	--	--	--	--	--
A. douglasii	--	IV	--	--	IV	--	--
A. laricis	--	III	--	--	--	--	--
A. microcarpum	--	I	--	--	I	--	--
A. pusillum	--	--	I	I	[2]	II	--
A. tsugense	III	IV	--	--	--	--	IV

[1] I = Principal host, II = secondary host, III = occasional host, IV = rare host and V = immune; "--" dwarf mistletoe not observed within range of the tree.

[2] On planted trees in Maine (U. S. Dep. Agr. 1960).

Extra-Limital and Unnatural Hosts

Several workers have inoculated dwarf mistletoes on trees that do not occur naturally within the range of a particular species of *Arceuthobium* (extra-limital hosts). The results of their studies, summarized in table 11, are discussed further under the dwarf mistletoes involved in the Formal Taxonomy section.

Perhaps conditions for infection and development of dwarf mistletoes are more favorable under artificial than natural situations, and plants grown under such conditions have occasionally become established on hosts that are not naturally infected. Weir (1918a) artificially grew *A. campylopodum* on *Abies concolor*. and we grew *A. cyanocarpum* on *Pinus strobiformis*. In nature, these trees are exposed to the two dwarf mistletoes, but we have not found natural infection of them.

Inoculation experiments are most useful for determining susceptibility of extra-limital hosts. Such studies do not reveal, however, how the parasite will act in the natural environment of a new host. We question whether life-cycle data could be based on artificial inoculations, because of the accelerated growth rates we noted in the greenhouse. For example, when we inoculated *Pinus strobiformis* with *A. cyanocarpum* in the greenhouse we obtained shoots within 5 months, and flowering within 7 months, of the date of inoculation. In nature, *A. cyanocarpum* shoots do not appear until 2 to 3 years after infection, and flowering does not begin until after at least one more year.

Observations of natural susceptibility of trees from outside the range of a mistletoe are sometimes economically important (table 12). For example,

Graham and Leaphart (1961) reported that plantation-grown *Pinus sylvestris* was so severely parasitized by the larch dwarf mistletoe (*A. laricis*) in Washington, that this tree should not be planted in areas where *A. laricis* occurs.

Nonhosts

Since the dwarf mistletoes parasitize so many western conifers we have recorded those in the western United States and Mexican Pinaceae not yet known to be naturally infected by *Arceuthobium*:[16]

Abies: (True firs)
  durangensis
  guatemalensis
  hickeli
  mexicana
  oaxacana
Picea: (Spruces)
  chihuahuana
  mexicana

Pinus: (Pines)
  chiapensis
  greggii
  maximartinezii
  nelsonii
  patula
  pinceana
  rzedowskii
  torreyana
  washoensis
Pseudotsuga: (Douglas-fir)
  macrocarpa

Host-Parasite Relationships

A peculiar feature of dwarf mistletoe parasitism, at least in the central Rocky Mountains, is the existence of a type of host exclusion between taxa (Hawksworth 1968). If the principal parasite of a certain host is present in an area, other dwarf-

[16] Kuijt (1960a) successfully inoculated *Pinus torreyana* with *A. occidentale*; *A. abietis-religiosae* possibly parasitizes *Abies guatemalensis*.

TABLE 11.—*Extension of host ranges of* Arceuthobium *as determined by artificial inoculations on unnatural hosts*

Host	Dwarf mistletoe	Reference
Abies		
concolor	*A. campylopodum*	Weir 1918a
grandis	do.	Do.
Larix		
europaea	*A. laricis*	Do.
leptolepis	do.	Do.
occidentalis	*A. campylopodum*	Do.
Do.	*A. tsugense*	Smith 1970a
Picea		
abies	*A. campylopodum*	Weir 1918a
Do.	*A. tsugense*	Smith 1965
glauca	do.	Do.
engelmannii	do.	Smith 1970b
pungens	do. ?	[1]
Pinus		
banksiana	*A. occidentale*	Hedgcock and Hunt 1917
bungeana	do.	Do.
mugo (as *P. montana*)	*A. campylopodum*	Weir 1918a
Do.	*A. americanum*	Do.
palustris	*A. occidentale*	Hedgcock and Hunt 1917
Pinus		
pinea	do.	Do.
ponderosa	*A. tsugense*	Smith and Craig 1968
radiata	do.	Do.
resinosa	*A. campylopodum*	Weir 1918a
strobiformis	*A. cyanocarpum*	[1]
strobus	do.	[1]
sylvestris	*A. campylopodum*	Weir 1918a
Do.	*A. tsugense*	Smith and Craig 1968
torreyana	*A. occidentale*	Kuijt 1960a
virginiana	do.	Hedgcock and Hunt 1917
Tsuga		
canadensis	*A. tsugense*	Weir 1918a

[1] From studies reported in this paper.

mistletoes rarely parasitize that tree. Conversely, if the principal parasite is absent, the chances of parasitism by other dwarf mistletoes is greatly increased. This is exemplified by *A. americanum* (principal host, in this instance, *Pinus contorta* subsp. *latifolia*) and *A. cyanocarpum* (principal host, *Pinus flexilis*). In mixed stands where *A. americanum* is present, parasitism of *P. contorta* by *A. cyanocarpum* has not been found. Conversely, in stands where there is no *A. americanum*, *A. cyanocarpum* frequently occurs on this host. A comparable, and reciprocal, situation exists for *P. flexilis*. Another example is the relative frequency of *A. americanum* on *Pinus ponderosa* var. *scopulorum* and *A. vaginatum* subsp. *cryptopodum* on *Pinus contorta*, which shows a similar relationship to that above (Hawksworth 1968).

Wiens (1962) has recorded a comparable situation in *Phoradendron* parasitizing junipers. The explanation for this host exclusion principle is unknown and presents a fascinating field for research.

The dwarf mistletoes seem to show an "all or nothing" parasitism of trees that are rarely infected. Such trees are usually immune, but when infection does occur such individuals are often moderately to highly parasitized. An example of this is the parasitism of *Picea engelmannii* by *A. americanum*. Usually less than 1 percent of the spruces are infected in stands where the mistletoe is common on the associated *Pinus contorta*. However, the individual *P. engelmannii* trees that are parasitized may bear 100 infections or more (Hawksworth and Graham 1963).

Our field studies suggest that some very rare trees have little resistance to dwarf mistletoes. For example, *Pinus culminicola* is readily parasitized by *Arceuthobium vaginatum* subsp. *vaginatum*, and *Picea breweriana* is infected by *A. abietinum* f. sp. *concoloris* (fig. 8), *A. californicum*, and *A. tsugense* in every instance where we have seen them exposed to these dwarf mistletoes. The situation for *Abies bracteata* may be similar (because *Arceuthobium* has been collected on it), but we have not observed this tree associated with dwarf mistletoe. No dwarf mistletoe occurs within the range of *Pinus torreyana*, but Kuijt (1960a) inoculated this tree with *A. occidentale* and found it susceptible.

Features that often indicate host-parasite incompatibility are poor (sometimes lack of) shoot development and unusually large swellings at the point of infection (table 13).

Host Reactions

The first external symptom that a dwarf mistletoe has become established in a branch is usually a swelling of the host tissues at the point of infection. As the infection becomes older, the swellings enlarge and eventually become fusiform. Typically, dwarf mistletoe infection leads to the production of profuse, dense masses of distorted host branches called "witches' brooms" (figs. 8–14).

Two basic types of witches' brooms are formed (Kuijt 1960b, Hawksworth 1961a): (1) Systemic (isophasic) types in which growth of the endophytic system keeps pace with growth of the infected

TABLE 12.—*Reports of extra-limital hosts naturally infected by dwarf mistletoes*

Host	*Arceuthobium*	Locality	Reference
Cupressus			
macrocarpa	*A. oxycedri*	U.S.S.R.	Zefirov 1955
Larix			
europaea	*A. tsugense*	British Columbia	Kuijt 1964
Picea			
abies	*A. laricis*	Idaho	U. S. Dep. Agr. 1963
pungens	*A. pusillum*	Maine	U. S. Dep. Agr. 1960
Pinus			
banksiana	*A. laricis*	Idaho	Graham 1959a
pinaster	*A. campylopodum*	California	Kuijt 1960b
resinosa	*A. laricis*	Idaho	U. S. Dep. Agr. 1962
sylvestris	do.	Washington	Graham and Leaphart 1961
Do.	*A. americanum*	do.	Do.
Do.	do.	Alberta	Powell 1968
Do.	*A. campylopodum*	Idaho	J. R. Weir, unpubl.[1]

[1] Specimen at the University of Illinois.

branch, dwarf mistletoe shoots are scattered along the host branch, often concentrated at the branch girdles and, (2) nonsystemic (anisophasic) types in which the shoots remain concentrated near the original site of infection. These two types of broom formation, however, are species constant and therefore of taxonomic value. *Arceuthobium americanum*, *A. douglasii*, *A. guatemalense*, *A. minutissimum*, and *A. pusillum* consistently form systemic brooms. Herbarium specimens reveal that *A. chinense*

TABLE 13.—*Reported incompatible host-parasite relationships*

Arceuthobium	Host	Reference
A. abietinum f. sp.		
concoloris	*Pinus lambertiana*	R. F. Scharpf[1]
Do.	*Pinus contorta* subsp. *murrayana*	D. A. Graham[1]
A. americanum	*Pinus albicaulis*	Weir 1918b
Do.	*Picea pungens*	[2]
Do.	*Pseudotsuga menziesii*	R. S. Peterson[1]
A. pusillum	*Larix laricina*	Tainter and French 1967
A. tsugense	*Larix europaea*	Kuijt 1964
Do.	*Larix occidentalis* (inoculations)	R. B. Smith[1]
Do.	*Picea engelmannii*	[2]
Do.	*Picea sitchensis*	Laurent 1966

[1] Personal communications, 1965–69.
[2] First reported in this paper.

and *A. pini* also cause systemic brooms, but whether this host reaction is consistent is not known. The nonsystemic type is much more common, although most dwarf mistletoes will sometimes cause systemic brooms. In a few host-parasite combinations, little or no witches' brooms of either type are formed.

In *Pinus contorta* branches older than about 5 years, *A. americanum* shoots on systemic brooms are formed only at the girdles and not on the segments (Kuijt 1960b). Similarly, our limited observations of systemic infections of *A. abietis-religiosae* on *Abies religiosa* suggest that here, also, the dwarf mistletoe shoots are produced only at the girdles.

Within a host genus, the parasite and not the host determines the type of brooms formed (Hawksworth 1956a, Kuijt 1960b, Weir 1916). For example, the witches' brooms formed by *A. americanum* on any pine are basically similar, but are distinctly different on spruce (Hawksworth and Graham 1963, Kuijt 1960b).

Although systemically infected branches are usually immune to secondary infection, Muir (1968) reported several secondary pistillate and staminate infections on a pistillate systemic broom of *A. americanum* on *Pinus banksiana* in northeastern Alberta. The secondary infections were detectable because of the location of their shoots, differences in shoot color, and formation of swellings. We have observed similar situations (one instance each) in the following: *A. americanum* on *Pinus contorta* in Colorado, *A. vaginatum* subsp. *cryptopodum* on *P. ponderosa* in Arizona, and *A. guatemalense* on *P. ayacahuite* in Guatemala.

Kuijt (1960b) reported that cones usually are not produced on witches' brooms, particularly systemic ones. Bonga (1964), however, noted fertile cones on an aberrant broom in *Picea mariana* caused by *Arceuthobium pusillum*. We have observed cones on several systemic witches' brooms on *Pinus contorta* (caused by *A. americanum*) but all were sterile.

Effects on Hosts

The dwarf mistletoes are serious pathogens of North American forest trees, and in many parts of the West they are the most damaging disease agents. They not only cause extensive losses through direct mortality, but also adversely affect growth rates of infected trees. In addition, the dwarf mistletoes reduce seed production and wood quality, and in some hosts, particularly *Abies* and *Tsuga*, provide entrance points for decay fungi. The extent of the damage caused by these parasites is estimated to total 3.2 billion board feet annually in the western United States (Shea and Howard 1969). At 1970 prices, this annual loss totals about $75 million. The commercially important trees that are most seriously damaged are *Pinus ponderosa*, *P. contorta*, *P. banksiana*, *P. lambertiana*, *Pseudotsuga menziesii*, *Abies magnifica*, *A. concolor*, *Larix occidentalis*, and *Tsuga heterophylla*. *Arceuthobium pusillum*, considered the most serious cause of timber loss in *Picea mariana* in the Lake States, also causes serious losses in *Picea glauca* along the coast of Maine.

Dwarf mistletoe infection reduces the tree's growth rate in both height and diameter, but there is no significant reduction until the upper half of the tree's crown is parasitized. Then the growth rate declines rapidly as the degree of infection in the upper crown increases (Hawksworth 1961a).

Heavy dwarf mistletoe infection eventually kills the tree. However, the length of time required for the parasite to kill a tree varies considerably, and depends on many factors: the host and dwarf mistletoe species involved; the amount of infection

in a tree; the vigor of the tree; the ecological and climatic situation under which the tree is growing; and activity of secondary pests, particularly bark beetles, which often attack and help kill heavily infected trees. Some host-parasite combinations in which tree mortality is particularly high are:

Dwarf mistletoe	Hosts
A. abietinum f. sp. *magnificae*	*Abies magnifica*
A. americanum	*Pinus contorta*, *P. banksiana*
A. cyanocarpum	*P. flexilis*, *P. albicaulis*
A. douglasii	*Pseudotsuga menziesii*
A. laricis	*Larix occidentalis*
A. microcarpum	*Picea engelmannii*, *P. pungens*
A. pusillum	*Picea mariana*, *P. glauca*
A. vaginatum subsp. *cryptopodum*	*Pinus ponderosa*

How dwarf mistletoes affect the growth of their host trees is not fully understood. Important factors, however, might be the appropriation of water, minerals, and other nutrients by the parasite and infected parts of the lower crown at the expense of upper parts of the crown. Once a branch becomes infected, it utilizes more than its share of nutrients. Thus, the diameter growth of infected branches is greatly enhanced. Infected branches may become several times as large as uninfected branches in the same whorl, and they tend to live long after the adjacent uninfected branches are shaded out. As progressively more and more nutrients are appropriated by infected branches, the vigor of the crown declines. Eventually, the effective photosynthetic surface area of noninfected branches is reduced below that necessary to sustain the tree, and death results.

Leonard and Hull (1965) found that several dwarf mistletoes in California obtained large quantities of photosynthate from their hosts at all seasons of the year. Although the dwarf mistletoes do contain chlorophyll and can manufacture a small part of their required carbohydrates, neither material is translocated to the host. Physiological work on the water balance of dwarf mistletoe-infected trees is needed.

MECHANISMS AND TRENDS OF EVOLUTION

The Genetic System and Recombination Potential

Arceuthobium has a base chromosome number of $x = 14$ (that is, the lowest extant haploid number). Polyploidy is unknown. A base chromosome number of $x = 14$ is relatively high in the angiosperms, and one might suspect that $x = 14$ is a tetraploid on a base of seven. This is unlikely, however, because in

the Viscaceae as a whole the lowest known number is $x = 10$ (in *Viscum*). *Viscum* shows an aneuploid series ranging from $x = 10$–13 and may be the primitive genus in the Viscaceae. The putatively derived genera, *Phoradendron*, *Korthalsella*, and *Arceuthobium*, are all characterized by chromosome numbers of $x = 14$. Chromosome evolution in the Viscaceae as a whole is discussed in detail by Wiens and Barlow (1971). In view of the patterns of

Figure 8.—Effects of dwarf mistletoes on various hosts: *A, Arceuthobium abietinum* f. sp. *concoloris* on *Picea breweriana*, severely broomed tree killed by the parasite, Siskiyou National Forest, Oregon; *B, A. douglasii* on *Pseudotsuga menziesii*, most trees have been killed by the parasite, Mescalero Apache Reservation, New Mexico; *C, A. occidentale* on *Pinus sabiniana*, no brooms formed even though trees are heavily infected, both trees died within 2 years after the photograph was taken, North Fork, California; *D, A. microcarpum* on *Picea pungens*, note the small brooms and the trees killed by the mistletoe, Grand Canyon National Park, Arizona.

29

Figure 9.—Witches' brooms caused by *Arceuthobium americanum*: *A*, on *Pinus ponderosa* (left) and *P. contorta* (right) note similarity of the brooms; *B*, on *Picea engelmannii*, brooms are distinctly different from those in pines caused by same mistletoe; *C*, on *Pinus contorta*; (*A, B, C*, in Roosevelt National Forest, Colorado.) *D*, on *Pinus banksiana*, Golden Ridge, Saskatchewan; photograph by J. G. Laut, Canadian Department of Fisheries and Forestry.

Figure 10.—Witches' brooms on pines caused by five dwarf mistletoes: *A, Arceuthobium strictum* on *Pinus leiophylla* var. *chihuahuana* (left), and *A. verticilliflorum* on *P. engelmannii* (right) show difference in host reaction to the two mistletoes; *B, A. rubrum* on *Pinus teocote* (right), not in *P. engelmannii* (left) but elsewhere this tree is parasitized by *A. rubrum*; *C, A. gillii* subsp. *nigrum* severely damaging *Pinus leiophylla*; (*A, B, C,* near El Salto, Durango, Mexico.) *D, A. californicum* on *Pinus lambertiana*, Sierra National Forest, California.

31

Figure 11.—Effects of dwarf mistletoe on various pines: *A, B, C—Arceuthobium vaginatum* subsp. *cryptopodum. A,* on *Pinus engelmannii,* El Largo, Chihuahua, Mexico; *B,* massive witches' broom in *Pinus ponderosa,* Grand Canyon National Park, Arizona; *C,* group of *Pinus ponderosa* killed by dwarf mistletoe, Grand Canyon National Park, Arizona; *D, A. guatemalense* on *Pinus ayacahuite,* Sierra Cuchumatanes, Guatemala.

Figure 12.—Witches' brooms caused by two southern dwarf mistletoes. *A, B, Arceuthobium bicarinatum* on *Pinus occidentalis*, Constanza, Dominican Republic; *C, D, A. hondurense* on *P. oocarpa*, near Tegucigalpa, Honduras. In D, the dense clumps in the lower crown are epiphytic bromeliads.

Figure 13.—Witches' brooms caused by larch and hemlock dwarf mistletoes: *A* and *B*, *Arceuthobium laricis* on *Larix occidentalis*, Blue Mountains, Oregon. Photograph *B* by J. R. Weir. *C*, *A. laricis* on *Tsuga mertensiana*, Coeur d' Alene National Forest, Idaho; *D*, *A. tsugense* on *Tsuga mertensiana*, Stanislaus National Forest, California.

Figure 14.—Dwarf mistletoes on various conifers: *A, Arceuthobium pusillum* on *Picea mariana*, Minnesota; *B, A. pusillum* on *P. glauca*, Minnesota. Photographs *A* and *B* by D. W. French, University of Minnesota. *C, A. campylopodum* on *Pinus ponderosa*, near Spokane Washington; photograph by J. R. Weir; *D, A. minutissimum* on *Pinus griffithii*, Kashmir:

chromosome numbers and change in the family, the $x = 14$ in *Arceuthobium* appears to be the product of an increasing aneuploid series, rather than a tetraploid based on $x = 7$.

The apparent chromosome system in *Arceuthobium* is diploid with $x = 14$. The genetic system is presumably sexual and obligately out-crossing (the genus being dioecious). No evidence of asexual reproduction exists. These characteristics, coupled with the relatively high diploid chromosome number ($x = 14$) and high chiasma frequency (averaging perhaps 2 to 3 chiasma per bivalent), suggest a relatively high recombination index (Darlington 1958).

Progressive Evolution and Adaptive Radiation

The significance of a high recombination index depends on the evolutionary opportunities of the group. For the North American dwarf mistletoes, numerous habitats (host trees) became available for colonization because of the large development of *Pinus* during the Miocene (Mirov 1967). The genetic system of *Arceuthobium*—diploid with high recombination potential—theoretically should be well suited to progressive evolution.

If a large number of ecological niches (host species) are available for colonization, evolution should eventually produce an adaptive radiation into the available niches. The high proportion of North American Pinaceae presently parasitized by *Arceuthobium* (see table 5) indicates that such an adaptive radiation has occurred. With the exception of the eastern pines of North America, most of the major species of Pinaceae are parasitized by *Arceuthobium*.

A factor conceivably important in this adaptive radiation was the apparent lack of competition with other plants for the available niches. With the possible exception of *Phoradendron bolleanum* subsp. *pauciflorum*, which sometimes occurs on *Abies concolor* with *A. abietinum*, and a few tropical species of *Dendropemon*, *Psittacanthus*, and *Struthanthus*, no extant groups compete with *Arceuthobium*. Competition with epiphytes might be expected in tropical cloud forest situations, but this does not occur, presumably because only young shoots are susceptible to infection by dwarf mistletoes. Generally, emerging shoots are infected by dwarf mistletoe before epiphytes can become established.

On the basis of our criteria, a number of dwarf mistletoes have reached a high degree of specialization. This suggests that the basic adaptive radiation has already taken place, and that the adaption is now into increasingly more specialized niches. For example, *A. americanum* and *A. douglasii* are highly

specialized (reduced) morphologically, and also occupy narrow ecological niches, or host trees, to which they are almost exclusively confined. Furthermore, these hosts (*Pinus contorta* and *Pseudotsuga menziesii*) usually are not climax species, as are the hosts for the more primitive species, but are intermediates in the successional sequence of the ecosystems in which they occur. This suggests that the climax host species may have been colonized first by the primitive species of dwarf mistletoes. As these ecological niches were filled, further evolution required the more advanced species to occupy niches (host trees) characteristic of pioneering or intermediate stages of the ecological sere.

Absence of Hybridization and Polyploidy

One of the most significant factors in the evolution of vascular plants is the occurrence of natural hybridization. So pervasive is this phenomenon, that most groups of vascular plants studied by contemporary workers appear to show some evidence of natural hybridization.

In *Arceuthobium*, however, no evidence of natural hybridization has been discovered. In our cumulative years of field experience (and those of several knowledgeable colleagues) we have never encountered a single instance of natural hybridization, although we have consciously searched for such evidence, especially in our studies of sympatry (see table 3). Overlap occurs in a number of characters, especially quantitative traits which might be interpreted as evidence for natural hybridization. We believe, however, that the overlap is the result of evolutionary convergence. While a single character of one taxon might overlap with a trait of another, the majority of character combinations defining each taxon do not occur discordantly (Anderson 1951). Discordant variation occurs through hybridization when character combinations typical of more than one taxon occur together. Traits are concordant in *Arceuthobium*; they remain associated with their regular constellation of characters.

The absence of hybridization is apparently typical of both familes of mistletoes (Barlow and Wiens 1971, Wiens and Barlow 1971), and is not unique to *Arceuthobium*. In *Phoradendron*, a single clear instance of natural hybridization is known (Wiens 1962, Vasek 1966), and the hybrid is apparently sterile. The absence of natural hybridization in *Arceuthobium* as well as other mistletoes can be explained by occurrence of strong interspecific isolating mechanisms, particularly seasonal isolation.

A factor which might explain the apparent absence of hybrids in *Arceuthobium* is the lack of suitable habitats for their establishment. Most dwarf mistletoes have a principal host (see table 5) to which the species must be adapted. Because hybrids combine the genetic characteristics of two species, theoretically they should be adapted to intermediate habitats. However, intermediate habitats in parasitic groups theoretically could be produced only through hybridization of the hosts. In other words, "hybridization" of the habitat, as Anderson (1948) expressed it, would literally be necessary. Various pinaceous hosts of *Arceuthobium* do hybridize, but we are unfamiliar with any situations where two species of dwarf mistletoes parasitize hybridizing host populations. Where host pines do hybridize, for example, *P. jeffreyi* × *P. ponderosa* and *P. contorta* × *P. banksiana*, the hybridizing pair of species are so closely related that they are parasitized by the same dwarf mistletoe.

Another factor that may inhibit hybrid establishment also involves habitat. If intermediate hosts are not available, then hybrids of the dwarf mistletoes, even if they occurred, would be without a suitable habitat and might not survive. Hence, hybrids in *Arceuthobium* might not be detected. Whether or not hybridization in dwarf mistletoes is precluded by strong isolating mechanisms, or because hybrids fail to become established, the result is the same. In either case, there should be strong selective pressures against gene combinations that allow hybridization (Dobzhansky 1951).

The presumed absence of natural hybridization (or hybrid establishment) is an important basis for further evolutionary considerations in *Arceuthobium*. Not only have we failed to discover hybrids in dwarf mistletoes, but they are not reported in the extensive literature of the group. But if hybrids do not occur, we could hardly expect to find literature on the subject.

A theoretical explanation proposed for the absence of polyploidy in *Arceuthobium* (Wiens 1968) is based on the assumption that most polyploids are alloploids (Stebbins 1950), and depend on natural hybridization for their origin. If hybridization does not occur, alloploidy is precluded. Autoploidy might still occur, but its presence is probably of little evolutionary significance; probably the few cases of known polyploidy in the Loranthaceae and Viscaceae are of autoploid origin (Barlow and Wiens 1971, Wiens and Barlow 1971).

Evolutionary Patterns and Taxonomic Structure

Arceuthobium is apparently a sexual, outcrossing group which could be expected to produce a relatively wide pattern of variation. A high recombination potential and open niches on the Pinaceae could provide the fundamental conditions to produce an adaptive radiation onto most North American Pinaceae. In the absence of hybridization and polyploidy, the species have apparently maintained distinct evolutionary lines. This feature has important evolutionary and taxonomic consequences, because distinct phyletic lines should produce dendritic evolutionary patterns.

Such evolutionary patterns are typical of most animals. In vascular plants, however, reticulate evolution is the rule, and is almost certainly produced through natural hybridization. Alloploidy may stabilize hybrid genomes into true-breeding species. Hybridization and polyploidy, therefore, have the result of combining the characteristics of different evolutionary lines and thereby produce reticulate evolutionary patterns characteristic of vascular plants.

In contrast, a dendritic evolutionary pattern appears to characterize *Arceuthobium*, but the situation is obscured by the extreme morphological reduction attendant with the parasitic habit. The species of *Arceuthobium* are relatively distinct, but the characters separating them are often cryptic or discernible for only short periods of the life cycle. Even though individual characters are not always clearly evident, when the characters are analyzed in their totality, the taxa become well differentiated. This is evident from our numerical analyses which show that all taxa have a relatively high degree of integrity and tend to be more distinct than in other groups where hybridization has played an important evolutionary role (Sokal and Sneath 1963).

The two subgenera or phyletic lines (based on branching patterns) which Kuijt (1970) proposed seem valid, but the reduction of shoots in species such as *A. pusillum* sometimes obscures the relationship. In *Arceuthobium* the evolutionary pattern is further characterized by three stages of evolutionary divergence. These three stages appear to be present in both the New and Old Worlds, but are better developed in the former.

Because of the dendritic evolutionary patterns, these evolutionary stages can be defined taxonomically and basically correspond to the primitive, intermediate, and advanced species groups we propose in the New World subgenera (see discussion under the subgenera and fig. 15). We have constructed a subgeneric taxonomy based on what appear to be definable evolutionary stages in distinct phyletic lines. We believe that the taxonomic treatment given here generally represents the phyletic history of *Arceuthobium*.

Evolutionary Trends

Evolutionary trends in *Arceuthobium* are inferred (Gill 1935), but the course of evolution is far from

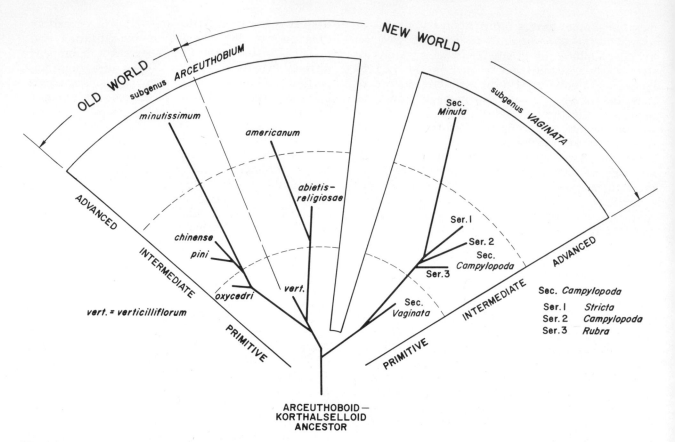

Figure 15.—Presumed phyletic evolution of *Arceuthobium* showing two primary lines of diversification—subgenera *Arceuthobium* and *Vaginata*. Subgenus *Arceuthobium* is divided into Old World and New World groups with three and four species, respectively. Subgenus *Vaginata* contains a primitive group (Sec. *Vaginata*), an intermediate group (Sec. *Campylopoda*), and an advanced group (Sec. *Minuta*).

understood. Some evolutionary tendencies that we recognize are summarized below:

Characteristic	Primitive	Advanced
Host specificity	Low	High
Shoot size	Large	Small
Fruit maturation period	Long	Short
Shoot longevity	Long	Short
Polymorphism	High	Low
Flowering group	Direct	Indirect
Branching type	Verticillate	Flabellate
Witches' brooms	Nonsystemic	Systemic

By most of Gill's criteria, *A. pusillum* and *A. douglasii* are the most advanced species, and *A. vaginatum* and *A. campylopodum* the most primitive. We use the concepts of Davis and Heywood (1963) that primitive groups are not necessarily ancient: "Primitive or advanced groups may be ancient or recent according to whether they became separate entities early or late in evolution." "Primitive" merely connotes a character that occurs in both the modern species and its ancestors, while "advanced" implies derived characters not present in ancestral stock.

Wiens (1968) studied the flowering characteristics of the New World dwarf mistletoes. He hypothesized that the different flowering groups arose as the genus moved northward from Mexico (the present area of greatest species diversity) into latitudes of greater annual variation in photoperiod. He concluded that taxa with indirect, spring flowering (*A. americanum, A. douglasii, A. pusillum*) were derived from those with direct, summer flowering (the *campylopodum* group, *A. rubrum*, and *A. strictum*), which in turn are derived from those with direct, spring flowering (*A. abietis-religiosae, A. globosum, A. verticilliflorum*, and *A. vaginatum*).

Kuijt (1970) presents evidence that flabellate branching pattern in *Arceuthobium*, common in most North American taxa, is a derived character. The more primitive, verticillate type of branching is present in the two Old World species in which this trait was studied (*A. oxycedri* and *A. chinense*). The diminutive *A. minutissimum*, and the New World *A. pusillum*, are so reduced that their basic branching type is not determinable. In the New World, *A. americanum* and *A. abietis-religiosae* exhibit verticillate branching. *Arceuthobium verticilliflorum* is anomalous because the flowers are verticillate, but the stems show no secondary branching. However, Kuijt (1970) states the branching pattern in *A. verticilliflorum* is basically verticillate.

The formation of systemic (or isophasic) witches' brooms (see p. 26) is an additional feature that probably indicates an advanced degree of evolution. Although systemic types of witches' brooms are occasionally induced by several dwarf mistletoes, they are consistently formed by only five species: *A. pusillum*, *A. douglasii*, *A. guatemalense*, and *A. americanum* in the New World, and *A. minutissimum* in the Himalayas. Some host-parasite combinations, where witches' brooms are not consistently formed, may represent a primitive state that preceded nonsystemic broom formation, which, in turn, may have preceded systemic broom formation. Systemic witches' brooms seem to be of adaptive advantage because they greatly increase the reproductive potential of the dwarf mistletoe. By formation of systemic witches' brooms, the endophytic system from a single seed can ramify through hundreds of linear feet of host branches and produce a profusion of shoots, flowers, and fruit.

Most dwarf mistletoes eventually kill their hosts, but mortality occurs much sooner in some host-parasite combinations than in others. Parasites that are less lethal to their hosts are presumably better adapted. This factor is apparently not related, however, to the relative stage of advancement as measured by other factors. For example, *A. pusillum*, *A. americanum*, and *A. douglasii* are presumably advanced species, but are ultimately very damaging to their hosts. However, this could be explained if these species are relatively newly evolved and neither the host nor the dwarf mistletoe are yet co-adapted—the dwarf mistletoe for less pathogenicity and the host for greater resistance. Within the *campylopodum* group there are some taxa that cause severe host mortality (for example, *A. laricis* on *Larix occidentalis*), and some in which host mortality is relatively low (*A. divaricatum* on pinyons).

We consider *A. pusillum* and *A. douglasii* to be

the most advanced New World species, because they exhibit the following features: (1) very small shoots, (2) very specific host associations, (3) derived flowering type, (4) flabellate branching, in *A. douglasii*, and probably in *A. pusillum*, and (5) consistent formation of systemic witches' brooms. Conversely, the Mexican species, *A. verticilliflorum*, probably represents the most primitive species because of its (1) large shoots and extremely large fruits, (2) less specific association, (3) primitive flowering type, (4) verticillate branching, and (5) formation of nonsystemic witches' brooms.

Arceuthobium is primarily a parasite of *Pinus*, since 22 of the 32 taxa occur principally on this genus (see fig. 7). Of the 22 taxa, 15 parasitize *Diploxylon* and 7 *Haploxylon* pines. Mirov (1967) recognizes 73 *Diploxylon* and 32 *Haploxylon* pines, so about one-fifth of each group is parasitized. The oldest known pine fossils are from the Jurassic period, and even then the pines had differentiated into the subgenera *Haploxylon* and *Diploxylon*, the former possibly preceding the latter (Mirov 1967).

In both the Old and New Worlds, *Pinus* (*Diploxylon* and *Haploxylon*) and *Abies* are hosts of *Arceuthobium*. However, four other genera (*Larix*, *Picea*, *Pseudotsuga*, and *Tsuga*) that occur in both hemispheres are parasitized only in the New World. *Juniperus*, which is common throughout the Northern Hemisphere, is a host only in the Old World. *Keteleeria*, a genus not found in the New World, is parasitized in China.

We surmise that the primitive *Arceuthobium* stock was a relatively large, verticillately branched parasite of pines in northeastern Asia. Chromosomal and morphological studies suggest that *Korthalsella* is the closest related living genus, and that the two genera arose from common ancestral stocks (Wiens and Barlow 1971). One species, *Korthalsella dacrydii*, occurs on conifers (*Podocarpus*) and even has mildly explosive fruit (Danser 1937). *Korthalsella* is now distributed from Hawaii through the South Pacific to Africa (Danser 1937). *Arceuthobium*, conversely, spread westward to the Mediterranean region, south into Africa, and northeastward through the Bering Straits region into the New World. In the New World, the genus apparently found ideal conditions for rapid expansion, and many new species evolved. Generally, in the Tertiary period, the angiosperms have evolved more rapidly than the gymnosperms (Leopold 1967). Consistent with this trend, the dwarf mistletoes probably evolved much more rapidly than their coniferous hosts.

SYSTEMATICS OF *ARCEUTHOBIUM*

Taxonomic Considerations

Arceuthobium has long been considered to be a taxonomically difficult genus. This is primarily because the genus has undergone extreme morphological reduction due to its parasitic habit. Also, the general morphological aspects of all members of the group are similar and there are few gross discontinuous variables. Many of the morphological features such as leaves and trichomes commonly used in the classification of other mistletoe groups are not present in the genus. In all species, the flowers are small (2–4 mm. in diameter) and generally similar in form.

Gill (1935) segregated the members of the *Arceuthobium campylopodum* and *A. vaginatum* groups into host forms, that is, "taxa delimited exclusively on the basis of the host relationships, without regard to biological parity." Although Gill's system provided an effective and facile method for naming the various dwarf mistletoes, it obscured the systematic difficulties in the group. Gill realized his classification system was unnatural, but available data were too limited for a more natural treatment. Gill noted that the "forms are not all of equal rank in the sense of being biologically distinct. Some are well-developed strains showing a marked affinity for a limited group of host species, while others are admittedly artificial categories, into which infrequent or even accidental host relationships of the better defined forms have been cast." Gill further stated that a system of forms based exclusively on hosts "though without good taxonomic precedent, should be tolerable as a temporary device, pending a complete revision of the genus based on further field and experimental evidence." As will be shown, we consider Gill's host forms in *Arceuthobium campylopodum* and *A. vaginatum* to be morphologically distinct; hence, they warrant higher taxonomic rank.

Danser (1950) stated that the function of taxonomy is to classify life cycles. Danser was a student of the Old World mistletoes, and how much his experience with mistletoes influenced his thinking is unknown. However, such a concept is particularly well suited to the classification of *Arceuthobium*, where general reduction and convergence of gross features of the sporophyte have obscured the relationships of the species. The idea that all aspects of an organism are potentially useful taxonomically is not new, but we have not seen the idea expressed in quite the same context as Danser. We believe that Danser's idea of classifying life cycles provides a useful theoretical model on which to base systematic studies. As a corollary, discontinuities between life cycles should determine taxonomic units.

The term "life cycle" is used in this paper to encompass all aspects of the biology of a dwarf mistletoe, and includes interactions with host and environment. All phases of the life cycle are considered here as potentially valid taxonomic criteria, and the first priority is to determine the basic features of the life cycle in the group and to isolate discontinuities between them. The test of valid discontinuities rests on genetic control and consistency of occurrence. Other valid taxonomic criteria we have considered are physiological characters such as time of meiosis, anthesis, period of seed dispersal, time of seed germination, host specificity, and brooming response of the host because they are measurable and consistent. We therefore disagree with Davis and Heywood (1963) who question the use of physiological characters in taxonomy. Quantitative and qualitative morphological characters may also be utilized in classification. The quantitative difference, while often small, may be statistically and taxonomically significant.

Previous difficulties in the genus are therefore the result of the extreme reduction and lack of precise data on morphology and life cycles. There appear to be few other plant groups in which a knowledge of living populations is so essential for their classification.

At certain stages of their life cycle, some dwarf mistletoes may be difficult to identify. The herbarium taxonomist, confronted by an individual specimen, might well experience difficulty in identification because of the particular stage of the life cycle represented in the specimen before him. For example, in a nonflowering specimen the time of anthesis might not be obvious. Color, generally consistent in living plants, may be altered in drying; *A. rubrum* is a dark, shiny red in nature but becomes dull brown when dried. Characteristics of habit, obvious in living plants, such as *A. globosum* which forms open spherical masses, may be completely obliterated by careless pressing or fragmentation. Because *Arceuthobium* is difficult to preserve and fragments easily, general botanists seldom collect these plants. Some suggestions for collecting and curating dwarf mistletoes are given on page 61.

The monographer's duty is to extensively study the life cycles of various taxa to determine their significant differences and similarities. Whether these differences are easily discernible in a particular specimen in no way affects their intrinsic taxonomic value. The distinctions between classification and ease of identification should not be confused.

Fortunately, characters such as host specificity may provide an easy method of identification, but this does not infer that our classification is based on hosts alone, because no characters in our system are weighted.

The key we have prepared reflects natural relationships, and includes characters manifest at various stages of the life cycle. In addition, an artificial key to facilitate identification is included.

Natural hybrids apparently do not exist in *Arceuthobium*, so the taxa should be easily delimited unless they represent intermediate stages of gradual evolutionary divergence. In *Arceuthobium* the taxa appear to be reasonably well defined, and significant discontinuous variation occurs in a number of characters. The amount of infra-taxon variation is about what one would expect in a sexual, outcrossing group. Even the subspecific categories appear to be demarcated by relatively sharp discontinuities, although of less magnitude than those separating species.

Problems in Classification

Based on our exhaustive field observations and experimental studies, we believe the taxa Gill (1935) classified as host forms in the *A. campylopodum* complex are distinct species. The most convincing evidence to support our position is that *when these dwarf mistletoes occur on trees other than the principal host, they maintain their morphological integrity and are identifiable*. Natural dwarf mistletoe crossovers from principal hosts to secondary, occasional, or rare hosts have been observed in all but 4 of the 13 members of the main *A. campylopodum* group (*A. apachecum*, *A. blumeri*, *A. guatemalense*, and *A. divaricatum*).

Various examples illustrate difficulties with Gill's host-form concept. At McKenzie Pass, Oregon, where *Arceuthobium tsugense* occurs on *Pinus albicaulis*, *Abies lasiocarpa*, and the principal host, *Tsuga mertensiana*, the parasities on all hosts are identifiable as *A. tsugense*. Under Gill's system, however, three different names (f. *cyanocarpum*, f. *abietinum*, and f. *tsugensis*, respectively) were assigned according to the host plant. At Priest River Experimental Forest, Idaho, *A. laricis*, common on its principal host (*Larix occidentalis*), is also found on *Pinus contorta* and on three introduced conifers, *P. banksiana*, *P. resinosa*, and *Picea abies*. Here, too, the morphological integrity of the dwarf mistletoe is retained. The host-form concept is difficult to apply when dwarf mistletoes occur on introduced hosts since, by definition, each form is restricted to a specific host. Strict adherence to such an unnatural system would require that a new name be coined for each new host-parasite combination.

Another disadvantage to Gill's treatment is that whenever more than one member of the *A. campylopodum* group parasitized the same host, all had the same name. For example, where *A. campylopodum*, *A. laricis*, and *A. cyanocarpum* parasitized *Pinus ponderosa*, all three were classified as *A. campylopodum* f. *camplyopodum*. Each dwarf mistletoe, however, is morphologically distinct on *P. ponderosa* as well as on any other of its hosts. This evidence also supports our contention that these are valid taxa rather than host forms, because of discontinuous variations among them.

In addition to morphological integrity, dwarf mistletoes show definite host preferences, even though they occasionally occur on trees other than their principal hosts. The reasoning employed when we assigned taxonomic ranks, particularly in the troublesome *A. campylopodum* group, can be illustrated by *A. campylopodum* and *A. occidentale*. *Pinus ponderosa* and *P. sabiniana*, respectively, are their principal hosts, and these dwarf mistletoes are restricted to their principal hosts even where the hosts of the other mistletoe occur sympatrically. This could be interpreted as evidence that these dwarf mistletoes simply represent ecotypic races; however, morphological and physiological differences (other than host) also characterize the two plants. Where the two populations occasionally occur together, the morphological type of each dwarf mistletoe occurs on its respective host. *Arceuthobium occidentale* also occurs on *Pinus radiata* and *P. muricata*, but not *P. ponderosa*. In these cases, it is easy to identify as that which predominately occurs on *P. sabiniana*. *Arceuthobium campylopodum*, whose principal host is the typical variety of *P. ponderosa*, is also found on some other pines such as *P. jeffreyi*, *P. attenuata*, *P. coulteri*, but not *P. sabiniana*. Again, the morphological and physiological characteristics of the dwarf mistletoe remain relatively stable and identifiable.

The peak flowering periods of *A. campylopodum* and *A. occidentale* differ, but there is some overlap. If mutual pollinating agents are available, gene exchange should occur if the plants are crossable. The problem of sympatry is complicated in parasitic groups (Dobzhansky 1951). However, we consider these two dwarf mistletoes to be sympatric because, in terms of temporal and spatial characteristics, gene exchange should be possible unless they are genetically isolated. Although one is tempted to weight sympatry in classification, we have not done so since the present data show sufficient diversification between the two taxa to warrant specific status. All members of the *A. campylopodum* group are sympatric with at least one other member of the group (see fig. 6). In all cases the morphological integrity of each dwarf mistletoe is maintained.

Our research indicates that the number of species in *Arceuthobium* is greater than that recognized by previous workers. We believe two criteria are fundamental in delimiting these taxa as species. First, and perhaps most critical, is that dwarf mistletoes maintain their morphological integrity when growing on trees other than their principal host. Secondly, taxa, recognized as species, are almost always sympatric, yet show no evidence of hybridization.

Some taxonomists may question why many taxa we recognize as species should not be considered ecotypes. Ecotypes are usually defined as genetically distinct races physiologically adapted to localized habitats and sometimes differentiated morphologically, particularly by quantitative characters. The taxa we recognize as species should not be considered ecotypes because of their morphological integrity on nonprincipal hosts, and the lack of intermediates between sympatric taxa. Also, ecotypes are not reproductively isolated and usually are not distributed as widely as the taxa we recognize as species. *A. microcarpum* has the most restricted range of any dwarf mistletoe outside of Latin America; it is found only within a 300-mile area in Arizona and New Mexico. Most dwarf mistletoes have ranges at least twice this large. Conceivably, some of the dwarf mistletoes we recognize as species might correspond to regional ecotypes, but most taxonomists consider regional ecotypes to be comparable to subspecies so the taxonomic treatment would not be greatly different.

We believe that ecotypes occur in *Arceuthobium*, but they do not exhibit the level of differentiation of taxa we recognize as species or subspecies. Species of dwarf mistletoe with more than one principal host probably are ecotypically differentiated in various parts of their range. For example, *Pinus ponderosa* is one of the principal hosts of *A. campylopodum*, and this tree is parasitized from Washington to southern California. In parts of northern California and southern Oregon, however, where the principal host of *A. campylopodum* is *Pinus attenuata*, associated *P. ponderosa* is seldom infected. Within a dwarf mistletoe, however, cross infection between the principal hosts occurs. Therefore, we do not believe a useful purpose is served by taxonomic recognition of populations we consider as ecotypes.

Subspecific Classification

Subspecies in *Arceuthobium* are interesting because they do not conform to commonly accepted definitions. Geographically associated morphological variation occurs in two species of North American mistletoes, *A. gillii* and *A. vaginatum*. Usually no gradation of characteristics or "shading-off" occurs between the *Arceuthobium* population systems that constitute subspecies, as is common in many plant groups. The presence of discontinuous variation between such population systems might suggest that they should be species, even though the differences are small. This situation might be comparable to that in *Carex* where the species are often based on small, yet apparently consistent, differences. We believe, however, that geographically restricted populations, delimited by relatively few but consistent variations, are best classified as subspecific units.

In *A. abietinum*, we have used the category of *forma specialis*, to avoid confusion with the usual concept of *forma* which denotes morphological distinction. Special forms designate physiological races without morphological differences. Scharpf and Parmeter (1967) have shown experimentally that the dwarf mistletoe on *Abies magnifica* will not infect *Abies concolor*, and vice versa. However, the form on *A. concolor* will also infect *Abies grandis*, and the form on *A. magnifica* will parasitize *A. procera* (see discussion under *A. abietinum*). This high specificity is confirmed from field studies in mixed fir stands. If the races of *A. abietinum* could parasitize either species of fir, their presence would be expected in mixed stands where millions of dwarf mistletoe seeds from each type of fir are deposited yearly on the other species. Yet, cross infection does not occur.

CRITERIA FOR CLASSIFICATION

In our treatment of *Arceuthobium*, we considered many morphological, palynological, cytological, physiological, and chemical features of the genus. Some traits, for example, branching and flowering season, are classical characters used by Engelmann and Gill. Other characters such as pollen, flowering group, and shoot pigments, have not been previously used in the classification of the genus.

Morphological Characters

Plant Size and Habit

Shoot size varies considerably within the genus from a mean of about 0.5 cm. for *A. minutissimum* to over 70 cm. for *A. globosum*. Thus the size of mature plants may be over 100 times larger in some species than in others. Hooker (1886) reported *A. minutissimum* as the smallest dicotyledonous plant, but *Pilostyles thurberi* (Rafflesiaceae), a parasite of leguminous trees in Southwestern deserts, probably is smaller.

Within a taxon, shoots on systemic witches' brooms are somewhat smaller than nonsystemic infections on the same host. In our descriptions, (see Formal Taxonomy section) the shoot dimensions for the most common situation for each species are given; that is, for systemic brooms for *A. americanum*, *A. douglasii*, *A. guatemalense*, *A. minutissimum*, and *A. pusillum*, but for nonsystemic infections for all other taxa. Also, shoot dimensions as given are for both pistillate and staminate plants. Plants of one sex are occasionally larger than those of the other, but the differences usually are not significant.

Plant size varies somewhat because the vigor of the dwarf mistletoe depends directly on the vigor of the host plant. Mean dimensions shown for each species are based on the most frequently observed situations; in addition, we have indicated the tallest shoots measured for each taxon.

Growth habit is a distinguishing character for some species. Shoots may form dense spherical masses (*A. globosum* and *A. occidentale*), be scattered along the stem (as in most taxa), or so dense that the host twigs are obscured (*A. cyanocarpum* and *A. apachecum*).

Shoots

Gill (1935) used branching as a major taxonomic character in classifying *Arceuthobium*. All species have decussate primary branching (Kuijt 1970), and in some taxa branching proceeds no further (*A. pusillum*, *A. minutissimum*, and *A. verticilliflorum*). In most taxa, however, secondary branching is apparent and is of two basic types: verticillate or flabellate (see fig. 1). Kuijt (1970) considers the verticillate habit to be a primitive feature present in the Old World taxa, *A. oxycedri*, *A. chinense*, and presumably in *A. minutissimum*, and in three New World taxa, *A. americanum*, *A. abietis-religiosae*, and *A. verticilliflorum*. The latter species does not actually exhibit secondary branching, although the flowers are verticillately arranged. The remaining New World taxa show flabellate branching. *A. pusillum*, however, is so reduced that the basic branching type cannot be determined, but it probably belongs in the flabellate group. Some taxa show little secondary branching, for example, *A. rubrum* (flabellate) or *A. abietis-religiosae* (verticillate).

Internode dimensions are useful criteria for distinguishing several species. We have consistently used the third internode from the base for this statistic. Length and standard deviation of the third internode are given for each taxon in the Formal Taxonomy section. Frequently the basal and second internodes are not normally elongated. Because dwarf mistletoe shoots have a basal meristem, individual shoot internodes elongate for several years. For this reason, Kuijt (1970) has questioned the validity of our use of internode dimensions as a taxonomic character. However, the overall mature internode dimensions among taxa differ so much that internodal elongation does not negate the usefulness of the characters in certain cases (fig. 16). When we analyzed the length/width ratio of the third internode (table 14), we found less variation than in length alone.

Some species show sexual dimorphism in shoot characteristics. For example, the staminate shoots of the two subspecies of *A. gillii* are more divaricate than the pistillate ones. In *A. strictum*, the staminate shoots show no branches in annual growth segments,

TABLE 14.—*Length/width ratio of third internode of the North American taxa of* Arceuthobium

Taxon	Length/width ratio	Number of collections
A. americanum	10.1:1	20
A. abietinum f. sp. *magnificae*	8.8:1	5
A. occidentale	7.1:1	11
A. californicum	7.0:1	8
A. abietinum f. sp. *concoloris*	6.7:1	15
A. guatemalense	6.7:1	3
A. microcarpum	6.2:1	9
A. divaricatum	6.1:1	19
A. laricis	6.1:1	12
A. tsugense	6.1:1	15
A. hondurense	6.1:1	3
A. campylopodum	5.6:1	27
A. abietis-religiosae	5.5:1	4
A. blumeri	5.5:1	8
A. bicarinatum	5.2:1	5
A. apachecum	4.8:1	12
A. cyanocarpum	4.7:1	15
A. gillii subsp. *gillii*	3.8:1	9
A. globosum	3.7:1	6
A. douglasii	3.6:1	29
A. rubrum	3.4:1	5
A. vaginatum subsp. *durangense*	3.3:1	5
A. gillii subsp. *nigrum*	2.9:1	6
A. vaginatum subsp. *vaginatum*	2.9:1	11
A. vaginatum subsp. *cryptopodum*	2.5:1	25
A. pusillum	1.9:1	13
A. strictum	1.6:1	5
A. verticilliflorum	0.9:1	5

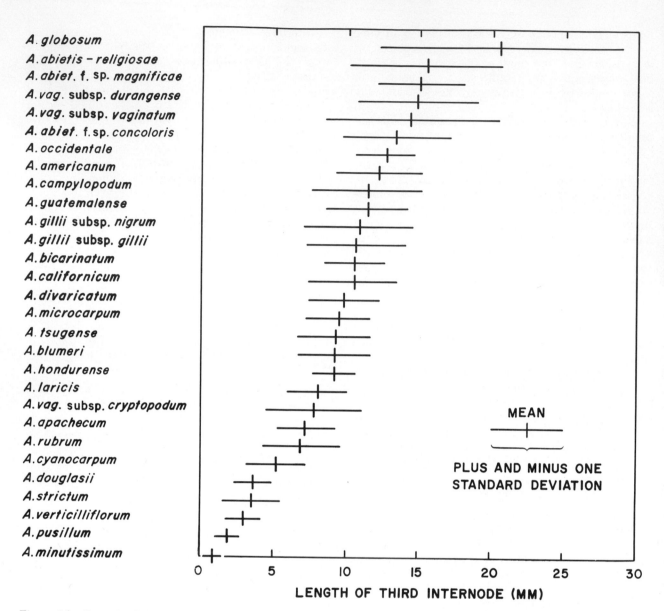

Figure 16.—Length of the third internode of the New World taxa of *Arceuthobium* and the Old World *A. minutissimum*.

but the pistillate shoots are abundantly branched.

Several species can be readily distinguished by shoot color (see color photographs). Shoot color is a useful taxonomic character even though it may vary slightly within a taxon, and the shade of the staminate shoots may be different from the pistillate shoots (for example, in *A. campylopodum*). Colors range from black, purple, brown, red, orange, green, to light gray, and carefully preserved dried specimens usually retain the original color. An exception is *A.*

rubrum; the bright red living shoots become dull brown when they are dried.

Shoots are typically erect, but they may be somewhat pendant in the larger individuals of the *A. vaginatum* group. Shoots of most species live for many years, but only for 1 or 2 years in some of the smaller species such as *A. pusillum*.

A single shoot axis that originates from a basal cup characterizes all species except *A. minutissimum*; in this species numerous shoots arise from the basal cup.

44

Inflorescence

Characters of the inflorescence are of taxonomic value. For example, the size of staminate spikes prior to flowering is useful in separating some members of the *A. campylopodum* group; the branching pattern of the staminate spikes helps distinguish the subspecies of *A. vaginatum*.

Buds and Flowers

The lateral staminate buds of *A. douglasii* and *A. americanum* are spherical, but those of the other taxa are lenticular.

The flowers are pedicillate in some taxa and sessile in others. Gill (1935) used the "pedicillate joint" of the staminate flowers as taxonomic features of *A. americanum* and, to a lesser extent, *A. douglasii*. Kuijt (1970) has shown that this "pedicillate joint" is an annual dichasial unit. Kuijt (1970) first reported pedicillate pistillate flowers on the main axis in some taxa. We consider this feature to be of taxonomic value because it is present in some groups (the *A. campylopodum* complex) and absent in others (*A. vaginatum, A. gillii*, and *A. globosum*).

Both the staminate and pistillate flowers of *Arceuthobium* are structurally simple and remarkably uniform throughout the genus (Cohen 1968, 1970).

The color, size, and number of perianth lobes of the staminate flowers are useful taxonomic characters. The inner surface of the staminate flowers is the same color as the shoots in all species except *A. abietis-religiosae, A. douglasii*, and *A. hondurense*. The staminate flowers are about 2–3 mm. in diameter for most taxa but average 4 mm. in *A. verticilliflorum*. The lateral staminate flowers are predominantly 3-merous except for *A. verticilliflorum* (4-merous), *A. guatemalense* (2- to 3-merous), *A. blumeri* (4- to 6-merous) and *A. strictum* (3- to 7-merous). The terminal flowers are frequently 4-merous in most taxa. Length and width of staminate perianth segments, closely related to overall flower size, are sometimes useful taxonomic characters. Staminate flowers that do not fully expand is a unique feature of *A. rubrum*.

A nectary or "central cushion" is present in the center of each staminate flower (Cohen 1968). We have not found any valid taxonomic features of this nectary, although it is more prominent in some specimens than in others.

Anthers

Anther diameter is discontinuously variable among some species, and may be as large as 1 mm. in *A. verticilliflorum*, and less than half this size in others.

Engelmann (in Watson 1880) used the location of the anther on the perianth segment to help distinguish some taxa, but our analyses indicate that this character has little taxonomic value.

Fruit

The mature fruit in most species ranges from 3 to 5 mm., but is 15 mm. long in *A. verticilliflorum*. All species have bicolored fruits, and the relative size of the proximal and distal portions is a useful taxonomic character. The distal portion of the fruit may account for 45 percent of the total fruit length in *A. gillii*, but only 25 percent in *A. abietis-religiosae*. Dimensions of dried fruits are usually 15 to 25 percent less than that of fresh specimens. Shrinkage is more pronounced in the distal portion (25 to 35 percent) than the proximal portion (10 to 20 percent). Thus the proximal/distal ratio tends to be somewhat higher in dried plants.

The fruit surface, also useful in taxonomy, may be either glaucous, nonglaucous and dull, or nonglaucous and shiny. Seed size is directly correlated with fruit size so it was not analyzed separately, but it does vary among taxa.

Kuijt (1970) noted that some species, for example, *A. bicarinatum*, typically have one or two sterile nodes just below the terminal fruit on the main axis of each pistillate shoot. This condition was evident in all populations of *A. bicarinatum* we have studied.

In most taxa, the base of the mature fruit fuses smoothly into the receptacle of the pedicel. In *A. guatemalense* and *A. vaginatum* subsp. *durangense*, however, the receptacle, slightly wider than the base, forms a characteristic ring at the base of the fruit.

Palynological Characters

No comprehensive pollen studies have previously been made in *Arceuthobium*, although pollen grains of a few taxa have been measured or illustrated: *A. chinense* (Lecomte 1915), *A. minutissimum* (Bhandari and Nanda 1968), *A. oxycedri* (Erdtman 1952, Heinricher 1915a), and *A. pusillum* (Gill 1935, Pomerleau 1942, Whitehead 1963, Whitehead and Barghoorn 1962).

Our preliminary findings are reported here, but we plan to publish details later. In collaboration with Dr. Estella B. Leopold of the U.S. Geological Survey, we plan to use standard palynological techniques, including electron scanning photomicrography, to analyze all members of the genus.

We have examined all *Arceuthobium* taxa, although some of our study samples were meager. We analyzed one to eight collections of each taxon and measured at least 10 pollen grains in each collection. Our analyses here are based primarily on the appearance of dried pollen grains mounted in glycerin; however, we have used the electron scanning system to study two taxa, A. pusillum and A. verticilliflorum.

The pollen grains of *Arceuthobium* can be easily distinguished from other genera (Erdtman 1952). Approximately 20 to 30μ in diameter, the grains are roughly spherical in shape, but the equatorial diameter is 5 to 15 percent larger than the polar diameter (fig. 17). The grains are divided into six alternating spined and smooth sections that converge at the poles. The grains are 3-colpate (grooved), and as the pollen dries, these colpae become deeply grooved. Lying parallel to the colpae on the intervening walls are three pseudocolpae, or short grooves, which do not reach the poles, but become more prominent during drying.

We have confirmed Gill's (1935) suggestion that pollen characteristics might be of taxonomic value, although we did not find, as he reported, that A. *pusillum* has larger pollen grains than the other species. In our studies, pollen diameters ranged from a mean of 18μ in A. *minutissimum* to 28μ in A. *verticilliflorum*. Intra-taxon variation is usually limited to within 1 or 2μ of the mean. Another readily measured pollen feature of taxonomic value is the height of spines in relation to wall (exine and intine) thickness. In some species the spine height may be three times the wall thickness (A. *tsugense*), while in others the wall thickness greatly exceeds the spine height (A. *verticilliflorum*). These taxa and a few others are so distinct that they may be identified solely on the basis of pollen characteristics.

Our electron scanning photomicrographs of two species reveal detail in *Arceuthobium* pollen grain morphology (fig. 18) that has not been apparent in light microscope studies. For example, the wall of the grain in A. *pusillum* is scabrate (with low, widely spaced warts), while the wall in A. *verticilliflorum* is more uniformly roughened. The spines of A. *verticilliflorum* are smaller and less abundant than those of A. *pusillum*. Spines are absent in the grooves

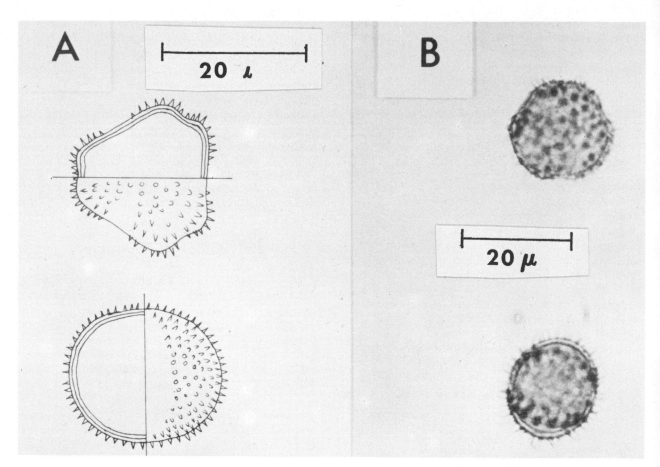

Figure 17.—*Arceuthobium* pollen grains: A, Diagrammatic drawing of pollen. Upper, polar aspect showing cross-sectional and external views. Lower, lateral aspect showing cross-sectional and external views. B, *Arceuthobium americanum* pollen showing polar (upper) and lateral views.

in *A. verticilliflorum* but present in *A. pusillum*. Also, the bases of the spines seem to be more distinct with vertical sides in *A. pusillum* but are more spreading in *A. verticilliflorum*.

Cytogenetical Characters

The chromosome number of all dwarf mistletoes studied is $n = 14$ (fig. 19), and the base generic chromosome number is considered to be $x = 14$. In the New World, Dowding (1931) first reported $n = 14$ for *Arceuthobium americanum* which Wiens (1964) confirmed. Wiens also obtained the same number for five additional taxa, and in 1968, reported counts for 10 additional New World taxa. Chromosome counts for 12 more taxa are included in this paper, so 23 of the 28 New World taxa have now been studied. The five taxa not yet examined

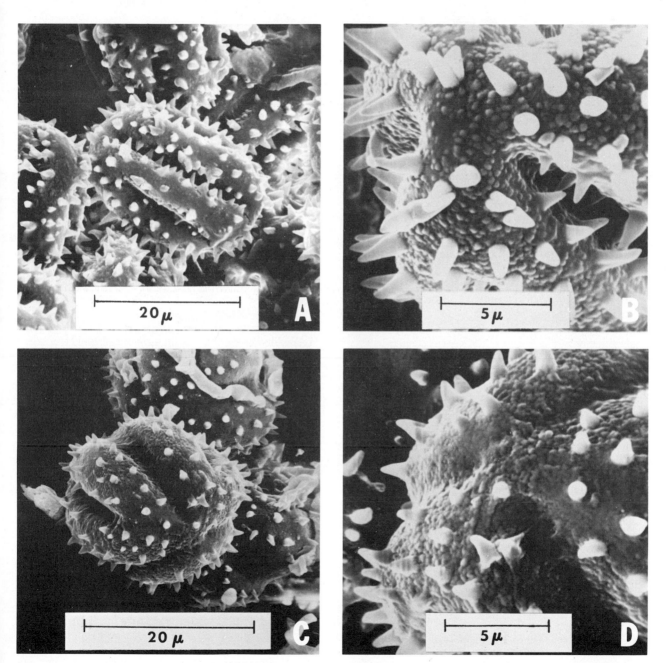

Figure 18.—Electron scanning photomicrographs of *Arceuthobium* pollen: *A*, Pollen of *A. pusillum*; *B*, Detail of spines and pollen surface; *C*, Pollen of *A. verticilliflorum*; *D*, Detail of spines and pollen surface. Photographs provided through the courtesy of Drs. Estella B. Leopold of the U.S. Geological Survey, and Charles Drew of the U.S. Navy Department.

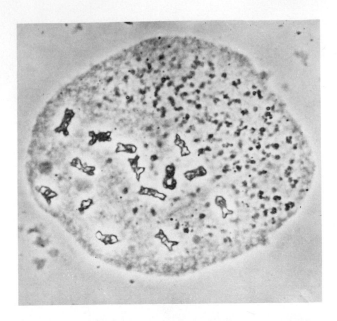

Figure 19.—Chromosomes in *Arceuthobium gillii* subsp. *gillii* at early meiotic metaphase. Magnification ca. 950.

include two Mexican species (*A. globosum* and *A. rubrum*), the Central American *A. guatemalense*, and two subspecies of *A. vaginatum* (subsp. *vaginatum* and *durangense*).

In the Old World, only *A. oxycedri* has been studied cytologically (Pisek 1924). This species is apparently $n = 14$, but Pisek also reported the existence of $n = 13$.

Although the chromosome numbers in *Arceuthobium* are consistently $n = 14$, preliminary observations suggest that other karyotypic differences may distinguish some species. For example, *A. douglasii* and *A. gillii* possess a bivalent significantly smaller than other members of the genome. Both species undergo meiosis in late summer but flower in late winter or early spring of the following year. Initial observations of *A. americanum* and *A. pusillum*, which have similar patterns of meiosis and flowering, did not show small bivalents, although most of the meiotic cells examined did not spread well, and a small bivalent could have gone undetected. The karyotypes of these two species should be examined with regard to this karyological feature.

A thorough karyotypic study of the dwarf mistletoes would be a useful contribution to our knowledge of the group. The difficulties of obtaining mitotic cells in large numbers, however, pose technical problems. For example, there are no root tips, in the usual sense, but the dwarf mistletoes have a basal meristem similar to grasses, which is active primarily in the spring. The radicular apex of the developing embryo and axillary buds were investigated as a possible source of mitotic cells, but mitosis was too sporadic and occurred in numbers too small for effective karyotypic work (Wiens 1968). The radicular apex of germinating seeds might contain mitotic cells, but this source has not been fully investigated.

Physiological Characters

Phenology

Gill (1935) used time of flowering (spring vs. summer) as a principal taxonomic character. His "summer" flowering group (the *campylopodum* group) contains some significant interspecific variation. For example, *A. occidentale* flowers as late as November or December, and *A. californicum* flowers as early as June (fig. 20).

A taxon generally flowers at given periods each year, although normal altitudinal, latitudinal, and seasonal variation occurs. For the summer or fall flowering species, flowering usually begins at the higher elevation first (Scharpf 1965) while the opposite seems to be true for the spring flowering taxa.

Whether meiosis occurs immediately before flowering or 5 to 8 months preceding anthesis is an important taxonomic criterion not previously utilized in this genus. Wiens (1968) has established three basic flowering groups in *Arceuthobium* (table 15): Group I, spring flowering species that undergo meiosis directly preceding anthesis; Group II, mid- or late-summer flowering species that undergo meiosis directly preceding anthesis; and Group III, spring flowering species that undergo meiosis during the preceding late summer or early fall. Group Ia was established for *A. gillii* and *A. verticilliflorum* which undergo meiosis in late summer and flower in early spring, a characteristic in which they resemble the species in Group III. General floral development and other traits, however, appear to place the two species in a transitional position between Groups I and II.

Time of seed dispersal and fruit maturation periods are useful taxonomic criteria. Relatively consistent for a given taxon, peak seed dispersal may occur as early as July in *A. globosum* or as late as November to January in *A. occidentale* (fig. 21). Also, fruits of *A. pusillum* mature in about 5 months, while those of all other taxa require at least 12 months; fruits of *A. gillii* require 19 months to reach maturity (fig. 22).

Too little data are available to attach taxonomic significance to time of seed germination and length of the incubation period (time from infection until

TABLE 15.—*Flowering groups in the North American dwarf mistletoes* (*Wiens 1968*)

Group I (direct flowering) February–April	Group Ia (indirect flowering) February–March	Group II (direct flowering) July–September	Group III (indirect flowering) February–May
A. abietis-religiosae?	A. gillii subsp. gillii	A. abietinum f. sp. concoloris	A. americanum
A. globosum	A. gillii subsp. nigrum	A. abietinum f. sp. magnificae	A. douglasii
A. vaginatum subsp. vaginatum	A. verticilliflorum	A. apachecum	A. pusillum
A. vaginatum subsp. cryptopodum		A. bicarinatum	
A. vaginatum subsp. durangense		A. blumeri	
		A. californicum	
		A. campylopodum	
		A. cyanocarpum	
		A. divaricatum	
		A. guatemalense	
		A. hondurense	
		A. laricis	
		A. microcarpum	
		A. occidentale	
		A. rubrum	
		A. strictum	
		A. tsugense	

initial shoot appearance). *A. guatemalense, A. vaginatum* subsp. *cryptopodum*, and probably other southern species germinate in the fall, while all North American species in the temperate zone germinate in late winter or spring.

Hosts

The host, important in the classification of dwarf mistletoes, was discussed earlier. In most instances a dwarf mistletoe will be collected on its principal host. If a collection is made on other hosts, it is important for identification to record the principal host in the immediate vicinity. For example, if a mistletoe occurs on *Pinus flexilis*, it is usually *A. cyanocarpum*. However, if the dwarf mistletoe is a rare crossover of *A. americanum*, information that the mistletoe was rare on *Pinus flexilis*, but common on associated *Pinus contorta*, would help to identify the parasite. Situations are relatively rare where two species of dwarf mistletoe are both common in a given stand and, in such situations, crossovers are extremely rare.

Witches' Brooms

The dwarf mistletoes cause two basic types of witches' brooms, systemic or nonsystemic (see p. 26). Since the type formed is usually consistent with a host-parasite combination, this taxonomic feature can be used to help classify the species. Five taxa (*A. americanum, A. douglasii, A. guatemalense, A. minutissimum,* and *A. pusillum*) consistently cause systemic brooms. Most other taxa cause the non-systemic type. In Guatemala, *A. globosum* forms witches' brooms, but in Mexico it does not. Witches' broom formation is not exhibited, or is inconspicuous, in these host-parasite combinations: *A. divaricatum* on *Pinus monophylla, A. blumeri* on *Pinus strobiformis,* and *A. occidentale* on *Pinus sabiniana*.

Chemical Characters

Our analysis of the phenolic constituents of *Arceuthobium* is the first comprehensive chemotaxonomic study in the mistletoes.

Greenham and Leonard (1965), who compared the amino acids of three dwarf mistletoes (*A. abietinum* f. sp. *concoloris* and *magnificae* and *A. occidentale*) with their respective host trees, reported some similarities in amino acid composition between host and parasite, but their results did not help explain host specificity.

Relatively little information on the phenolics of the mistletoes is available; hence, we are presenting a brief review of the known literature.

VISCACEAE.—Bate-Smith (1962) made preliminary studies of the phenolic compounds in the European *Arceuthobium oxycedri* and *Viscum album*. Kuang-Fang and Shih-Chueh (1957) recorded four flavonoids in *V. album* subsp. *coloratum* from China.

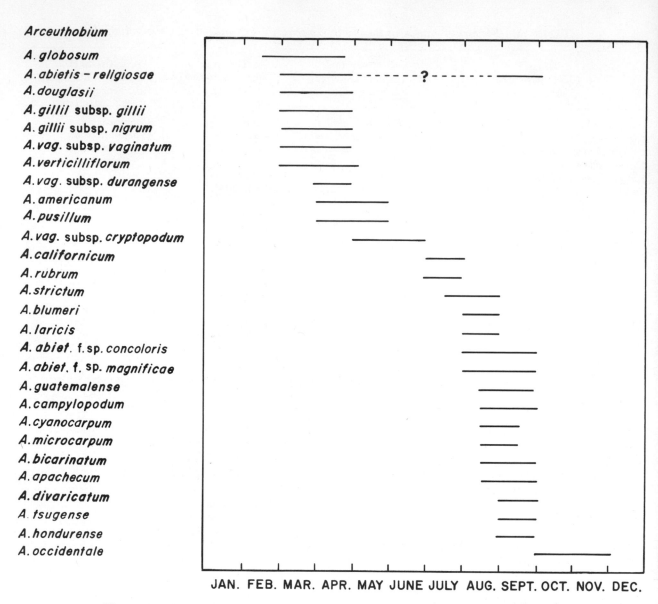

JAN. FEB. MAR. APR. MAY JUNE JULY AUG. SEPT. OCT. NOV. DEC.

Figure 20.—Approximate periods of anthesis for the New World dwarf mistletoes.

LORANTHACEAE.—Some phenolic constituents have been isolated from the Australian species *Nuytsia floribunda* (Bate-Smith 1962), and from two South American mistletoes *Psittacanthus cuneifolius* and *Phrygilanthus flagellaris* (Graziano, Widmer, Juliani, and Coussio 1967; Widmer and Coussio 1969). Several Asian species have also been studied, and the flavonoid quercitin has been found in *Loranthus pentandrus* and *L. globosus* (Wester 1921). This flavonoid and arabinoside have been reported in *Loranthus parasiticus* (Kuang-Fang and Chung-Liang 1957). Khanna, Viswanathan, Tewari, and others (1968) found a relatively high concentration of phenolics in the mistletoe *Dendrophthoe falcata* and two other parasitic angiosperms in India.

A relatively wide range of shoot colors is known in *Arceuthobium*. Although there is some infraspecific variation, shoot color is relatively constant within a species. We attempted to determine whether these color differences were associated with specific pigments.

Preliminary analyses indicated that a dark species (*A. rubrum*) contained anthocyanins, whereas a yellow species (*A. strictum*) did not. These fragmentary data suggested that anthocyanins might be positively correlated with the dark coloration (red or black) characteristic of many species, and negatively correlated with the lighter coloration (greens, yellows, and oranges) of others. We then surveyed all dwarf mistletoe taxa to determine the

50

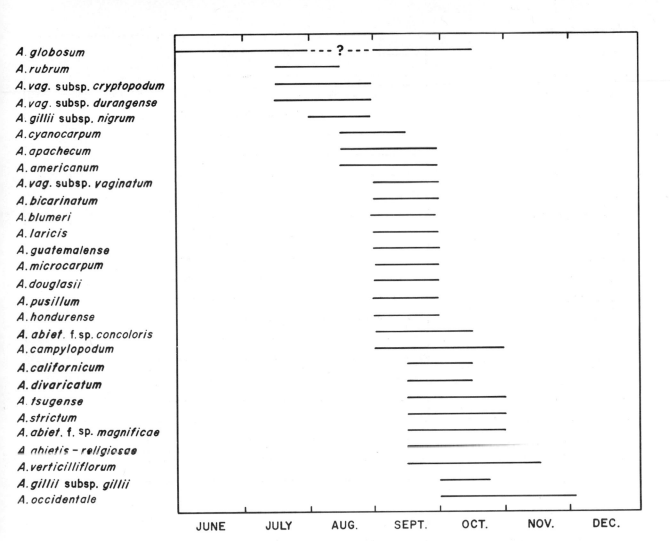

Figure 21.—Approximate periods of seed dispersal for the New World dwarf mistletoes.

relationship between anthocyanin content and shoot coloration. In addition, we evaluated several additional phenolic compounds (flavones, flavonols, and cinnamic acid derivatives) because they could be chromatographically isolated from the original extracts in ethyl acetate along with the anthocyanins, and appeared to be valuable taxonomic characters in classification of *Arceuthobium*. Alston, Rösler, Naifeh, and Mabry (1965) found the phenolic compounds to be of chemotaxonomic value because, at least for the flavonoids, Mendelian mechanisms apparently govern their qualitative differences.

Methods

The tissue utilized for extraction represented approximately the terminal centimeter of growth, and was obtained from staminate herbarium ma-terial. The internodes were ground to powder with a mortar and pestle with the aid of glass beads. The phenolic compounds were extracted in 5 ml. of 1 percent hydrochloric acid (HCl) in absolute methanol (v/v), followed by four additional washes of the same volume. The extracts were then com-bined and concentrated at 40°C. to approximately 3 to 4 ml. by evaporation into nitrogen. After initial concentration, approximately 5 ml. of 0.5 percent aqueous HCl was added and the solution then reconcentrated to about 2 ml. Carotenoids were removed by phasing with petroleum ether (30–60°C fraction).

Non-anthocyanin phenolic compounds were re-moved from the aqueous phase with ethyl acetate. The organic phase was then back extracted with 0.5 percent aqueous HCl.

The extracts were immediately applied to What-man #3 MM chromatographic paper with finely

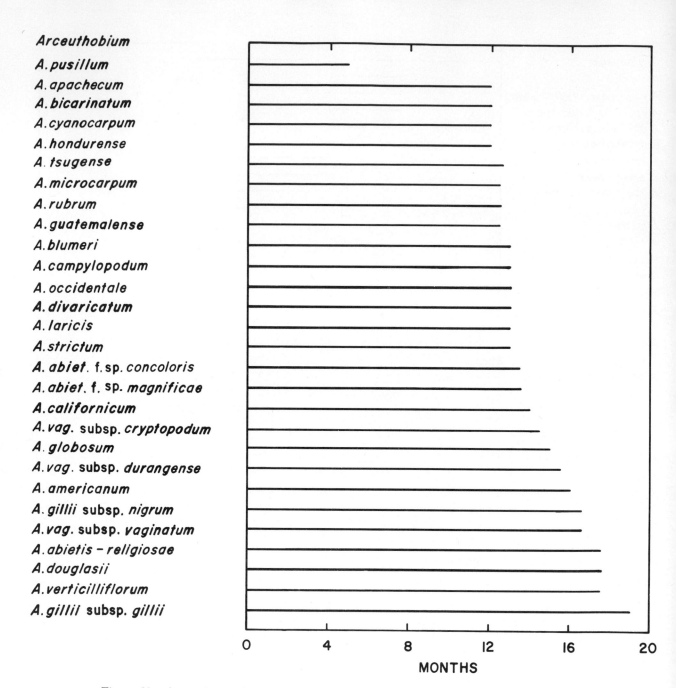

Figure 22.—Approximate fruit maturation periods for the New World dwarf mistletoes.

drawn Pasteur pipets. For one-dimensional chromatography, the extracts were applied in strips 3 cm. long. For two-dimensional development, they were applied in spots about 2 cm. in diameter.

The anthocyanin-containing fraction was chromatographed in water: glacial acetic acid:12 N HCl in the ratio 82:15:3 (v/v). Development time was 18 hours. The ethyl acetate fraction was chromatographed in 15 percent aqueous acetic acid (v/v) for 6 hours. The various bands were consistently discernible under 3440 A° ultraviolet (UV) light both before and after drying.

Results

All species and subspecies of *Arceuthobium*, except *A. chinense* and *A. pini*, were analyzed chromatographically (table 16). These data must be considered as preliminary, however, because of the small number of individuals analyzed in some species, and because the bands are only tentatively identified. Furthermore, the ethyl acetate fraction contained many compounds which cochromatographed in 15 percent aqueous acetic acid, but were separable when developed in the second dimension with BAW (12:3:5). In the numerical analyses, however, these paired bands were scored as unit characters, as were the chromatographically pure bands. No attempt was made to analyze quantitative differences, although these were sometimes obvious. The chromatogram of *A. microcarpum* (fig. 23) contains most of the flavonoid compounds presently known in *Arceuthobium*, and shows the band numbering system used in our studies.

ANTHOCYANINS.—The aqueous phase that remained after extraction with ethyl acetate contained up to three magenta bands discernible in visible light. After hydrolysis, the aglycon from each band was shown to be cyanidin. This conclusion was derived from the results of cochromatography with authentic cyanidin in several solvent systems, and of UV and visible spectrophotometry.

The specific distribution of cyanidin is interesting because it occurs not only in all species with dark coloration, which we suspected, but also in many which are yellow, greenish yellow, or orangish in coloration.

FLAVONOLS. — A conspicuously yellow fluorescing band (Y), observable under UV, contains two compounds, one of which is probably quercitin, as determined by cochromatography with known quercitin. The second component of the band is unknown, but may be derived from kaempferol. The unknown band YO has some flavonol-like properties, and, in at least two species (*A. campylopodum* and *A. microcarpum*) is separable into two compounds when developed in the second dimension in BAW (12:3:5). The yellow fluorescing band, along with the BG bands of putative cinnamic acid derivatives (vid infra), are of nearly universal occurrence in the populations studied. Band Y occurred consistently in every sample except *A. vaginatum* subsp. *durangense*. The single and rare YG band is also tentatively placed here.

FLAVONES.—The most interesting feature of the chromatograms viewed under UV is the occurrence of 4 (rarely 5 or 6) purple bands (A bands) that appear to be glycosides of flavones. These bands turn yellow with age or when fumed with ammonia. Preliminary observations in *A. microcarpum* show that bands A_1 and A_3 are separable into two compounds when developed in the second dimension. Also, the single D band, presently unique to *A. guatemalense*, probably belongs in this group of compounds.

The flavones exhibit more discontinuous variation and perhaps less infrataxon variation than most of

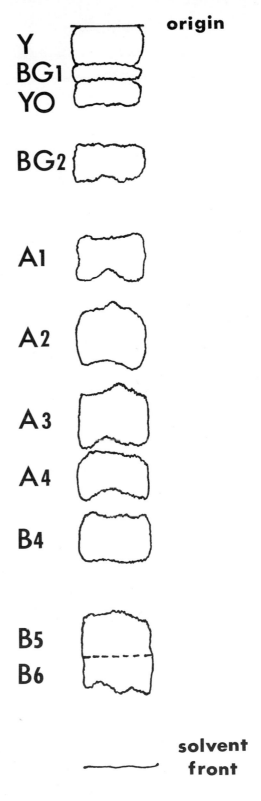

Figure 23.—Chromatogram of *Arceuthobium microcarpum* showing typical separation of compounds soluble in ethyl acetate.

TABLE 16.—*Phenolic constituents of Arceuthobium as determined by chromatography*[1]

Arceuthobium	Anthocyanins			Flavones, flavonols, and cinnamic acid ester derivatives																		
	1	2	3	Y_1	D	B_1	Y_2	BG_1	YO	B_2	BG_2	A_1	YG	A_2	B_3	A_3	A_4	B_4	A_5	B_5	B_6	A_6
A. abietinum f. sp. concoloris	+	+	--	++	--	--	--	++	++	--	++	++	--	++	++	++	++	++	--	++	--	--
A. abietinum f. sp. magnificae	++	+	-+	+++	--	--	--	+++	+++	--	+++	+++	--	+++	+++	+	+	+++	--	+	--	--
A. abietis-religiosae	++	-+	--	+++	--	--	--	+++	+++	--	+++	+++	--	-+	++	+++	++	++	--	+	--	-+
A. americanum	-+	-+	-+	+++	--	--	--	+++	+++	--	+++	+++	--	+++	++	+++	++	++	--	++	--	++
A. apachecum	++	+	++	+++	--	++	--	+++	+++	-+	+++	+++	--	+++	-+	+++	++	-+	+	+++	-+	--
A. bicarinatum	-+	--	--	+++	--	-+	--	+++	+++	-+	+++	+++	--	+++	++	+++	+++	+++	++	+++	++	--
A. blumeri	-+	++	-+	+++	--	--	--	+++	+++	--	+++	+++	--	+++	++	+++	++	+++	--	+++	++	--
A. californicum	-+	-+	--	+++	--	-+	--	++	+++	--	+++	+	--	++	+	++	++	++	+	++	--	--
A. campylopodum	--	--	--	+++	-+	--	-+	+++	++	--	+++	+++	--	+++	--	+++	+++	++	--	++	--	--
A. cyanocarpum	++	--	--	+++	-++	--	-+	+++	+++	--	+++	+++	--	+++	--	+++	+	-+	--	+	--	--
A. divaricatum	-+	-+	--	+++	--	+	--	+++	++	--	+++	-+	--	++	-+	++	+	++	--	+++	++	+
A. douglasii	++	++	--	+++	--	+	--	+++	+++	--	+++	++	--	++	++	+++	+++	++	--	+++	++	++
A. gillii subsp. gillii	++	++	--	+++	--	--	--	+++	+++	--	+++	++	--	++	++	+++	+++	++	--	+++	--	--
A. gillii subsp. nigrum	++	-+	--	+++	--	--	--	+++	+++	--	+++	++	--	++	++	+++	+	+	--	+	--	--
A. globosum	-+	--	--	+++	--	+	-+	+++	+++	--	+++	+	--	++	-+	++	+	-+	--	--	--	--
A. guatemalense	++	--	--	+++	--	--	--	+++	+++	--	+++	++	--	++	++	+	+	-+	--	+	--	--
A. hondurense	-+	--	--	+++	--	--	--	+++	+++	--	+++	++	--	++	--	+++	+	--	--	+++	--	--
A. laricis	--	-+	--	+++	--	+	-+	+++	+++	--	+++	++	--	++	-+	+++	+++	++	--	+++	++	+
A. microcarpum	-+	++	--	+++	--	+	-+	+++	+++	--	+++	+++	--	+++	++	+++	+++	++	+	++	+	--
A. minutissimum	--	++	--	+++	--	--	--	+++	+++	--	+++	+++	--	+++	-+	+	+	-+	-+	+++	--	--
A. occidentale	--	-+	--	+++	--	--	-+	+++	++	--	++	+	--	+++	--	+	+	+	--	+++	--	--
A. oxycedri	-+	--	--	+++	--	+	-+	+++	+++	--	++	+	--	+++	--	+	-+	--	--	+	--	--
A. pusillum	++	-+	--	+++	--	--	--	+++	+++	--	+++	++	--	++	++	+	+	++	+	++	--	--
A. rubrum	++	-+	--	+++	--	--	--	+++	+++	--	+++	++	--	++	++	+	+	+	--	++	--	--
A. strictum	++	-+	--	+++	--	--	--	+++	+++	--	+++	+++	--	+	-+	+	+	-+	--	+	--	--
A. tsugense	+	+	--	++	--	-+	--	+	+++	--	+++	++	--	++	--	+	+	--	--	--	--	--
A. vaginatum subsp. vaginatum	++	+	--	++	--	--	--	+	++	--	++	+	--	++	--	+	+	--	--	--	--	--
A. vaginatum subsp. cryptopodum	++	--	--	++	--	--	--	+	++	--	++	+	--	++	--	+	+	--	--	--	--	--
A. vaginatum subsp. durangense	--	--	--	-+	--	--	--	++	-+	--	-+	-+	--	-+	--	+	+	--	--	--	--	--
A. verticilliflorum	--	--	--	++	--	--	--	++	++	--	++	++	--	++	--	++	-+	--	--	--	--	--

++, Present in all specimens. +, Sometimes present. --, Not detected.

the other chemical classes; they are totally lacking in *A. bicarinatum*, *A. vaginatum* subsp. *cryptopodum* and subsp. *durangense*, *A. oxycedri*, and *A. rubrum*. This group of compounds might provide the best possibility for further chemotaxonomic study in *Arceuthobium*.

CINNAMIC ACID DERIVATIVES.—A conspicuous feature of most chromatograms of *Arceuthobium* extracts is a series of bright blue fluorescing bands (B bands) which are probably cinnamic acid derivatives. With two exceptions, all B bands appear to contain single components. The exceptions are the B_5 and B_6 bands which are separable in the second dimension in *A. campylopodum*, *A. microcarpum*, and *A. minutissimum*. These two bands are also difficult to separate in the single dimension, and were arbitrarily scored as B_5 unless, as in the three cases mentioned, the results of second dimension chromatograms confirmed the existence of both bands. As with the A bands, this group of compounds displays considerable interspecific diversity. Several species contain none of these presumed cinnamic acid derivatives: *A. bicarinatum*, *A. gillii* subsp. *nigrum*, *A. rubrum*, *A. vaginatum* (including all of its subspecies), and *A. verticilliflorum*; *A. gillii* subsp. *gillii* contains only a single blue fluorescing band, which was found in only one of four populations analyzed.

In addition to the bands fluorescing bright blue, two additional bands fluorescing a light blue green under UV are tentatively placed in this class of compounds. The most significant aspect of the BG bands is their occurrence in every species analyzed and in all but two of the populations sampled. Furthermore, both of these bands are separable when chromatographed in the second dimension.

Discussion and Conclusions

Anthocyanins were found in all the species with dark-colored shoots, and more than half of the light colored ones (table 16). We also found a light magenta color pattern in the living staminate flowers of two light-colored species that resembled the anthocyanin bands we had isolated chromatographically from their shoots. Since the color pattern is evident in the outer portions of living staminate flowers of *A. americanum* and *A. douglasii*, we suspect its function is to visually attract pollinators (apparently Diptera in these species). We plan to study the living flowers of all the light-colored species to determine if a similar light magenta coloration might be present.

CHROMATOGRAPHIC VARIATION.—Three aspects of variation were considered: qualitative, quantitative, and comparison of living and dead specimens. Qualitative infrataxon variation in chromat-

ographic patterns (presence or absence) often occurred among the populations of a particular species. To determine the extent of such variation within a species, 34 populations of *A. americanum* were analyzed. The variables included: (1) hosts—*Pinus contorta* (two subspecies), *P. ponderosa*, and *P. banksiana*; (2) geographical distribution—West Coast, and the southern Rocky Mountains to central Canada; (3) time since collection—specimens collected a few days to over 50 years before analysis; and (4) season of collection—most months. Analyses showed that 30 of the 34 populations of *A. americanum* were qualitatively uniform (table 16). In the four chromatograms that varied, the variation was due to the visible anthocyanin band 2, and the bands of phenolic compounds visible under *UV* (B_3, B_4, A_6), with the most obvious variation in the B_3 and B_4 bands. The A_3 and A_4 bands are in close proximity, and when small quantities of the compounds are present interpretation becomes difficult, but some variation was suggested in our samples.

Quantitative variation in virtually all of the bands was a common feature of the chromatograms. Detecting compounds at low levels of concentration probably introduced some variability in the results.

The Y band, which contains two quantitative phases, was consistently detectable (except in some samples of *A. vaginatum* subsp. *durangense*). We thought the lighter phase might indicate the presence of only one of the two compounds that compose this band (see Results) but when a sample of *A. americanum* that contained the light phase was chromatographed in the second dimension, the Y band still separated into two parts.

Although both qualitative and quantitative variation exists in the chromatographic patterns of dwarf mistletoes, our experience with *A. americanum* suggests that, where large samples are available, chemical data can provide reliable taxonomic information. The data could also be more useful if two dimensional analyses were available for each compound.

To determine whether chromatographic variation existed, we analyzed living and dried shoots from a putative clone of *A. americanum*. The chromatograms varied little, except that the BG_2 band, apparent in all dried samples, was noticeably absent in the live specimens, which suggests that it may be a degradation product. Also, in the chromatogram for the living shoots, a single band fluorescing yellow under UV occurred between the BG_2 band location and the A band.

TAXONOMIC IMPLICATIONS.—Although the chemical data do not show discontinuous variation among all taxa, many species are distinct chromatographically, and can be readily identified by this means. *A. americanum* is the only species we intensively analyzed, but our preliminary studies indicate that comparable differences will be obvious when the other taxa are studied.

A. bicarinatum, one of the most chromatographically distinctive of all dwarf mistletoes, lacks all the A and B bands, and although we first confused *A. hondurense* with *A. bicarinatum*, the chromatographic differences we found suggested these two taxa were specifically distinct.

Other species such as *A. abietis-religiosae*, *A. rubrum*, *A. strictum*, and *A. vaginatum* subsp. *cryptopodum* and *durangense* are similar chromatographically; they lack the A bands but are distinctive in other ways. Although all five are Mexican species, they do not appear to form a phyletic group, but are scattered throughout various subgenera and sections. Thus, although certain species appear to be mutually distinct chromatographically, no chromatographic features seem to be associated with the various subgeneric groupings.

NUMERICAL ANALYSES

The use of computer techniques in taxonomy (taximetrics), essentially a development of the 1960's (Sokal and Sneath 1963; Rogers, Fleming, and Estabrook 1967), is a powerful new tool for making taxonomic decisions. Although some classical taxonomists view this development with suspicion, most numerical taxonomists have emphasized that taximetric analyses will supplement but not replace conventional systematics techniques (Rogers and Appan 1969). How good the taximetric analyses are for a particular group depends on the taxonomist's ability to discern significant characters in the group and to separate them into meaningful states. Both the numerical taxonomist and the classical taxonomist need to thoroughly understand the group in question before they can make systematic decisions.

Methods

The Graph Theory Clustering Program[17] is the computer technique we found best suited to analyze our extensive taxonomic data (table 17). We made a preliminary taximetric analyses of the characters of *Arceuthobium* (Hawksworth, Estabrook, and Rogers 1968), then chose the following taximetric methods for classifying the species:

1. On the basis of our field and herbarium experience with the dwarf mistletoes, we selected a number of qualitative and quantitative characters that we considered taxonomically significant. Because these plants are leafless and extremely reduced morphologically, we emphasized other types of characters in addition to morphological ones.

2. Each selected character was subdivided into 2 to 18 states, depending on the range of variation shown in the particular character. The number of states we selected for each character was based on the work by Rogers and Fleming (1964) and Estabrook and Rogers (1966).

3. We adjusted the number of states for each character so the range of overlap (Estabrook and Rogers 1966) was either one or zero. This overlap value, for example, is used for shoot height (character No. 2, table 17), where three states are based on the relative height of the staminate and pistillate shoots: (1) staminate shoots tallest, (2) staminate and pistillate shoots about the same, and (3) pistillate shoots tallest. Examination of many collections showed that within a taxon, ratings were usually 1 and 2, but not 3; other taxa were rated as either 1, 2, or 3; while others were 2 and 3, but not 1. Thus an overlap value of 1 was assigned, which indicates that only states that are more than 1 unit apart (or in this instance states 1 and 3) are computed as different. In many other characters, (for example, Principal hosts, character No. 38, table 17) an overlap value of zero is used, which indicates that differences in any two states are calculated as equally distinct.

4. The 60 characters used in this study (see table 17) are divided as follows: shoots (12), flowers (11), pollen (5), fruit (5), phenology (4), hosts and host reactions (3), and shoot pigments (21).

5. In the analyses we gave all characters equal weight because of the difficulty of assigning meaningful weights to the various characters. As will be shown, however, certain characters contain much more taxonomic information than others and thus contribute more to the resulting classification.

6. A total of 212 specimens representing all known 28 North American taxa were examined and rated in each of the 60 characters. The number of specimens per taxon varied from 12 to as few as 3 in some of the seldom-collected Central American and Mexican taxa. The specimens were selected on the following basis: (a) those that yielded the most information, and (b) those that represented the

---

[17] Details of the Program and its application are summarized in Estabrook 1967; Estabrook and Rogers 1966: Irwin and Rogers 1967; Rogers and Appan 1969; and Wirth, Estabrook, and Rogers 1966.

SHOOTS:

1. *Mean plant height*
   (overlap—1 unit)
   1. Less than 1 cm.
   2. 1–2 cm.
   3. 3–5 cm.
   4. 6–10 cm.
   5. 11–13 cm.
   6. 14–18 cm.
   7. 19–23 cm.
   8. Over 24 cm.
2. *Shoot height*
   (overlap—1 unit)
   1. Staminate shoots tallest
   2. About the same
   3. Pistillate shoots tallest
3. *Mean basal diameter*
   (overlap—1 unit)
   1. 0.1 cm.
   2. 0.2 cm.
   3. 0.3 cm.
   4. 0.4 cm.
   5. 0.5 cm.
   6. 0.6 cm.
   7. 0.7 cm.
   8. Over 0.8 cm.
4. *Third internode length*
   (overlap—1 unit)
   1. 1.0–2.9 mm.
   2. 3.0–4.9 mm.
   3. 5.0–6.9 mm.
   4. 7.0–8.9 mm.
   5. 9.0–10.9 mm.
   6. 11.0–12.9 mm.
   7. 13.0–14.9 mm.
   8. 15.0–16.9 mm.
   9. Over 17.0 mm.

5. *Third internode width*
   (overlap—1 unit)
   1. Up to 1.0 mm.
   2. 1.1–2.0 mm.
   3. 2.1–3.0 mm.
   4. 3.1–4.0 mm.
   5. 4.1–5.0 mm.
   6. 5.1–6.0 mm.
6. *Third internode length/width ratio*
   (overlap—1 unit)
   1. Less than 2.0
   2. 2.1–4.0
   3. 4.1–6.0
   4. 6.1–8.0
   5. Over 8.1
7. *Branching*
   (overlap—none)
   1. No accessory branches
   2. Accessory branches sometimes verticillate
   3. Accessory branches always flabellate
8. *Sexual dimorphism*
   (overlap—none)
   1. Branching similar
   2. Branching different
9. *Shoot color*
   (overlap—none)
   1. Pistillate and staminate shoots of same color
   2. Pistillate and staminate shoots of different color

10. *Color of pistillate shoots*
    (overlap—1 unit)
    1. Green
    2. Yellow
    3. [1]
    4. Orange
    5. Red
    6. Purple
    7. [1]
    8. Brown
    9. [1]
    10. Black
11. *Shoot density*
    (overlap—none)
    1. Shoots densely clustered around host branch
    2. Shoots not densely clustered around host branch
12. *Overall plant shape*
    (overlap—none)
    1. Plants in globose masses
    2. Plants not as above

FLOWERS:

13. *Staminate floral buds*
    (overlap—none)
    1. Spherical
    2. Lenticular
14. *Pre-flowering lateral staminate spikes—length*
    (overlap—1 unit)
    1. None
    2. 1–2 mm.
    3. 3–4 mm.
    4. 5–6 mm.
    5. 7–8 mm.
    6. 9–10 mm.
    7. 11–13 mm.
    8. 14–16 mm.
    9. Over 17 mm.

15. *Pre-flowering lateral staminate spikes—width*
    (overlap—1 unit)
    1. None
    2. 1 mm.
    3. 2 mm.
    4. 3 mm.
    5. 4 mm.
    6. 5 mm.
16. *Staminate flowers*
    (overlap—none)
    1. Verticillate
    2. Opposite, with pedicellate joints
    3. Opposite, no pedicellate joints

17. *Number of staminate perianth segments*
    (overlap—1 unit)
    1. 2 or 3 (approx. equally divided)
    2. All 3's
    3. Mostly 3, few 4's
    4. 3 or 4 (approx. equally divided)
    5. Mostly 4, few 3's
    6. 3, 4, or 5 (approx. equally divided)
    7. Mostly 5 or more.
18. *Staminate flower diameter*
    (overlap—1 unit)
    1. 1.0–1.4 mm.
    2. 1.5–1.9 mm.
    3. 2.0–2.4 mm.
    4. 2.5–2.9 mm.
    5. 3.0–3.5 mm.

6. Over 3.5 mm.
19. *Anther diameter*
 (overlap—1 unit)
 1. 0.3–0.4 mm.
 2. 0.5–0.6 mm.
 3. 0.7–0.8 mm.
 4. 0.9–1.0 mm.
20. *Anther distance from perianth tip* (overlap—1 unit)
 1. 0.3–0.4 mm.
 2. 0.5–0.6 mm.
 3. 0.7–0.8 mm.
 4. 0.9–1.0 mm.

21. *Staminate perianth length*
 (overlap—1 unit)
 1. 0.6–0.9 mm.
 2. 1.0–1.3 mm.
 3. 1.4–1.7 mm.
 4. Over 1.8 mm.
22. *Staminate perianth width*
 (overlap—1 unit)
 1. 0.6–0.9 mm.
 2. 1.0–1.3 mm.
 3. 1.4–1.7 mm.
 4. Over 1.8 mm.
23. *Pistillate flowers*
 (overlap none)
 1. Verticillate
 2. Opposite

POLLEN:
24. *Length*
 (overlap—1 unit)
 1. 18–19μ
 2. 20–21μ
 3. 22–23μ
 4. 24–25μ
 5. 26–27μ
 6. 28–29μ
25. *Width*
 (overlap—1 unit)
 1. 18–19μ
 2. 20–21μ
 3. 22–23μ
 4. 24–25μ
 5. 26–27μ
 6. 28–29μ

26. *Spine length*
 (overlap—1 unit)
 1. 0.5–0.9μ
 2. 1.0–1.4μ
 3. 1.5–1.9μ
 4. 2.0–2.5μ
27. *Wall thickness*
 (overlap—1 unit)
 1. 0.5–0.9μ
 2. 1.0–1.4μ
 3. 1.5–1.9μ
 4. 2.0–2.4μ

28. *Spine/wall ratio*
 (overlap—1 unit)
 1. 0.3–0.7
 2. 0.8–1.2
 3. 1.3–1.7
 4. 1.8–2.2
 5. 2.3–2.7
 6. 2.8–3.2
 7. 3.3–3.8

FRUIT:
29. *Surface*
 (overlap—none)
 1. Glaucous
 2. Nonglaucous, dull
 3. Nonglaucous, shiny
30. *Length*
 (overlap—1 unit)
 1. 2 mm.
 2. 3 mm.
 3. 4 mm.
 4. 5 mm.
 6. [1]
 7. Over 10 mm.
PHENOLOGY:

31. *Distal portion as percent of total fruit length* (overlap—1 unit)
 1. 21–25 percent
 2. 26–30 percent
 3. 31–35 percent
 4. 36–40 percent
 5. 41–45 percent
32. *Sterile nodes near tips of pistillate shoots*
 (overlap—none)
 1. Present
 2. Absent

33. *Pedicellate fruits on main axis*
 (overlap—none)
 1. Common
 2. Occasional or rare
 3. None

34. *Peak flowering period*
 (overlap—1 unit)
 1. March–April
 2. May–June
 3. July
 4. August
 5. September
 6. October or later
35. *Peak seed dispersal period*
 (overlap—1 unit)
 1. July
 2. August
 3. September
 4. October
 5. November or later

36. *Mean fruit maturation period*
 (overlap—1 unit)
 1. ca. 5 months
 2. [1]
 3. ca. 12 months
 4. ca. 13 months
 5. [1]
 6. Over 14 months
37. *Time of meiosis in relation to flowering*
 (overlap—none)
 1. Spring flowering, spring meiosis
 2. Winter flowering, fall meiosis
 3. Summer flowering, summer meiosis
 4. Spring flowering, fall meiosis

HOSTS AND HOST REACTIONS:

38. *Principal hosts*
    (overlap—none)
    1. *Abies (concolor, grandis)*
    2. *Abies magnifica*
    3. *Abies (other species)*
    4. *Pseudotsuga*
    5. *Picea (mariana, glauca)*
    6. *Picea (engelmannii, pungens)*
    7. *Larix*
    8. *Tsuga*
    9. *Pinus lambertiana*
    10. *Pinus (flexilis-aristata)*
    11. *Pinus strobiformis*
    12. *Pinus ayachauite*
    13. *Pinus (pinyons)*
    14. *Pinus (Leiophyllae)*
    15. *Pinus (Australes)*
    16. *Pinus (Ponderosae)*
    17. *Pinus (Sabinianae and Oocarpae)*
    18. *Pinus (Contortae)*

39. *Witches' broom formation*
    (overlap—none)
    1. None
    2. Rare or occasional
    3. Consistent

40. *Type of witches' brooms*
    (overlap—none)
    1. Brooms systemic
    2. Brooms nonsystemic
    3. No brooms

CHROMATOGRAPHY OF SHOOT PHENOLICS:[2]

41. to 43.
    Anthocyanins
    (overlap—none)
    1. Consistently present
    2. Sometimes present
    3. Absent
41. *Anthocyanin #1*
42. *Anthocyanin #2*
43. *Anthocyanin #3*
44. to 60.
    Flavones, flavonols and cinnamic acid derivatives
    overlap—none
    1. Consistently present
    2. Sometimes present
    3. Absent

44. *Phenolic Y_1*
45. *Phenolic D*
46. *Phenolic B_1*
47. *Phenolic Y_2*
48. *Phenolic BG_1*
49. *Phenolic YO*
50. *Phenolic BG_2*
51. *Phenolic A_1*
52. *Phenolic YG*

53. *Phenolic A_2*
54. *Phenolic B_3*
55. *Phenolic A_3*
56. *Phenolic A_4*
57. *Phenolic B_4*
58. *Phenolic A_5*
59. *Phenolic B_5*
60. *Phenolic B_6*

---

[1] A skipped state number indicates that the two adjacent states are calculated as distinct when the overlap value is 1 unit.

[2] See table 16. Two compounds (B_2 and A_6) listed in table 16 were not used in the taximetric analyses because their occurrence was too erratic.

---

geographic and host range of the taxon. The specimens used in these analyses are indicated in the specimens examined lists.

7. Data were entered on IBM cards and analyses were made on a CDC 6400 computer at Colorado State University.

8. A measure of similarity was then calculated between each specimen and every other one in the analysis. This similarity was based on the fraction of the characters which were coded for both specimens. For example, if two specimens were rated the same in all characters, their similarity would be 1.00.

9. The clustering program compares the overall

similarity (the averaged similarities of each state for which information is given) of each specimen with all others in the study. The specimens are then clustered in accordance with the rank of their relative similarity. For example, specimens that have a similarity ratio of 1.00 are separated first, then additional specimens are clustered as the similarity ratio is relaxed, and the program continues until all specimens are included in a single group.

Results

A numerical analysis of the New World taxa of *Arceuthobium* (fig. 24) shows the relationships of the taxa based on average similarity of all characters listed in table 17.

Because the characters and states used in each taximetric study are different, the results of our *Arceuthobium* study cannot be compared with those in other groups. The taxa of *Arceuthobium*, however, were found to be unusually distinct, and all species were formed by similarity level 0.85. The analyses suggest that the genus consists of two major groups plus several smaller ones, some of which contain only a single taxon.

Arceuthobium verticilliflorum, *A. abietis-religiosae*, and *A. americanum*, the most distinctive North American species (fig. 24), share few features in common, except all have verticillate branching of the shoots or flowers (Kuijt 1970).

Two distinctive taxa, *Arceuthobium pusillum* and *A. douglasii*, which form another group, are characterized by their small size, indirect spring flowering, high host specificity, and formation of systemic witches' brooms.

A major group (the *vaginatum* group) consists of

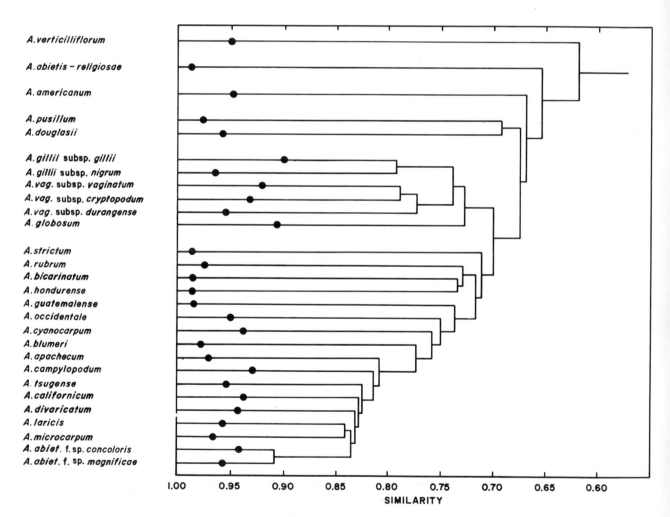

Figure 24.—Dendrogram showing taximetric analyses of the New World dwarf mistletoes. The scale shows similarity, based on combined analyses of all 60 characters used. Vertical lines indicate the level at which two taxa were joined. Length of the horizontal line indicates the distinctness of each taxon. Dot shows the similarity level at which all specimens of the particular taxon were first united.

six taxa comprising three species and three subspecies: *A. globosum*; *A. gillii* subsp. *gillii* and *nigrum*; *A. vaginatum* subsp. *vaginatum*, *cryptopodum*, and *durangense*. The analyses of this group illustrate our use of subspecies in *Arceuthobium*. For example, although subsp. *gillii* and *nigrum* are distinct, and maintain their identities to about level 0.79, common features unite them for about another 0.05 similarity unit before the group joins with the *A. vaginatum* complex. A comparable situation exists for *A. vaginatum*. These are the only instances where we believe that a subspecific category is appropriate in *Arceuthobium*. This *vaginatum* group contains relatively unspecialized taxa with large shoots and broad host ranges on pines, and is centered in Mexico. All exhibit spring flowering.

The other major group, the *campylopodum* group, contains 17 taxa: *A. abietinum* f. sp. *concoloris* and *magnificae*, *A. apachecum*, *A. blumeri*, *A. californicum*, *A. campylopodum*, *A. cyanocarpum*, *A. divaricatum*, *A. guatemalense*, *A. laricis*, *A. microcarpum*, *A. occidentale*, and *A. tsugense*; the less closely related group *A. bicarinatum*, *A. hondurense*, *A. rubrum*; and the even more distinct *A. strictum*. The 13 principal members of this group are concentrated in the western United States, but some range from southeastern Alaska to northern Guatemala. *Arceuthobium bicarinatum*, *A. hondurense*, and *A. rubrum* form a distinct southern subgroup and occur in Hispaniola, Honduras, and central Mexico, respectively. The analyses suggest that *A. strictum* is the most distinct member of the entire *campylopodum* group. *Arceuthobium guatemalense* is the most distinct of the main 13-member subgroup.

The black dot in figure 24 indicates the similarity level by which all specimens of a particular taxon had been united. Thus, the distance of the dot from the 1.00 similarity level indicates variability within a taxon; species with dots closest to 1.00 (for example, *A. abietis-religiosae*, *A. strictum*, *A. pusillum*, *A. bicarinatum*, *A. hondurense*, *A. guatemalense*, and *A. blumeri*) are least variable while those with the dot farthest from 1.00 (*A. gillii* subsp. *gillii* and *A. globosum*) are the most variable. In general, the *vaginatum* group seems to be the most variable. Perhaps this is correlated with the primitive status of the group.

The length of the horizontal line from the dot to the point where it joins another taxon is a direct indication of the distinctness of the particular taxon. For example, *A. verticilliflorum*, *A. abietis-religiosae*, *A. americanum*, *A. pusillum*, *A. douglasii*, and *A. strictum* are the most distinct, and their lines range from 0.25 to 0.33 similarity unit in length. Conversely, the *formae speciales* of *A. abietinum* are the least distinct and their lines are only 0.03 to 0.05 unit long.

Character analyses of *Arceuthobium* (Hawksworth, Estabrook, and Rogers 1968) provide data on the *quality* of information contributed by each character toward the overall classification of the genus based on the synthesis of all characters used. The analyses showed that the five characters with the highest quantity of information, that is, those that contributed the most to the classification were, in order:

> No. 39—principal hosts (most information)
> No. 3—mean basal diameter of dominant shoots
> No. 38—time of meiosis in relation to time of flowering
> No. 15—length of lateral staminate spikes
> No. 16—width of lateral staminate spikes.

Similarly, the five characters that contributed least to the final classification were:

> No. 27—height of pollen spines
> No. 23—width of perianth segment on staminate flowers
> No. 8—sexual dimorphism of branching
> No. 9—difference in color of pistillate and staminate plants
> No. 21—location of anther on perianth lobe (least information).

COLLECTING AND CURATING TECHNIQUES

At many of the herbaria we visited, the *Arceuthobium* specimens were broken or fragmented. Invariably the plants were fragmented if a large branch with an attached dwarf mistletoe had been pressed.

In preserving our specimens, we had little fragmentation if we pressed individual shoots rather than preserving the entire dwarf mistletoe plant. To include the basal shoot internodes, which we found useful taxonomically, we cut the host branch so that a small portion of the host bark remained attached to each shoot. For smaller species such as *A. douglasii* or *A. pusillum*, we pressed the entire infected host branch if it measured less than about one-fourth inch in diameter. Also, we retained enough of the host branch for identification, and collected both staminate and pistillate dwarf mistletoe plants.

On many herbarium specimens we studied, collection data were meager. Information that should be recorded includes the host, ecological data about the site, and shoot characters such as habit size, sexual dimorphism, and original color. Also, the presence or absence of witches' brooms should be recorded and, if more than one host species is involved, their relative susceptibility noted. Any additional information that will help identify either the parasite or its host should be recorded.

Our herbarium specimens are better preserved when we used the following technique for mounting: Before the plants became totally dry, we applied a heavy coat of adhesive to the back of each specimen, and mounted them on heavy grade herbarium paper. Another satisfactory method is to use a cotton-backed envelope or a Riker Mount. A modification of the latter is to place the dried specimen directly on Tomac,[18] and file it in a large envelope with a transparent window so it can be observed with little handling.

Formal Taxonomy

Generic Description

ARCEUTHOBIUM M. BIEB. DWARF MISTLETOE

Razoumofskya Hoffman, Hort. Mosq., unpaged, 1808. *Arceuthobium* M. Bieb. Fl. Taur.-Caucasica 3(IV) Suppl.: 629, 1819. *Nom. Cons.* 2091.

Herbs or shrubs from 0.5 cm. to approximately 70 cm. high, parasitic on coniferous trees of the Pinaceae or Cuppressaceae; plants glabrous, variously colored from greenish yellow to orange; reddish and black, dioecious; stems without a central xylem cylinder; leaves reduced to minute, opposed, connate scales; internodes angled (at least when young); flowers generally decussate or rarely whorled on young shoots, 2–4 mm. in diameter; staminate flowers with a central nectary, perianth segments usually 3–4 (rarely 2 and up to 7) bearing a sessile, uniloculate, circular anther on each perianth segment; pollen spherical with 6 alternating spiny and smooth section; pistillate flower manifestly ep-i gynous, with one style, perianth segments persistent, adnate to ovary, 2-merous; ovary 1-chambered; fruit an ovoid berry, 1-seeded, mucilaginous and bicolored (distal and basal portions of different shades), explosive at maturity; seeds without true integuments, usually 3–5 mm. long, ovate-lanceolate; containing a single, distal, cylindrical embryo, with copious endosperm. Basic chromosome number, $x = 14$.

A genus of approximately 32 taxa mostly in the United States and Mexico; apparently four species in the Old World.

Type species: *A. oxycedri* (DC.) M. Bieb.

Subgeneric Classification and Natural Keys to the Species

Ours is the first attempt to establish a formal below-genus classification in *Arceuthobium* (fig. 25). We recognized two subgenera, *Arceuthobium* and *Vaginata*, based on the type of secondary branching, verticillate and flabellate, respectively. Although Kuijt (1970) suggested that secondary branching could be the basis for natural subdivision of the genus, he did not formally name the subdivisions. We are not fully satisfied because this system emphasizes a single character (branching type), but we have not discovered other groups of characters that might form a better basis for natural subgenera. Another difficulty is that some species (for example, *A. pusillum*) are so reduced that their basic type of secondary branching cannot be determined. Their placement into subgenera, then, is based on assumed relationships and is obviously tentative.

The subgenus *Vaginata* is exclusively New World, and contains 25 taxa. This subgenus has been divided into three sections (*Vaginata*, *Campylopoda*, and *Minuta*), with the largest section *Campylopoda*, further subdivided into three series: *Campylopoda*, *Rubra*, and *Stricta*. We believe the three sections represent a phyletic sequence from primitive (*Vaginata*), to intermediate (*Campylopoda*), to advanced (*Minuta*) species.

---

[18] Dr. W. A. Weber substituted Tomac for cotton because it did not cling to the back of the specimen. Tomac is manufactured by the American Hospital Supply Corporation, North Kansas City, Missouri.

Genus Arceuthobium						
Subgenus Arceuthobium		Subgenus Vaginata				
No sections designated - 4 taxa	No sections designated - 3 taxa	Section Vaginata	Section Campylopoda			Section Minuta
			Series Campylopoda	Series Rubra	Series Stricta	
		6 taxa	13 taxa	3 taxa	1 taxon	2 taxa
OLD WORLD	NEW WORLD					

Figure 25.—Taxonomic summary of the genus *Arceuthobium* (Hawksworth and Wiens 1970b).

The subgenus *Arceuthobium* contains four Old World and three New World species. We have not proposed formal subdivisions of this subgenus because detailed information on the Old World taxa is lacking and there are only three New World taxa in this group. We believe the Old and New World members are probably sectionally distinct, but we hesitate to establish sections based exclusively on geography. However, since the two groups apparently have been isolated since at least the Miocene, it seems likely that, when the Old World species are studied in detail, sufficient additional differences will be found to warrant establishment of sections. In the New World, the three members of subgenus *Arceuthobium* seem to represent a phyletic sequence similar to that shown by the sections in subgenus *Vaginata*. We consider *A. verticilliflorum* to be primitive, *A. abietis-religiosae* intermediate, and *A. americanum* advanced (see fig. 15). The three species are quite distinct and each should perhaps be accommodated by separate series if sectional status is established. Probably a comparable situation exists in the Old World, where *A. oxycedri* is primitive, *A. chinense* and *A. pini* intermediate, and *A. minutissimum* advanced.

A synopsis of our classification of *Arceuthobium* (see fig. 25) follows. The taxon numbers correspond with those used in the alphabetical listing for the New and Old World species.

I. Subgenus *Arceuthobium* (No formal sections designated)
    New World Species
      2. *A. abietis-religiosae* Heil
      3. *A. americanum* Nutt. ex Engelm.
     24. *A. verticilliflorum* Engelm.
    Old World Species
     25. *A. chinense* Lecomte
     26. *A. minutissimum* Hook. f.
     27. *A. oxycedri* (DC.) M. Bieb.
     28. *A. pini* Hawks. & Wiens
II. Subgenus *Vaginata* Hawks. & Wiens
    A. Section *Vaginata*
     12. *A. gillii* Hawks. & Wiens
       12a. subsp. *gillii*
       12b. subsp. *nigrum* Hawks. & Wiens
     13. *A. globosum* Hawks. & Wiens

63

23. *A. vaginatum* (Willd.) Presl
    23a. subsp. *vaginatum*
    23b. subsp. *cryptopodum* (Engelm.) Hawks. & Wiens
    23c. subsp. *durangense* Hawks. & Wiens
B. Section *Campylopoda* Hawks. & Wiens
  a. Series *Campylopoda*
     1. *A. abietinum* Engelm. ex Munz
       1a. f. sp. *concoloris* Hawks. & Wiens
       1b. f. sp. *magnificae* Hawks. & Wiens
     4. *A. apachecum* Hawks. & Wiens
     6. *A. blumeri* A. Nels.
     7. *A. californicum* Hawks. & Wiens
     8. *A. campylopodum* Engelm.
     9. *A. cyanocarpum* Coulter & Nelson

10. *A. divaricatum* Engelm.
14. *A. guatemalense* Hawks. & Wiens
16. *A. laricis* (Piper) St. John
17. *A. microcarpum* (Engelm.) Hawks. & Wiens
18. *A. occidentale* Engelm.
22. *A. tsugense* (Rosendahl) G. N. Jones
  b. Series *Rubra* Hawks. & Wiens
     5. *A. bicarinatum* Urban
    15. *A. hondurense* Hawks. & Wiens
    20. *A. rubrum* Hawks. & Wiens
  c. Series *Stricta* Hawks. & Wiens
    21. *A. strictum* Hawks. & Wiens
C. Section *Minuta* Hawks. & Wiens
    11. *A. douglasii* Engelm.
    19. *A. pusillum* Peck

Key to the Subgenera

1. Stems with at least some of the branching, or the staminate flowers, whorled.

                                 1. subgenus *Arceuthobium*

1. Stems flabellately branched; staminate flowers never whorled.

                                   2. subgenus *Vaginata*

Subgenus *Arceuthobium*

Stems with at least some of the branching, or the staminate flowers, occurring in whorls; Old and New World.

    Type species. *A. oxycedri* (DC.) M. Bieb.

No formal subdivision of this subgenus is made, although a practical division used here is occurrence in the Old or New Worlds. A natural key to the New World species follows. We do not have sufficient data to construct a comparable natural key for the Old World species but we have prepared an artificial key for them (see p. 70).

Key to the New World Species

1. Staminate flowers usually in whorls of 6; fruit at maturity about 15 mm. long; staminate inflorescences deciduous, internodes about as long as wide.

                               24. *A. verticilliflorum*

1. Staminate flowers opposite, fruit at maturity about 4 mm. long; staminate inflorescences not deciduous (but individual flowers deciduous); internodes at least 5 times longer than wide.
  2. Stems with branching occasionally whorled; fruit opposite; internodes about 5 times longer than wide; staminate buds lenticular; parasite on *Abies*.

                             2. *A. abietis-religiosae*

  2. Stems with branching always whorled; fruit occurring in whorls; internodes about 10 times longer than wide; staminate buds rounded; parasite on *Pinus*.

                             3. *A. americanum*

Subgenus *Vaginata*

Hawksworth & Wiens, Brittonia 22: 265, 1970.
Stems flabellately branched; staminate flowers decussate, never in whorls; New World.
    Type species: *A. vaginatum* (Willd.) Presl

Key to the Sections

1. Pistillate plants usually more than 4 cm. high; shoots in individual clusters; host generally not forming systemic brooms.
   2. Plants flowering in winter or spring; internodes usually less than 4 times as long as wide.
   Section 1. Vaginata
   2. Plants flowering in summer and fall; internodes at least 5 times as long as wide.
   Section 2. Campylopoda
1. Pistillate plants usually less than 4 cm. high; shoots scattered along the host stem near the apex; host forming systemic brooms.
   Section 3. Minuta

Section 1. *Vaginata*

Anthesis in winter or spring; tallest shoots usually over 15 cm. high; internodes less than 4 times as long as wide.

Type species: *A. vaginatum*

Key to the Species

1. Fruit markedly whitish-blue glaucous on proximal portion; staminate plants often markedly divaricate, pistillate plants erect; parasite on *Pinus* section *Leiophylla*, occasionally on *P. teocote*.
   12. A. gillii
1. Fruit not markedly glaucous on proximal portion; staminate plants and pistillate plants erect; parasite on *Pinus* sections *Ponderosae*, *Australes*, and *Oocarpae* (rare on *P. teocote*).
   2. Plants forming conspicuous, dense, globose clusters several dm. in diameter; stems pale to greenish yellow; pedicels on mature fruit usually 4–5 mm. long; hosts usually not forming witches' brooms; anthesis from February to April.
   13. A. globosum
   2. Plants usually scattered along the host branch, not forming dense, globose clusters; stem blackish or orange; pedicels ca. 3 mm. long; hosts forming conspicuous witches' brooms; anthesis from April through May.
   23. A. vaginatum

Section 2. *Campylopoda*

Hawksworth & Wiens, Brittonia 22: 266, 1970.

Anthesis summer or fall; tallest shoots usually less than 10 cm. high; internodes generally 5 times as long as wide.

Type species: *A. campylopodum*

Key to the Series

1. Staminate shoots unbranched except at base, some staminate flowers 6-or 7-merous.
   Series 1. Stricta
1. Staminate shoots abundantly branched, staminate flowers 3- or 4-merous, rarely 5.
   2. Tallest shoots usually over 10 cm. high; shoots dark red or redish brownish; secondary branching rare.
   Series 2. Rubra
   2. Tallest shoots usually under 10 cm. high; shoots yellow, green, gray or purple; secondary branching consistent.
   Series 3. Campylopoda

Series 1. *Stricta*

Hawksworth & Wiens, Brittonia 22: 266, 1970.

Staminate shoots unbranched in annual growth segments, usually only branched near base; staminate flowers 3- to 7-merous.

Type species: *A. strictum*, the only representative

Series 2. *Rubra*

Hawksworth & Wiens, Brittonia 22: 266, 1970.

Plants usually over 15 cm. tall; shoots dark, reddish or brownish; secondary branching rare.

Type species: *A. rubrum*

Key to the Species

1. Staminate flowers ca. 1.5 mm. in diameter; shoots dark red; fruit shiny, ca. 3 mm. long, central Mexico.

> 20. *A. rubrum*

1. Staminate flowers ca. 3 mm. in diameter; shoots red to brownish red; fruits dull, ca. 4–5 mm. long, Hispaniola or Honduras.
    2. Shoots brownish red; internodes often twisted in dried specimens; basal diameter of older shoots 2–3 mm.; nodes not swollen on older shoots; mature fruits ca. 4 × 2 mm., reddish; nectary in staminate flower with three similar lobes; parasite on *Pinus occidentalis;* Hispaniola.

> 5. *A. bicarinatum*

    2. Shoots olive brown to grayish green; internodes not twisted; basal diameter of older shoots 3–9 mm.; nodes of older shoots swollen; mature fruits ca. 5.5 × 3 mm., greenish; nectary of staminate flower with two large and one small lobe; parasite on *Pinus oocarpa;* Honduras.

> 15. *A. hondurense*

Series 3. *Campylopoda*

Plants usually under 10 cm. tall; plants variously colored but not dark reddish or dark brown; secondary branching consistent.

Type species: *A. campylopodum*

Key to the Species

1. Parasites on *Pinus.*
    2. Parasites on *Pinus* subgenus *Haploxylon* (soft or white and pinyon pines).
        3. Shoots olive green to brownish; parasite on pinyon pines.

> 10. *A. divaricatum*

        3. Shoots generally yellowish green to light gray or purplish; parasites on white pines.
            4. Plants forming systemic witches' brooms; receptacle larger than the base of the mature fruit; staminate flowers often 2–merous; parasite on *Pinus ayacahuite.*

> 14. *A. guatemalense*

            4. Plants rarely forming systemic witches' brooms; receptacle the same diameter as the base of the mature fruit; staminate flowers rarely 2–merous, usually 3– to 5–merous; never parasitic on *Pinus ayacahuite.*
                5. Staminate spikes in summer less than 3 mm. long, about twice as long as wide; staminate plants less than 2 cm. high; parasitic principally on *Pinus flexilis, P. aristata,* or *P. albicaulis;* California, Great Basin, and Rocky Mountain States.

> 9. *A. cyanocarpum*

                5. Staminate spikes in summer over 5 mm. long, about 5 times as long as wide; staminate plants at least 4 cm. high; parasitic principally on *Pinus lambertiana* or *P. strobiformis;* California, southern Oregon, Southwest, and northern Mexico.
                    6. Anthesis primarily in July; plants ca. 8 cm. high; shoots greenish to bright yellow; parasitic on *Pinus lambertiana;* California and southern Oregon.

> 7. *A. californicum*

                    6. Anthesis primarily August and September; plants ca. 4 to 6 cm. high; shoots generally yellow to light gray; parasitic on *Pinus strobiformis;* Arizona, New Mexico, and northern Mexico.
                        7. Plants ca. 6 cm. high; staminate spikes in summer over 10 mm. long; shoots not densely clustered; straw to light gray; extreme southern Arizona (Huachuca and Santa Rita Ranges) and in Chihuahua, Durango, and Nuevo León, Mexico.

> 6. *A. blumeri*

                        7. Plants ca. 4 cm. high; staminate spikes in summer 5–7 mm. long; shoots densely clustered, yellow; southern Arizona and New Mexico, northern Coahuila, Mexico.

> 4. *A. apachecum*

    2. Parasites on *Pinus* subgenus *Diploxylon* (hard or yellow pines).
        8. Staminate spikes in summer ca. 5 mm. long, less than 3 times as long as wide; anthesis in August and September; parasite primarily on *Pinus ponderosa.*

> 8. *A. campylopodum*

8. Staminate spikes in summer over 10 mm. long, more than 5 times as long as wide; anthesis in October and November; parasite primarily on *Pinus sabiniana*.

18. *A. occidentale*

1. Parasites on *Abies, Larix, Tsuga,* or *Picea*.
    9. Parasite on *Abies;* plants usually over 10 cm. high; usually yellowish; staminate buds same color as the subtending bracts.

    1. *A. abietinum*

    9. Parasite on *Larix, Tsuga,* or *Picea;* plants usually under 8 cm. high; dark, usually purplish; staminate buds conspicuously lighter than the subtending bracts.
        10. Parasite on *Larix;* anthesis usually in August; terminal internodes of staminate shoots ca. 2 mm. long.

        16. *A. laricis*

        10. Parasite on *Tsuga* or *Picea;* anthesis usually in September terminal internodes of staminate shoots over 3 mm. long.
            11. Parasite on *Tsuga;* staminate spikes in summer over 5 mm. long; staminate flowers sometimes 4–merous; basal internodes of mature plants usually rounded.

            22. *A. tsugense*

            11. Parasite on *Picea;* staminate spikes in summer less than 4 mm. long; staminate flowers rarely 4–merous; basal portions of older shoots angular.

            17. *A. microcarpum*

Section 3. *Minuta*

Hawksworth & Wiens, Brittonia 22: 266, 1970.

Anthesis in spring; plants less than 4 cm. high; shoots scattered along the host stem near the apex. Type species: *A. douglasii*

Key to the Species

1. Plants usually less than 2 cm. high, without secondary branching; fruit developing in one season (ca. 5 months); parasite on *Picea;* northeastern North America.

    19. *A. pusillum*

1. Plants usually more than 2 cm. high, generally with secondary branching; fruit development requiring two seasons (ca. 17–18 months); parasite principally on *Pseudotsuga;* Mexico and western North America.

    11. *A. douglasii*

Artificial Key to the New World Species of *Arceuthobium*

The color photographs will also aid in identification.
1. Mexico, Central America, or Hispaniola.
    2. Hispaniola or Honduras.
        3. Hispaniola; parasite on *Pinus occidentalis*.

        5. *A. bicarinatum*

        3. Honduras; parasite on *Pinus oocarpa*.

        15. *A. hondurense*

    2. Mexico, Guatemala, or British Honduras.
        4. Parasites on *Abies* or *Pseudotsuga*.
            5. Plants 1–3 cm. high; parasite on *Pseudotsuga*.

            11. *A. douglasii*

            5. Plants 10–15 cm. high; parasite on *Abies*.

            2. *A. abietis-religiosae*

        4. Parasites on *Pinus*.
            6. Baja California.
                7. Parasite on pinyons; plants olive green; internodes ca. 1–2 mm. wide.

                10. *A. divaricatum*

                7. Parasite on *Pinus Jeffrey;* or *P. Coulteri* plants yellow; internodes ca. 2–4 mm. wide.

                8. *A. campylopodum*

6. Mainland Mexico (not Baja California) or Central America.
  8. Parasites on *Pinus* subgenus *Haploxylon* (soft or white pines).
    9. Guatemala (possibly in southern Mexico); parasite on *Pinus ayacahuite;* plants greenish purple to purple.

      14. *A. guatemalense*
    9. Northern Mexico; parasite on *Pinus strobiformis;* plants yellow or grayish.
      10. Northern Coahuila; plants yellowish; ca. 4 cm. or less high.

        4. *A. apachecum*
      10. Chihuahua, Durango, Nuevo León; plants gray, usually over 6 cm. high.

        6. *A. blumeri*
  8. Parasites on *Pinus* subgenus *Diploxylon* (hard or yellow pines).
    11. Parasites principally on *Pinus* section *Leiophylla* and occasionally on *P. teocote.*
      12. Staminate plants strongly divaricate; internodes more than 3 times as long as wide; fruit markedly bluish white glaucous.

        12. *A. gillii*
      12. Staminate plants unbranched; internodes less than twice as long as wide; fruit slightly glaucous, but never markedly bluish white.

        21. *A. strictum*
    11. Parasites on pines other than section *Leiophylla;* staminate plants erect; fruit not plants erect; fruit not markedly glaucous.
      13. Plants dark reddish or blackish.
        14. Plants 20 cm. or more high; blackish; basal internodes about 5 mm. wide.

          23. *A. vaginatum*
        14. Plants 15 cm. or less high, dark reddish; basal internodes about 2 mm. wide.

          20. *A. rubrum*
      13. Plants greenish, yellowish, brownish, or orange.
        15. Staminate flowers in whorls; fruit generally over 7 mm. long; internodes about as long as wide; plants under 10 cm. high.

          24. *A. verticilliflorum*
        15. Staminate flowers opposite; fruit 6 mm. or less long; internodes at least 3 times as long as wide; plants over 15 cm. high.
          16. Plants greenish to pale yellow, generally diffusely and openly branched; pedicels of mature fruit ca. 4–5 mm. long.

            13. *A. globosum*
          16. Plants orangish, generally densely branched along a principal axis; pedicels of mature fruit ca. 3 mm. long.

            23. *A. vaginatum*
1. In the United States and Canada.
  17. Parasites principally on *Pinus.*
    18. Parasites on *Pinus* subgenus *Haploxylon* (white or soft pines or pinyon).
      19. Parasite on pinyons.

        10. *A. divaricatum*
      19. Parasites on white or soft pines.
        20. Parasite on *Pinus strobiformis.*
          21. Plants usually under 4 cm. high; yellow; southern Arizona and southern New Mexico.

            4. *A. apachecum*
          21. Plants usually over 6 cm. high; gray; Huachuca and Santa Rita Mountains, Arizona.

            6. *A. blumeri*
        20. Parasite on other white pines.
          22. Staminate plants usually over 8 cm. high; not densely clustered around the stem; parasite principally on *P. lambertiana.*

            7. *A. californicum*
          22. Staminate plants usually less than 2 cm. high, densely clustered around the stem; parasite principally on *P. flexilis, P. aristata,* or *P. albicaulis.*

            9. *A. cyanocarpum*

18. Parasites of *Pinus* subgenus *Diploxylon* (hard or yellow pines).
    23. Shoots branching in whorls; parasite principally on *Pinus contorta* vars. *murrayanna* and *latifolia* or *P. banksiana*.

                    3. *A. americanum*
    23. Shoots branching flabellately; parasites principally on other pines.
        24. Arizona, Utah, and eastward.
            25. Parasite on *Pinus leiophylla* var. *chihuahuana;* fruit markedly bluish white glaucous.

                    12. *A. gillii*
            25. Parasite on *Pinus ponderosa* vars. *scopulorum* and *arizonica* and *P. engelmannii;* fruits not markedly bluish white glaucous.

                    23. *A. vaginatum*
        24. Pacific Coast States, British Columbia, and Idaho.
            26. Pacific Coast from Oregon northward; parasite on coastal *Pinus contorta* var. *contorta* (generally associated with infected *Tsuga*, which is usually the principal host).

                    22. *A. tsugense*
            26. California, southern Oregon and northward east of the Cascades; parasite on other hard or yellow pines.
                27. Parasite principally on *Pinus ponderosa, P. ponderosa, P. jeffreyi,* and *P. attenuata;* California to Washington and Idaho; staminate spikes in summer ca. 5 mm. long, less than 3 times as long as wide; anthesis in August and September.

                    8. *A. campylopodum*
                27. Parasite principally on *Pinus sabiniana, P. radiata,* and *P. muricata;* California; staminate spikes in summer over 10 mm. long, more than 5 times as long as wide; anthesis in October and November.

                    18. *A. occidentale*
17. Parasites principally on *Abies, Larix, Picea, Pseudotsuga,* and *Tsuga.*
    28. Parasites on *Tsuga, Larix,* or *Pseudotsuga.*
        29. Parasite on *Pseudotsuga;* plants less than 4 cm. high, scattered along the host stem near the apex.

                    11. *A. douglasii*
        29. Parasites on *Larix* and *Tsuga;* plants over 5 cm. high, occurring randomly in clusters.
            30. Parasite on *Larix.*

                    16. *A. laricis*
            30. Parasite on *Tsuga.*
                31. Pacific Coast from Alaska to central California, Cascades-Sierra Nevada west of the crest; basal internodes of mature plants rounded; staminate spikes in summer over 5 mm. long; terminal internodes of staminate shoots over 3 mm. long; lateral staminate flowers frequently 4–merous; anthesis usually in September; parasite on *Tsuga heterophylla* or *T. mertensiana.*

                    22. *A. tsugense*
                31. Idaho and Montana; basal internodes of mature plants angular; staminate spikes in summer less than 3 mm. long; terminal internodes of staminate shoots less than 2 mm. long; lateral staminate flowers rarely 4–merous; anthesis usually in August; parasite on *Tsuga mertensiana* (associated with infected *Larix* which is generally the principal host).

                    16. *A. laricis*
28. Parasites on *Abies* or *Picea.*
    32. Parasites on *Abies.*
        33. Northern Arizona, southern Utah, Nevada, California, southern Oregon northward to southern Washington east of the crest of the Cascades; plants usually over 10 cm. high, yellowish; staminate buds same color as the subtending bracts.

                    1. *A. abietinum*

33. Pacific Coast from Oregon northward to Alaska and westward to the crest of the Cascades; plants usually less than 6 cm. high, green to purplish; staminate buds conspicuously lighter than the subtending purplish bracts (associated with infected *Tsuga* which is the principal host).

22. *A. tsugense*

32. Parasites on *Picea*.
    34. Lake States and Saskatchewan eastward to the Atlantic; plants less than 2 cm. high, unbranched; parasites on *Picea glauca* and *P. mariana*.

19. *A. pusillum*

    34. Arizona and New Mexico; plants usually over 5 cm. high, secondarily branched; parasites on *Picea engelmannii* and *P. pungens*.

17. *A. microcarpum*

Artificial Key to the Old World Species of *Arceuthobium*

1. Parasite on *Juniperus;* north Africa and southern Europe from the Atlantic eastward to the Himalayas and southward to Kenya.

27. *A. oxycedri*

1. Parasites on *Abies, Keteleeria,* or *Pinus;* Himalayan region and eastward to Szechwan, and Yunnan.
    2. Plants usually less than 1 cm. high; host forming systemic brooms with numerous mistletoe shoots concentrated near the apex of the host branches; parasite on *Pinus griffithii;* western Himalayan region.

26. *A. minutissimum*

    2. Plants usually over 5 cm. high; host probably not consistently forming systemic brooms, mistletoes not concentrated near the apex of the host branches; parasites on *Pinus tabulaeformis, Abies,* or *Keteleeria;* eastern Himalayas to southwestern China.
        3. Parasite on *Pinus tabulaeformis;* plants ca. 10–20 cm. high; internodes ca. 10 mm. long; anthesis in May and June.

28. *A. pini*

        3. Parasite on *Abies* and *Keteleeria,* plants ca. 5 cm. high; internodes ca. 5 mm. long; anthesis in August–September.

25. *A. chinense*

1. *Arceuthobium abietinum* f. sp. *concoloris* on *Abies concolor*. Staminate plant. California.

2. *Arceuthobium abietinum* f. sp. *magnificae* on *Abies magnifica*. Pistillate plant. California.

3. *Arceuthobium abietis-religiosae* on *Abies religiosa.*
Dried herbarium specimen. Staminate plant (center and upper left) and pistillate plant (upper
right). Note verticillate branching. Mexico, D.F.

4. *Arceuthobium americanum* on *Pinus contorta.* Staminate plant. Colorado.

5. *Arceuthobium americanum* on *Pinus contorta*. Pistillate plant. Colorado.

6. *Arceuthobium apachecum* on *Pinus strobiformis*. Staminate plant. Arizona.

73

7. *Arceuthobium apachecum* on *Pinus strobiformis.*
Pistillate plant. Arizona.

8. *Arceuthobium bicarinatum* on *Pinus occidentalis.*
Staminate plant. Dominican Republic.

9. *Arceuthobium bicarinatum* on *Pinus occidentalis.*
Pistillate plant. Dominican Republic.

10. *Arceuthobium blumeri* on *Pinus strobiformis.*
Staminate plant (lower) and pistillate plant
(upper). Arizona.

11. *Arceuthobium californicum* on *Pinus lambertiana*. Staminate plant (above) and pistillate plant (below). California.

12. *Arceuthobium campylopodum* on *Pinus ponderosa*. Staminate plant (left) and pistillate plant (right). California.

13. *Arceuthobium cyanocarpum* on *Pinus flexilis*. Pistillate plant. Colorado.

14. *Arceuthobium cyanocarpum* on *Pinus flexilis*.
Pistillate plant, note nectar droplets on flowers.
Colorado.

15. *Arceuthobium divaricatum* on *Pinus edulis*. Staminate plant. New Mexico.

16. *Arceuthobium divaricatum* on *Pinus edulis*. Pistillate plant. New Mexico.

17. *Arceuthobium douglasii* on *Pseudotsuga menziesii.*
Staminate plant. California.

19. *Arceuthobium gillii* subsp. *gillii* on *Pinus leiophylla*
var. *chihuahuana.* Staminate plant. Arizona.

18. *Arceuthobium douglasii* on *Pseudotsuga menziesii.* Pistillate plant. Idaho.

20. *Arceuthobium gillii* subsp. *gillii* on *Pinus leiophylla* var. *chihuahuana*. Pistillate plant. Chihuahua, Mexico.

21. *Arceuthobium gillii* subsp. *nigrum* on *Pinus leio-phylla*. Staminate plant. Durango, Mexico.

22. *Arceuthobium gillii* subsp. *nigrum* on *Pinus leio-phylla*. Pistillate plant. Durango, Mexico.

79

23. *Arceuthobium globosum* (right) and *A. vaginatum* subsp. *vaginatum* (left) on the same branch of *Pinus cooperi*. Durango, Mexico.

24. *Arceuthobium guatemalense* on *Pinus ayacahuite*. Systemic infections of pistillate plants (above) and staminate plants (below). Huehuetenango, Guatemala.

27. *Arceuthobium laricis* on *Larix occidentalis*. Staminate plant. British Columbia. Photograph by courtesy of R. B. Smith.

25. *Arceuthobium hondurense* on *Pinus oocarpa*. Staminate plant. Francisco Morazàn, Honduras.

26. *Arceuthobium hondurense* on *Pinus oocarpa*. Terminal portion of pistillate plant. Francisco Morazàn, Honduras.

28. *Arceuthobium laricis* on *Larix occidentalis*. Pistillate plant. British Columbia. Photograph by courtesy of R. B. Smith.

29. *Arceuthobium microcarpum* on *Picea pungens.*
Staminate plant. Arizona.

30. *Arceuthobium microcarpum* on *Picea pungens.*
Pistillate plant. Arizona.

31. *Arceuthobium occidentale* on *Pinus sabiniana.*
Staminate plant. California.

32. *Arceuthobium occidentale* on *Pinus sabiniana.*
Pistillate plant. California.

33. *Arceuthobium pusillum* on *Picea glauca*. Staminate plant. Manitoba. Photograph courtesy of J. G. Laut.

34. *Arceuthobium rubrum* on *Pinus teocote*. Staminate plant. Durango, Mexico.

35. *Arceuthobium rubrum* on *Pinus teocote*. Pistillate plant. Durango, Mexico.

36. *Arceuthobium strictum* on *Pinus teocote*. Staminate shoots. Durango, Mexico.

37. *Arceuthobium strictum* on *Pinus leiophylla* var. *chihuahuana*. Pistillate plant. Durango, Mexico.

38. *Arceuthobium tsugense* on *Tsuga heterophylla.*
Staminate plant. British Columbia. Photograph
by courtesy of R. B. Smith.

39. *Arceuthobium tsugense* on *Tsuga heterophylla.*
Pistillate plant. British Columbia. Photograph
by courtesy of R. B. Smith.

40. *Arceuthobium vaginatum* subsp. *cryptopodum* on *Pinus ponderosa* var. *scopulorum*. Staminate plant. Arizona.

41. *Arceuthobium vaginatum* subsp. *cryptopodum* on *Pinus ponderosa* var. *scopulorum*. Pistillate plant. Colorado.

42. *Arceuthobium vaginatum* subsp. *durangense* on *Pinus durangensis*. Staminate plants. Durango, Mexico.

44. *Arceuthobium verticilliflorum* on *Pinus engelmannii*. Staminate shoots in flower. Durango, Mexico.

43. *Arceuthobium vaginatum* subsp. *durangense* on *Pinus durangensis*. Pistillate plant. Durango, Mexico.

45. *Arceuthobium verticilliflorum* in *Pinus engel-mannii.* Pistillate plant with nearly mature fruits. Durango, Mexico.

46. *Arceuthobium minutissimum* on *Pinus griffithii.* Staminate shoots. Kashmir.

47. *Arceuthobium minutissimum* on *Pinus griffithii.* Pistillate shoot. Kashmir.

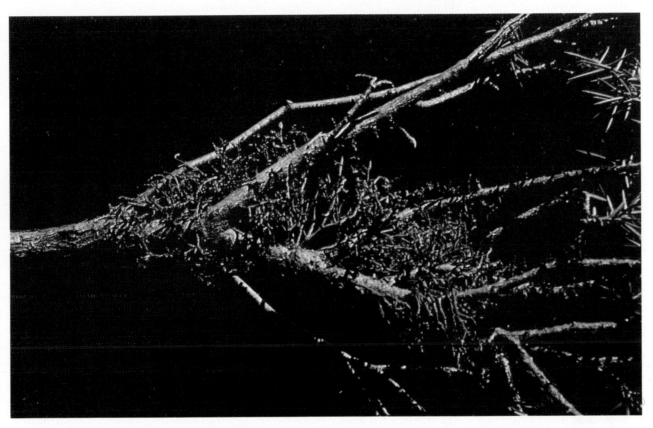

48. *Arceuthobium oxycedri* on *Juniperus oxycedrus*. Staminate plants. France. Photograph by courtesy of J. Gremmen.

New World Taxa

ARCEUTHOBIUM ABIETINUM
FIR DWARF MISTLETOE

1. *Arceuthobium abietinum* Engelm. ex Munz, Man. South. Calif. Bot.: 114, 1935*. LECTOTYPE: CALIFORNIA: Sierra Co.: Sierra Valley, on *Abies concolor, Lemmon* in 1875 (MO[4] Isotype GH). *Arceuthobium abietinum* Engelmann in Gray, Proc. Amer. Acad. Arts & Sci. 8: 401, 1872, *nomen nudum. Arceuthobium douglasii* Engelm. var. *abietinum* Engelm., in Watson, Bot. Calif. 2: 106, 1880. *Arceuthobium occidentale* Engelm. var. *abietinum* Engelm. in Watson, Bot. Calif. 2: 107, 1880. *Razoumofskya douglasii* (Engelm.) Kuntze var. *abietina* (Engelm.) Howell, Fl. N. W. Amer. 1: 609, 1902. *Razoumofskya douglasii* (Engelm.) Kuntze var. *abietina* (Engelm.) Piper, Contr. U.S. Nat. Herb. 11: 223, 1906. *Razoumofskya abietina* (Engelm.) Tubeuf forma *parvula* Tubeuf. Naturwiss. Z. Forst-u. Landwirt. 17: 219, 1919, *nomen nudum. Razoumofskya abietina* (Engelm.) Tubeuf forma *magna* Tubeuf, loc. cit.: 220, *nomen nudum. Razoumofskya abietina* (Engelm.) Abrams. Illus. Fl. Pac. States 1: 530, 1923. *Arceuthobium campylopodum* Engelm. forma *abietinum* (Engelm.) Gill, Trans. Conn. Acad. Arts & Sci. 32: 195, 1935.

DESCRIPTION: Mean shoot height ca. 8 cm. but up to 22 cm. Shoots yellow green to yellow, flabellately branched. Basal diameter of dominant shoots 1.5–6 mm. (mean 2 mm.). Third internode 4–23 mm. (mean 14) long and 1.5–4 mm. (mean 2 mm.) wide; length/width ratio ca. 7–9:1. Staminate flowers ca. 2.5 mm. in diameter; perianth 3-merous, sometimes 4, (not 7 as reported by Munz and Keck, 1959) apex acute; same color as shoots; segments ca. 1.2 mm. long and 1.0 mm. wide. Mean anther diameter 0.4 mm., centered 0.7 mm. from tip of segment. Pollen polar diameter 18–23 (mean 20μ); equatorial diameter 19–25 mean 22μ); polar/equatorial diameter ratio 1:1.07; spine height ca. 1.5–2 times greater than wall thickness (7 collections). Mature fruit ca. 4 mm. long and 2 mm. wide; proximal portion ca. 2.5 mm. long. Seeds 2.8 × 1.2 mm. Meiosis in July. Anthesis usually in August–September. Seeds mature in September or October of the year following pollination; maturation period averages 13–14 months. $n = 14$.

PRINCIPAL HOSTS: *Abies* spp.

---

*Dr. C. V. Morton of the U.S. National Museum has kindly pointed out that Munz raised Engelmann's varietal name to specific rank in 1935. Thus our published "new" combination of this transfer is superfluous (Brittonia 22: 268, 1970).

DISCUSSION: Parmeter and Scharpf (1963) first reported that, on the basis of field evidence and inoculation studies, the dwarf mistletoe on *Abies concolor* will not infect *A. magnifica*. Conversely, the parasite of *A. magnifica* does not parasitize *A. concolor*. Our observations in several mixed fir stands in the Sierra Nevada confirm Parmeter and Scharpf's conclusions. However, we have been unable to find morphological differences between these two mistletoes. Also, the two are similar phenologically although, in the same locality, seed dispersal begins about 1 week earlier for the red fir parasite (Scharpf and Parmeter 1967). Greenham and Leonard (1965) studied the amino acids of the two dwarf mistletoes and their respective hosts, but concluded that amino acid composition probably could not explain the specificity of the two mistletoes.

Since the host affinities of these two mistletoes are distinct, and because this is of considerable practical importance in forestry, we have designated them as *formae speciales* in accordance with recommendation 24B of the International Code of Botanical Nomenclature.

Key to the formae speciales

1. Parasitic principally on *Abies concolor* or *A. grandis*. Southern Washington to southern California and northern Arizona.
   1a. *Arceuthobium abietinum* f. sp. *concoloris*
1. Parasitic principally on *Abies magnifica* or *A. procera*. Southern Oregon to central California.
   1b. *Arceuthobium abietinum* f. sp. *magnificae*

ARCEUTHOBIUM ABIETINUM F. SP. CONCOLORIS,
WHITE FIR DWARF MISTLETOE

1a. *Arceuthobium abietinum* Engelm. ex Munz f. sp. *concoloris* Hawksworth & Wiens. Brittonia 22: 267, 1970.

DESCRIPTION: Mean shoot height ca. 10 cm., but up to 22 cm. (fig. 26). Basal diameter of dominant shoots 1.5–6 mm. (mean 2 mm.). Third internode 4–23 mm. (mean 13.3 ± 3.8 mm.) long and 1.5–4 mm. (mean 2.0 mm.) wide (15 collections), length/width ratio 6.7:1. Pollen polar diameter 18–23 (mean 20μ); equatorial diameter 19–25 (mean 22μ); polar/equatorial diameter ratio 1:1.07; spine height ca. 1.5μ slightly greater than wall thickness—ca. 1.1μ (5 collections). Peak anthesis usually during first half of August, with extremes from early July to late September. Seeds usually mature in September with extremes from late August to late October; maturation period averages 13–14 months. Seeds germinate from February through June (Scharpf and Parmeter 1967). $n = 14$.

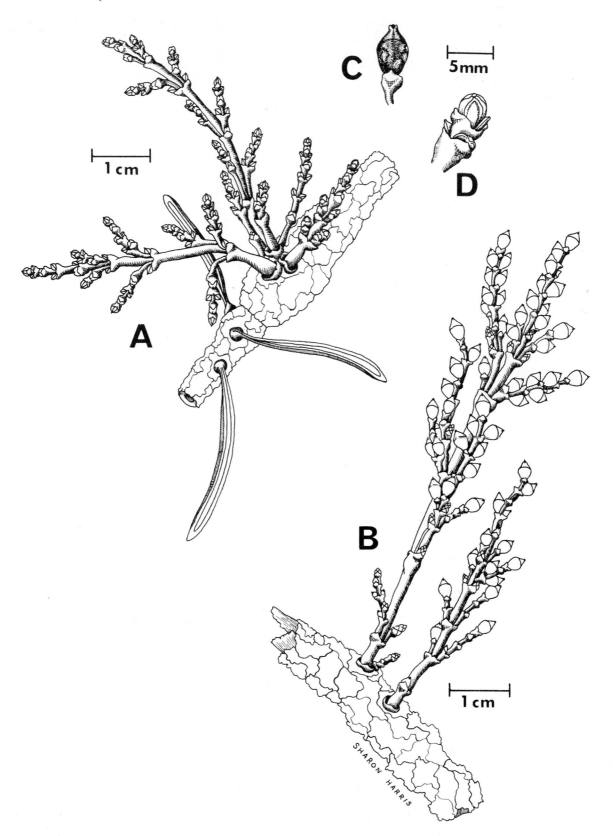

Figure 26.—*Arceuthobium abietinum* f. sp. *concoloris* in summer: *A*, Staminate plant; *B*, Pistillate plant; *C*, Detail of nearly mature fruit; *D*, Detail of staminate flower just prior to anthesis.

HOSTS: The principal hosts of this dwarf mistletoe are *Abies concolor* and *A. grandis*. The rare Brewer spruce, *Picea breweriana*, was found by Hawksworth, Wiens and Graham (1967) to be quite susceptible to this parasite on Flat Top Mountain, west of Grants Pass, Oregon (see fig. 9). On the North Rim of Grand Cayon, Arizona, *Abies lasiocarpa* is parasitized where this tree grows in association with infected *A. concolor*. Little is known of its occurrence on *A. amabilis*; only one collection is available on this host from the vicinity of Crater Lake, Oregon. *Pinus lambertiana*, *P. monticola*, and *P. contorta* are very rare hosts for the white fir dwarf mistletoe.

DISTRIBUTION: *Arceuthobium abietinum* f. sp. *concoloris* is widely distributed from southern Washington (Klickitat County) south through the Cascades and Sierra Nevada to the San Bernardino Mountains of California (fig. 27). It also occurs along the coast ranges from Mendocino County, California, to Curry County, Oregon. It is known in three isolated areas: the Charleston Mountains, Nevada; Grand Canyon National Park, Arizona; and northwestern Kane County, Utah.

This taxon occurs on *Abies concolor* throughout most of its range in California, Nevada, Arizona, and southern Oregon. *Abies grandis* is the principal host in central Oregon, southern Washington, and in the coastal mountains of Oregon and California. In the Siskiyou Mountains of Del Norte County, California, just south of the Oregon boundary, we found the parasite commonly infecting both *Abies concolor* and *A. grandis* in a in a mixed stand.

Several localities for *A. abietinum* recorded by Gill (1935) have since been found to be based on occasional parasitism of *Abies* by other species of *Arceuthobium:* Arizona, San Francisco Mountains, (*A. douglasii* on *Abies* sp.); Washington, Longmire and Ellensburg, (*A. tsugense* on *Abies amabilis*); Arizona, Graham Mountains, and New Mexico, Mogollon, (*A. douglasii* on *Abies lasiocarpa* var. *arizonica*); Utah, Spring Lake and Charles Peak, (*A. douglasii* on *Abies concolor*); and Oregon, McKenzie Pass, (*A. tsugense* on *Abies lasiocarpa*).

The parasite occurs from near sea level along the California and Oregon coasts to over 8,500 feet in the Charleston Mountains of southern Nevada. Specimens examined: see appendix, p. 186.

DISCUSSION: In the Northwest, two other species of *Arceuthobium* occur on *Abies*: (1) *A. tsugense* on *Abies amabilis*, *A. lasiocarpa*, and *A. grandis*, and (2) *A. laricis* on *Abies lasiocarpa* and *A. grandis*. However, insofar as we know, neither is sympatric with *A. abietinum*. For these other taxa, general

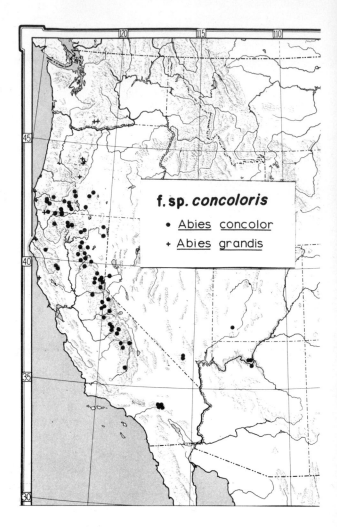

Figure 27.—Distribution of *Arceuthobium abietinum* f. sp. *concoloris* (based on collections only). Outline map copyrighted by Denoyer-Geppert Co., Chicago (used by permission).

infection of pure *Abies* stands does not occur, but occasional trees are infected in stands where the principal host is parasitized (for example *Larix* for *Arceuthobium laricis*, and *Tsuga* for *A. tsugense*). *Arceuthobium laricis* is readily distinguished from *A. abietinum* by its smaller, darker shoots, and small staminate spikes in summer (2–3 mm. long) vs. 5–7 mm. long in *A. abietinum*. *Arceuthobium tsugense* differs from *A. abietinum* by its smaller, green to purple shoots compared with the larger, yellowish shoots in *A. abietinum*.

Branch dying (flagging) is one of the most conspicuous field symptoms of *A. concolor* infected by dwarf mistletoe, particularly in California. Scharpf (1969c) has shown that flagging of dwarf mistletoe infected branches is often associated with the fungus *Cytospora abietis*.

ARCEUTHOBIUM ABIETINUM F. SP. MAGNIFICAE, RED FIR DWARF MISTLETOE

1b. *Arceuthobium abietinum* Engelm. ex Munz f. sp. *magnificae* Hawksworth & Wiens, Brittonia 22: 268, 1970.

DESCRIPTION: Mean shoot height ca. 6 cm., but up to 12 cm. Basal diameter of dominant shoots 1.5–3 mm. (mean 2 mm.). Third internode 10–22 mm. (mean 15.0 ± 3.1 mm.) long and 1.5–2 mm. (mean 1.7 mm.) wide (5 collections), length/width ratio 8.8:1. Pollen polar diameter 19–23 (mean 21μ); equatorial diameter 19–24 (mean 22μ); polar/equatorial diameter ratio 1:1.07; spine height ca. 2μ approximately twice wall thickness— ca. 1μ (2 collections). Peak anthesis usually in late August, with extremes from late July to late September. Seeds mature in September or October; maturation period averages 13–14 months. $n = 14$.

HOSTS AND DISTRIBUTION: This mistletoe is known on *Abies magnifica* (vars. *magnifica* and *shastensis*) from Oregon Caves National Monument in southern Oregon south to Sequoia National Park in California (fig. 28). It has been reported on *Abies procera* from three localities in southern Oregon, but its distribution and hosts in that State are poorly known, partly because of the difficulty of distinguishing *Abies magnifica* from *A. procera* in this area (Fowells 1965). It may be significant that the areas where dwarf mistletoe has been reported on *A. procera* are in the zone where the taxonomic status of the host is questionable. The parasite has not been found in the "typical" *A. procera* stands north of Crater Lake, Oregon. This mistletoe may occur in Nevada in the vicinity of Lake Tahoe. Known elevational range: 5,000 to 7,800 feet. Specimens examined: see appendix p. 188.

DISCUSSION: As noted under the discussion of *A. abietinum*, f. sp. *magnificae* is maintained here because, although it is morphologically similar to f. sp. *concoloris*, it will not infect *Abies concolor*. This mistletoe is a very common and serious disease agent of the *A. magnifica* forests of the Sierra Nevada. In a series of sample plots in California, this dwarf mistletoe was present on 46 percent of 103 *A. magnifica* plots and on 36 percent of the trees (Calif. Forest Pest Control Action Council 1968). Scharpf (1969b) discusses infection in young red fir stands, and gives recommendations for control of the dwarf mistletoe.

Branch flagging is one of the most conspicuous field symptoms of *A. magnifica* infected by dwarf mistletoe. Scharpf (1969c) has shown that flagging of dwarf mistletoe infected branches is often associated with the fungus *Cytospora abietis*.

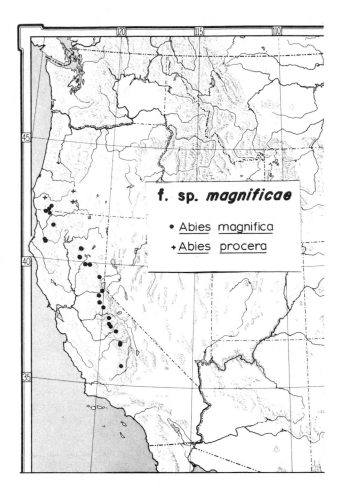

Figure 28.—Distribution of *Arceuthobium abietinum* f. sp. *magnificae* (based on collections only). Outline map copyrighted by Denoyer-Geppert Co., Chicago. (used by permission).

ARCEUTHOBIUM ABIETIS-RELIGIOSAE

2. *Arceuthobium abietis-religiosae* Heil, Centralbl. f. Bakt. Abt. 2: 28, 1923. NEOTYPE: MEXICO: Mexico: Between Amecameca and Paso de Cortez, near km. 78, below Popocatepetl and Ixtaccihuatl Nat. Park, on *Abies religiosa*, *Hawksworth & Wiens 3339* in 1963 (COLO, Isotypes F, FPF, INIF, MEXU, MO, US). (See Hawksworth and Wiens, Brittonia 17: 231, 1965).

DESCRIPTION: Mean shoot height ca. 10 cm., but up to 16 cm. (fig. 29). Shoots olive green, older shoots typically with black variegations. Occasionally verticillately branched. Basal diameter of dominant shoots 2–10 mm. (mean 4 mm.). Third internode 8–24 mm. (mean 15.4 ± 5.3 mm.) long and 1–4 mm. (mean 2.8 mm.) wide (3 collections), length/width ratio 5.5:1. Staminate buds 2–4 per node. Staminate flowers 2 mm. long and 2.4 mm. in diameter; perianth segments mostly 3, but often also 4, apex obtuse-acute; same color as shoots on

93

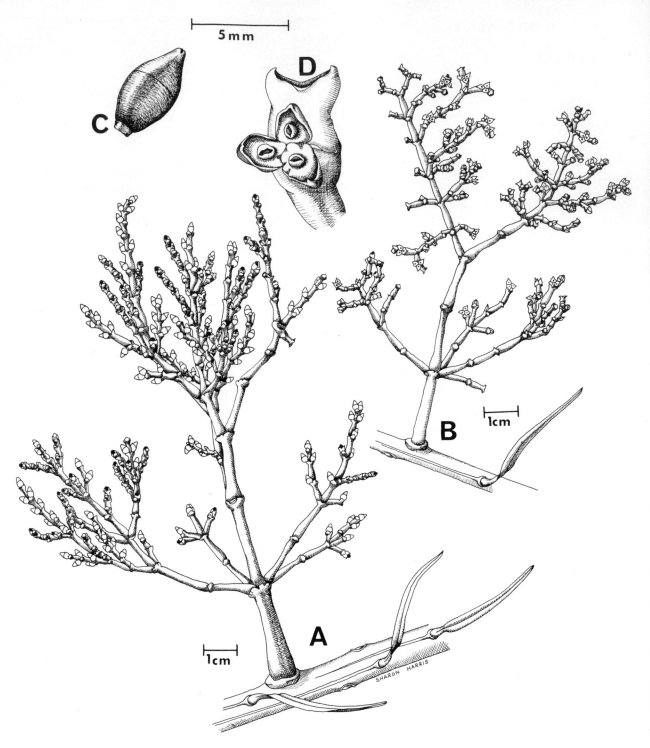

Figure 29.—*Arceuthobium abietis-religiosae* in March: *A*, Pistillate plant; *B*, Staminate plant; *C*, Detail of fruit; *D*, Detail of staminate flower.

outer surface, reddish on inner surface distal to anther; segments ca. 1.2 mm. long and 0.9 mm. wide. Mean anther diameter 0.4 mm., centered 0.8 mm. from tip of segment. Pollen polar diameter 17–23 (mean 20μ); equatorial diameter 22–26 (mean 24μ); polar/equatorial diameter ratio 1:1.22; spine height approximately equal to wall thickness—1.5μ (2 collections). Pistillate flowers ca. 1.0 mm. long and 0.5 mm. in diameter. Mature fruit 3.5 mm. long and 2 mm. wide; proximal portion ca. 2.5 mm. long. Seeds 2.2 × 1.0 mm. Meiosis in September. Peak anthesis in March and April but also observed in September. Seeds probably mature in October or November; maturation period apparently averages ca. 19 months. $n = 14$.

HOSTS: Known only on *Abies* spp., including *A. religiosa* and *A. vejarii*. It does not parasitize pines even where these trees are associated with infected *Abies*. Probably occurs on *Abies guatemalensis* at Copainalá, Chiapis, Mexico judging by the photograph of a tree with apparent witches' brooms published by Martínez (1963, p. 124).

DISTRIBUTION: This dwarf mistletoe is known only in Mexico from the Distrito Federal and the States of Mexico, Nuevo León, Jalisco, and Hidalgo, but can be expected in adjacent areas (fig. 30). Madrigal Sánchez (1967) reports that in the mountains around the Valle de Mexico *A. abietis-religiosae* generally occurs wherever *Abies religiosa* is found, and lists these localities: D. F.: Sierra de las Cruces; MEXICO: Sierra Nevada, Sierra de Calpulalpan, Sierras de Monte Alto and Monte Bajo; and HIDALGO: Sierra de Pachuca. The known elevational range of this dwarf mistletoe is from 8,200 to 10,600 feet. Specimens examined: see appendix, p. 189.

DISCUSSION: The nomenclature of this distinctive Mexican dwarf mistletoe is discussed by Hawksworth and Wiens (1965). The most distinguishing characteristics of the species are its occasionally verticillately branched shoots (a feature shared only with *A. americanum*), and its exclusive occurrence on *Abies*.

Additional items of interest in *A. abietis-religi-*

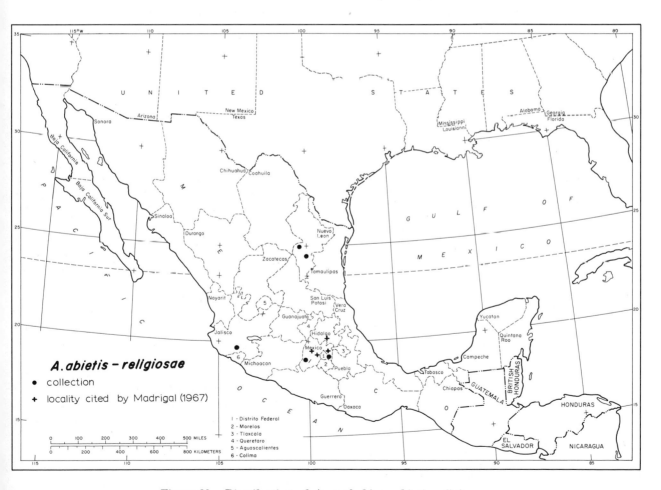

Figure 30.—Distribution of *Arceuthobium abietis-religiosae*.

osae include the occurrence of systemic witches' brooms and verticillate staminate floral buds. Systemic infections are not common in this species; on those few that we found, the dwarf mistletoe shoots had formed only at the girdles of the host branches.

The only other case in which verticillately arranged staminate flowers occur is in *A. verticilliflorum*, where the character is consistent and conspicuously developed. The discovery of this character in *A. abietis-religiosae* strengthens the presumed relationship between these two species.

Most dwarf mistletoes show definite and predictable phenological periodicity; however, several phenological characters such as flowering period and period of seed dispersal appear to be irregular in *A. abietis-religiosae*. Our observations are based on staminate flowers because of their larger size, even though the staminate and pistillate flowers appear to be synchronous.

In early April, the specimens we collected appeared to be in the peak flowering period, and the fruits in the initial stages of development. In September, when we made additional collections, we expected to find seed dispersal and floral buds in early developmental stages. Instead, we found most of the floral buds were already formed, and many staminate flowers already open. Only additional field observations at periodic intervals can help clarify the habits of this species, but we suggest two possibilities. Perhaps, *A. abietis-religiosae* has two flowering periods with peaks in late September and early March, or it may be an indirect flowering species similar to *A. douglasii* and *A. americanum* which complete floral development in late summer but do not flower until spring. If this is true, unusual environmental conditions could have induced the fall flowering of *A. abietis-religiosae*, as sometimes occurs in *A. douglasii* and *A. americanum*.

Heil (1923) stated that the fruits of *A. abietis-religiosae* mature in September. The fruits we observed in mid-September 1969, near Mexico City, however, were at least a month from maturity, and were maturing at the higher elevations first—a character common in most *Arceuthobium* species.

ARCEUTHOBIUM AMERICANUM LODGEPOLE PINE DWARF MISTLETOE

3. *Arceuthobium americanum* Nuttall ex Engelmann *in* Gray, Boston J. Natur. Hist. 6: 214, 1850. TYPE: OREGON, Blue Mountains, on *Pinus contorta, Douglas* in 1826 (MO!). *Razoumofskya americana* (Nutt. ex Engelm.) Kuntze, Rev. Gen. Pl. 2: 587, 1891.

DESCRIPTION: Mean shoot height ca. 6 cm., but up to 30 cm. (fig. 31). Shoots yellowish to olive green, verticillately branched. Basal diameter of dominant shoots 1–3 mm. (mean 1.5 mm.). Third internode 6–23 mm. (mean 12.1 ± 3.0 mm.) long and 1–2 mm. (mean 1.2 mm.) wide (20 collections), length/width ratio 10.1:1. Staminate flowers borne on pedicel-like joints. Staminate flowers ca. 2 mm. long and 2.2 mm. in diameter; perianth mostly 3-merous, sometimes 4, same color as shoots; segments ca. 1.1 mm. long and 1.0 mm. wide. Mean anther diameter 0.55 mm., centered 0.7 mm. from tip of segment. Pollen polar diameter 19–28 (mean 21μ); equatorial diameter 23–30 (mean 25μ); polar/equatorial diameter ratio 1:1.16; spine height (mean 1.8μ) equal to or slightly greater than wall thickness—mean 1.5μ (8 collections). Pistillate flowers verticillate; ca. 1.5 mm. long and 1.0 mm. in diameter; 2-merous. Mature fruit 3.5–4.0 mm. long (mean 4 mm.) and 1.5–2.5 mm. wide (mean 2 mm.); proximal portion ca. 2.5 mm. long. Seeds 2.4×1.1 mm. Meiosis in August. Anthesis usually in April and May, with extremes from March to June. Seeds mature in late August or September of the year following pollination; maturation period averages about 16 months; germination begins in May in Colorado. $n = 14$.

HOSTS: Principal hosts are *Pinus contorta* (subsp. *latifolia* and *murrayana*) and *P. banksiana* (see table 5). *Pinus ponderosa* var. *scopulorum* is frequently parasitized in Colorado, Utah, and Wyoming primarily where this tree is associated with infected *P. contorta*, but sometimes in pure stands. *Pinus ponderosa* var. *ponderosa* is an occasional host (Kuijt 1953) but it seems to be less susceptible than var. *scopulorum* (Hawksworth 1968). Other occasional hosts for *A. americanum* are *Pinus aristata*, *P. albicaulis*, and *P. flexilis*. Rare hosts are the spruces *Picea glauca*, *P. engelmannii*, and *P. pungens* (Hawksworth and Graham 1963; Kuijt 1960b; Molnar, Harris, Ross, and Ginns 1968). *Pseudotsuga menziesii* is an extremely rare host, and in the single case known (Shingle Creek, east of Kamas, Utah), small witches' brooms without mistletoe shoots were formed. Dissection of twigs on brooms revealed the endophytic system of the parasite.

Weir (1917) reports *A. americanum* on *Pinus attenuata* at Oregon Mountain, Josephine County, Oregon. His specimens are unquestionably *A. americanum*, but when we visited the same area in 1966, we were unable to find this parasite in the *Pinus attenuata* or *P. contorta* stands.

Weir (1918a) successfully inoculated seedlings of the European *Pinus montana* with *A. americanum*. This mistletoe has been found on planted

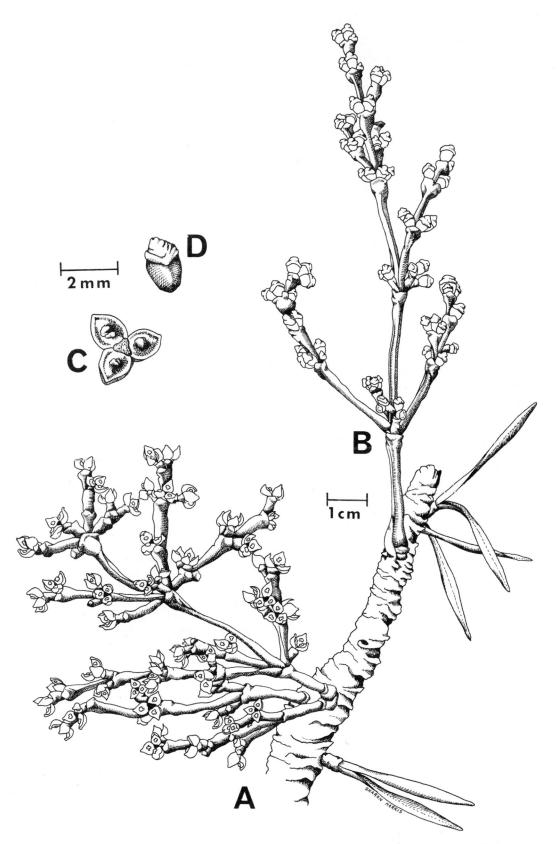

Figure 31.—*Arceuthobium americanum* in spring: *A*, Staminate plant; *B*, Pistillate plant; *C*, Staminate flower; *D*, Pistillate flower.

Pinus sylvestris in Washington (Graham and Leaphart 1961) and in Alberta (Powell 1968).

DISTRIBUTION: *Arceuthobium americanum* has the largest range of any North American dwarf mistletoe (figs. 32, 33, 34). Its latitudinal range, which is exceeded only by *A. douglasii*, is from Lake Athabasca in northern Saskatchewan south to the southern Sierra Nevada in California and to central Colorado. Its longitudinal distribution of nearly 1,500 miles extends from western Ontario to western British Columbia (Elliott, Laut, and Brandt 1967; Kuijt 1963; Larsen and Gross 1970; Zalasky 1956). *Arceuthobium americanum* occurs to nearly 60° N. latitude; thus it is one of the northernmost mistletoes in the world—possible rivals are *A. tsugense* in Alaska and *Viscum album* in Sweden (Wallden 1961). The general range of *A. americanum* is centered within that of its principal host *Pinus contorta*, particularly the subspecies *latifolia* and *murrayana*. An exception to this is in southern California and Baja California where subsp. *murrayana* extends about 300 miles south of the known range of the parasite.

Arceuthobium americanum does not occur within the range of shore pine (*P. contorta* subsp. *contorta*) except possibly in the Oregon Mountains near the Oregon-California border. Weir (1917) reported the parasite here on *Pinus contorta*, *P. jeffreyi*, and *P. attenuata*, but when we examined this area in 1966 we did not find *A. americanum*. All *Pinus contorta* we found was subspecies *contorta*, so Weir's report must refer to this subspecies. Verification of *A. americanum* here is needed because this area is approximately 60 miles from the main range of the species.

The parasite occurs in outliers of *Pinus contorta* subsp. *latifolia* in the Cypress Hills of southeastern Alberta, in the Little Rocky Mountains near Malta, Montana, and possibly in the Whitlash Mountains northeast of Shelby, Montana.

In central and northern Alberta, *A. americanum* occurs on *Pinus banksiana*, and is common on this host in Saskatchewan and Manitoba. The reports of *A. americanum* at White Otter Lake, in western Ontario (Hord and Quirke 1956) and near Sprague in extreme southeastern Manitoba (Zalasky 1956) apparently were based on a rare infection of *Pinus banksiana* by *A. pusillum* (Laut 1967; Sippell, Rose, and Larsen 1968). Recently, *A. americanum* has been confirmed in Ontario (Larsen and Gross 1970). Its discovery in the Sioux Lookout area, is nearly 150 miles east of the previous known eastern limit at the southern end of Lake Winnipeg, Manitoba.

Arceuthobium americanum only occurs in the western part of the range of *P. banksiana* so spread of the parasite onto this tree has probably been

relatively recent. It seems likely that *A. americanum* evolved as a principal parasite of *Pinus contorta*, then spread to *P. banksiana* through central Alberta where these two trees occur together and frequently hybridize. Yeatman (1967) suggests that *P. banksiana* first became parasitized by *A. americanum* after the Wisconsin glaciation, but available evidence indicates an earlier association (Zavarin, Critchfield, and Snajberk 1969).

Arceuthobium americanum has been found on the *Pinus contorta* × *banksiana* hybrid near Grand Prairie and Peace River, Alberta.[19] Also, *A. americanum* occurs on planted *P. contorta* in an infected *P. banksiana* stand at Prince Albert, Saskatchewan.[20] *Arceuthobium americanum* has an elevational range from about 700 feet near Lake Winnipeg in Manitoba to 11,000 feet in central Colorado. In the Rocky Mountains, the parasite occurs at the lower limits of *P. contorta*, but its upper limits are usually about 500 feet below the upper commercial limits of the host (Hawksworth 1956b).

Arceuthobium americanum distribution maps have been published by Kuijt (1963) for western Canada, Baranyay (1970) for Alberta, and by Zalasky (1956) for Manitoba and Saskatchewan. Specimens examined: see appendix, p. 189.

DISCUSSION: Gill (1935) discusses the typification problem of *A. americanum*. Engelmann thought that the specimen he was describing was collected by Nuttall, and it was designated as the type (Oregon, on *Pinus*). Gill states, however, that this specimen from Nuttall's collections was actually made by Douglas (Blue Mountains, Oregon on *Pinus contorta*) and thus we have designated it as the type specimen.

Despite the large geographic range of this parasite, we find no features that suggest ecotypic or subspecific division. In general, the plants are larger in the Cascades of Oregon and in northern Idaho than elsewhere, but this is probably associated with the more vigorous host growth in these areas. *A. americanum*, which induces the characteristic systemic brooms on *Pinus contorta* (Kuijt 1960b), causes the same type of broom on *P. ponderosa* (Hawksworth 1956a, Weir 1916c), but on *Picea engelmannii*, the brooms are nonsystemic (see fig. 9).

Kuijt (1960a) noted that *A. americanum* does not perpetuate itself for long periods of time on *Pinus jeffreyi* or *P. ponderosa* var. *ponderosa* in California. In northern Colorado and southern Wyoming, however, the parasite is aggressive in

---

[19] Personal communication, J. A. Baranyay, Canada Dep. Fisheries and Forestry, 1967.

[20] Personal communication, J. G. Laut, Canada Dep. Fisheries and Forestry, 1967.

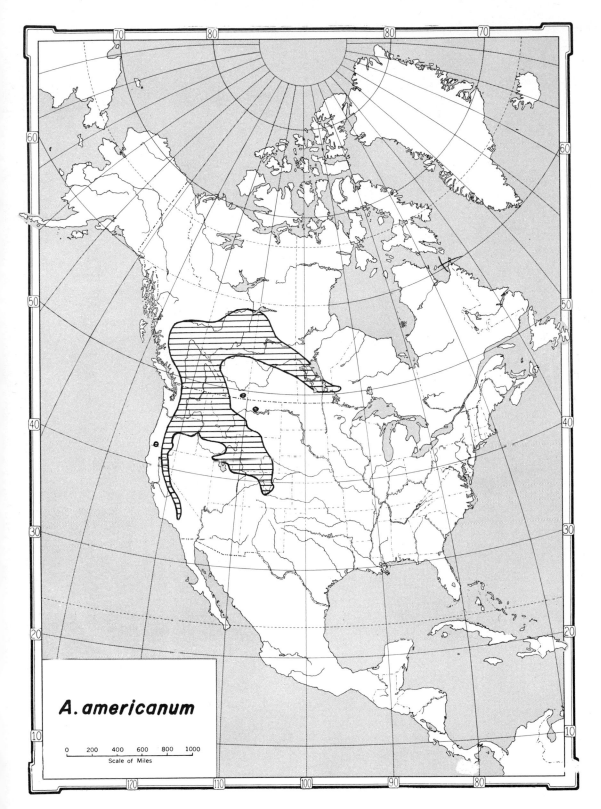

Figure 32.—General distribution of *Arceuthobium americanum*. Outline map copyrighted by Denoyer-Geppert Co., Chicago (used by permission).

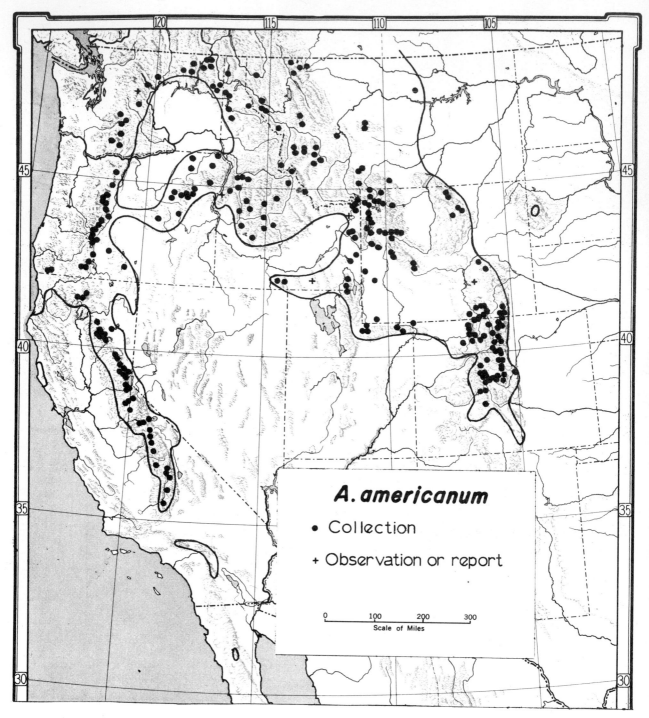

Figure 33.—Distribution of *Arceuthobium americanum* in the United States and the range of *Pinus contorta*. Outline map copyrighted by Denoyer-Geppert Co., Chicago (used by permission).

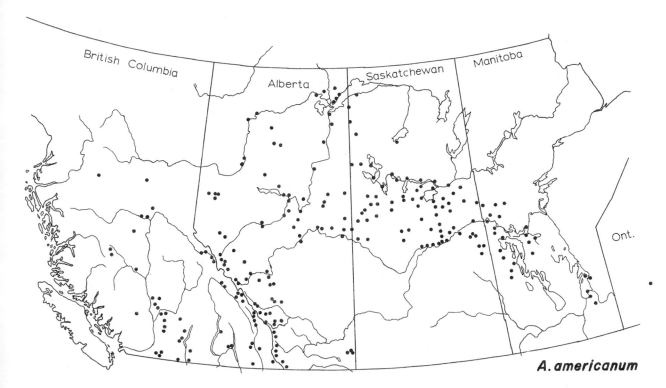

Figure 34.—Distribution of *Arceuthobium americanum* on all hosts in Canada, collections and reports combined.

several pure *P. ponderosa* var. *scopulorum* stands, some of which are several miles from the closest infection on *P. contorta*. Most areas where *A. americanum* occurs in pure *P. ponderosa* stands are outside the range of the common ponderosa pine dwarf mistletoe, *A. vaginatum* subsp. *cryptopodum* (Hawksworth 1968).

ARCEUTHOBIUM APACHECUM
APACHE DWARF MISTLETOE

4. *Arceuthobium apachecum* Hawksworth & Wiens, Brittonia 22: 266, 1970. TYPE: ARIZONA: Pima Co.: Santa Catalina Mountains near the summit of Mt. Lemmon at 9,100 feet, on *Pinus strobiformis*, *Hawksworth, Lightle*, and *Gilbertson 1110*, September 13, 1968. (US, Isotypes ARIZ, COLO, DS, FPF, MO, RM, UC, UT).

DESCRIPTION: Mean shoot height ca. 3–4 cm., but up to 7 cm. (fig. 35). Shoots yellow green, or reddish, flabellately branched and densely clustered. Basal diameter of dominant shoots 1–2 mm. (mean 1.8 mm.). Third internode 5–10 mm. (mean 7.2 ± 2.0 cm.) long and 1–2 mm. (mean 1.5 mm.) wide (12 collections), length/width ratio 4.8:1. Flowers axillary. Staminate flowers 2.7 mm. in diameter; perianth 3- or 4-merous; same color as shoots; segments ca. 1.3 mm. long and 0.9 mm. wide. Mean anther diameter 0.45 mm., centered 0.7 mm. from tip of segment. Pollen polar diameter 16–23 (mean 19μ); equatorial diameter 18–23 (mean 21μ); polar/equatorial diameter ratio 1:1.11; spine height 1.5μ slightly greater than wall thickness—ca. 1.1μ (4 collections). Mature fruit 4 mm. long and 2.5 mm. wide; proximal portion ca. 2.5 mm. long. Seeds 2.8 × 1.2 mm. Meiosis in July. Anthesis usually in early September. Seeds usually mature in September; maturation period averages ca. 12 months. $n = 14$.

HOST: Known only on *Pinus strobiformis*.

DISTRIBUTION: This species occurs from east-central Arizona (near Springerville) and New Mexico (Mangas, San Mateo, Magdalena, and Capitan Mountains) south to the Santa Catalina, Rincon, and Chiricahua Mountains of Arizona and to the Sierra del Carmen in northern Coahuila, Mexico (fig. 36). Elevational range: 7,700 to 9,800 feet. Specimens examined: see appendix, p. 195.

DISCUSSION: Gill's *Arceuthobium campylopodum* f. *blumeri* is here considered to comprise three non-sympatric species: *A. apachecum*, *A. blumeri*, and *A. californicum*. These differ in many characters including morphology, hosts, phenology, and distribution. Our numerical analyses confirm that these taxa should be regarded as species (see fig. 24).

The exclusive occurrence of two dwarf mistletoes on a single host species (*Pinus strobiformis*) is unique in *Arceuthobium*. In our early studies of *A. blumeri* and *A. apachecum*, we thought they might represent a single, variable taxon. However,

101

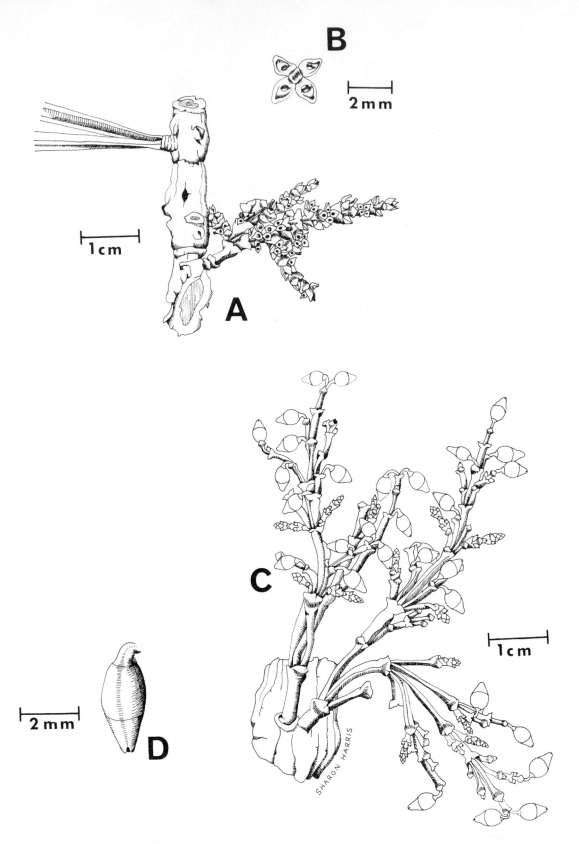

Figure 35.—*Arceuthobium apachecum* in September: *A*, Staminate plant; *B*, Detail of staminate flower; *C*, Pistillate plant; *D*, Detail of mature fruit.

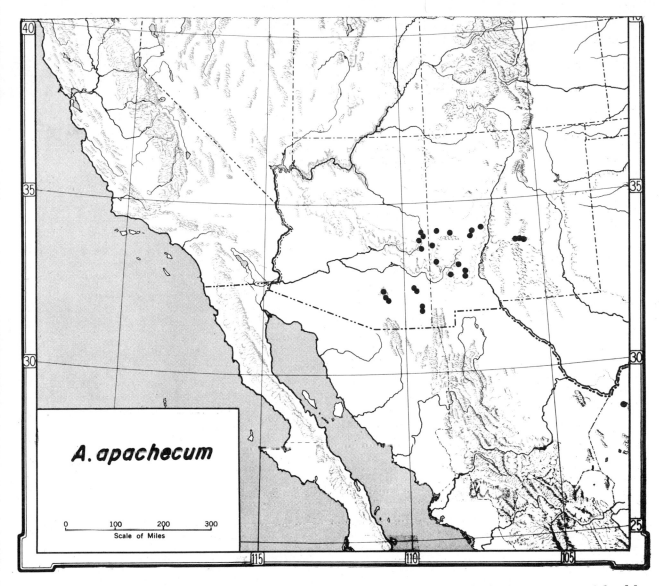

Figure 36.—Distribution of *Arceuthobium apachecum* (based on collections only). Outline map copyrighted by Denoyer-Geppert Co., Chicago (used by permission).

when further investigation revealed that the morphological differences were geographically consistent, we decided that separate taxonomic status was warranted. Also, under common conditions in a greenhouse at Fort Collins, Colorado, each species maintained its distinct morphological features. We have not found the two species in the same mountain range, although they occur about 40 miles apart in southern Arizona. *Arceuthobium apachecum* is abundant north and east from the Chiricahua, Graham, Santa Catalina, and Rincon ranges, and *A. blumeri* is south from the Huachuca and Santa Rita ranges.

A comparison of the two taxa is given in table 18. We do not have precise flowering data for *A. apachecum*, but its peak period of anthesis seems to be somewhat later (early September) than that

of *A. blumeri* (mid-August?). Fruits of both taxa, however, mature in September.

TABLE 18.—*Comparison of* Arceuthobium apachecum *and* A. blumeri

Characters	A. apachecum	A. blumeri
Shoots:		
Size, mean (maximum)	3–4 (7) cm.	6–7 (18) cm.
Color	Yellowish	Gray
Habit	Densely clustered around host branch	Not densely clustered
Lateral staminate spikes in summer	6 × 1 mm.	11 × 2 mm.
Witches' brooms	Consistent	Rare

103

ARCEUTHOBIUM BICARINATUM
HISPANIOLAN DWARF MISTLETOE

5. *Arceuthobium bicarinatum* Urban, Symb. Antillanae 7: 204, 1912. TYPE: DOMINICAN REPUBLIC: Constanza, on *Pinus occidentalis, von Turckheim 3241* in 1910 (Z! Isotypes BM, F, ILL, MO, NY, US). *Razoumofskya bicarinata* (Urban) Tubeuf, Naturwiss. Z. Forst-u. Landwirt. 17: 195, 1919.

DESCRIPTION: Mean shoot height ca. 10 cm., but up to 17 cm. (fig. 37). Shoots dark brownish red, terminal branches of living plants conspicuously whitish-blue glaucous, not glaucous when dried; shoots frequently twisted when dry, flabellately branched. Basal diameter of dominant shoots 2–4 mm. (mean 3 mm.). Third internode 6–14 mm. (mean 10.5 ± 2.1 mm.) long and 1.5–4 mm. (mean 2.0 mm.) wide (6 collections), length/width ratio 5.2:1. Staminate flowers ca. 3 mm. in diameter; perianth 3- (sometimes 4-) merous, apex acute, reddish; segments ca. 1.5 mm. long and 1.0 mm. wide. Mean anther diameter 0.5 mm., centered 1.0 mm. from tip of segment. Pollen polar diameter 21–25 (mean 23μ); equatorial diameter 25–28 (mean 26μ); polar/equatorial diameter ratio 1:1.14; spine height (ca. 3μ) about 3 times wall thickness—ca. 1μ (3 collections). Mature fruit ca. 4 mm. long and 2 mm. wide; proximal portion ca. 2.5 mm. long. Seeds 2.5×1.2 mm. Meiosis in August. Anthesis usually in September. Seeds mature in late August or September of the year following pollination; maturation period averages ca. 12 months. $n = 14$.

HOSTS: Known only on *Pinus occidentalis* on the island of Hispaniola (Haiti and the Dominican Republic).

DISTRIBUTION: *Arceuthobium bicarinatum* is common in both Haiti and the Dominican Republic (fig. 38). In Haiti, the dwarf mistletoe is common in the Morne la Selle and the Morne des Commissaires, in the southeastern part of the country.

A.bicarinatum

Figure 38.—Distribution of *Arceuthobium bicarinatum* in Hispaniola (based on collections only).

In the Dominican Republic, *A. bicarinatum* is damaging on all three major mountain ranges where *Pinus occidentalis* is found: The Cordillera Central, the Sierra de Neiba, and the Sierra de Baoruco. It is estimated that more than half of the pine forests in the Dominican Republic are infested, and damage is particularly severe in Santiago and San Juan Provinces.[21] In our studies of this parasite, mostly in La Vega Province, we observed *A. bicarinatum* commonly between 3,000 and 8,500 feet. Specimens examined: see appendix, p. 195.

DISCUSSION: This is a distinctive species restricted to Hispaniola (see fig. 12). Distinguishing features are the dark brownish-red color, sterile nodes near the tips of the pistillate shoots, and glaucous terminal internodes. Internodes on dried specimens often show a twist of about 1/4 turn, but this trait is not discernible in living plants. Some characteristics that distinguish this species from the related *A. hondurense* of Honduras are summarized in table 19.

The witches' brooms caused by *A. bicarinatum* are mostly nonsystemic (as illustrated by Marie-Victorin 1943). In one area near Valle Nuevo in the Cordillera Central, however, some witches' brooms were anomalous: they appeared to be systemic but dwarf mistletoe shoots were not regularly produced on the infected branches as is normally the case for systemic infections in other host-parasite combinations. Detailed studies are needed on the witches' brooms induced by *A. bicarinatum*.

At higher elevations in Haiti and the Dominican Republic a leafy mistletoe, *Dendropemon pycnophyllus* Krug & Urban, is common on *Pinus occidentalis* and frequently occurs on trees infected by *A. bicarinatum*.

ARCEUTHOBIUM BLUMERI

6. *Arceuthobium blumeri* A. Nelson, Bot. Gaz. 56: 65, 1913. HOLOTYPE: ARIZONA: Cochise Co.: Huachuca Mountains., on *Pinus strobiformis, Blumer* in Oct., 1910 (RM no. 78604!). *Razoumofskya blumeri* Standley, Proc. Biol. Soc. Wash. 29: 86, 1916. *Arceuthobium campylopodum* Engelm. forma *blumeri* (Engelm.) Gill, Trans. Conn. Acad. Arts & Sci. 32: 207, 1935 (in part).

DESCRIPTION: Mean shoot height ca. 6–7 cm., but up to 18 cm. in Durango, Mexico (fig. 39). Shoots gray to straw or light green, flabellately branched. Basal diameter of dominant shoots 1–3

[21] We wish to thank Anthony F. Gasbarro, Peace Corps Volunteer in the Dominican Republic during 1962 and 1963, for this information.

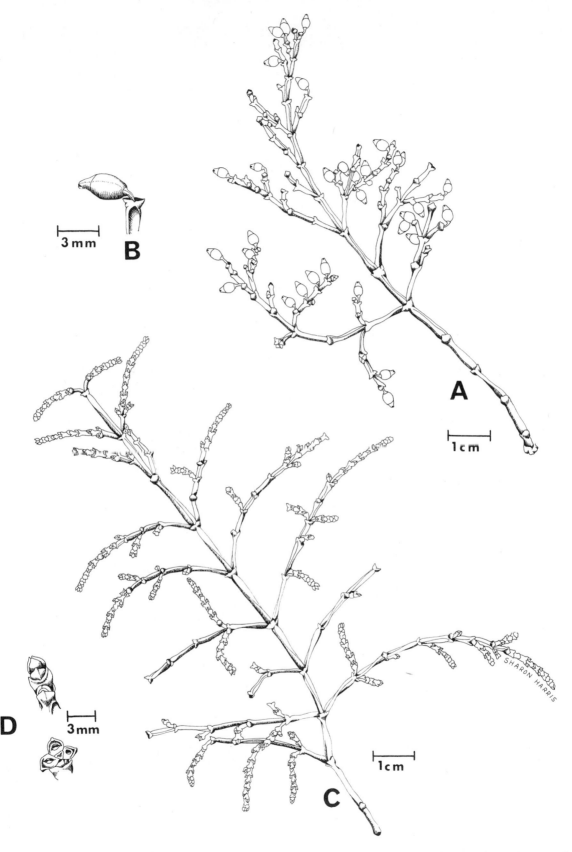

Figure 37.—*Arceuthobium bicarinatum* in September: *A*, Pistillate shoot; *B*, Detail of fruit; *C*, Staminate shoot; *D*, Detail of staminate flowers.

TABLE 19.—*Comparison of* Arceuthobium bicarinatum *of Hispaniola and* A. hondurense *of Honduras*

Characters	A. bicarinatum	A. hondurense
Host	*Pinus occidentalis*	*Pinus oocarpa*
Shoots:		
Basal diameter	2–3 mm.	3–9 mm.
Nodes on old shoots	Not swollen	Swollen
Color	Brownish red	Olive brown to grayish green
Mature fruits:		
Size, mean	2.0 × 4.0 mm.	3.0 × 5.5 mm.
Color	Reddish, nonglaucous	Greenish, glaucous
Stigmas	Not exserted	Markedly exserted
Staminate flowers:		
Perianth shape	Sides parallel, pointed tip	Rounded to tip
Nectary shape	Three lobes the same size	One lobe markedly smaller than the other two

mm. (mean 2.1 mm.). Third internode 5–14 cm. (mean 9.1 ± 2.5 cm.) long and 1–2 mm. (mean 1.6 mm.) wide (8 collections), length/width ratio 5.5:1. Staminate flowers ca. 2.5 mm. long and 2.5–3 mm. in diameter; perianth 4-, 5-, or 6-merous, apex acute; segments ca. 1.3 mm. long and 1.0 mm. wide. Mean anther diameter 0.6 mm., centered 0.4 mm. from tip of segment. Few pollen grains available for study, but those found had a polar diameter of ca. 19μ and an equatorial diameter of ca. 20μ; spine height and wall thickness each ca. 1μ (1 collection). Mature fruit ca. 4 mm. long and 2.5 mm. wide; proximal portion ca. 2.5 mm. long. Seeds 2.7 × 1.0 mm. Meiosis in July. Anthesis not precisely known but presumably in August. Seeds mature in September of the year following pollination; maturation period averages ca. 13 months. $n = 14$.

HOST: Known only on *Pinus strobiformis*.

DISTRIBUTION: This mistletoe ranges southward from the Huachuca and Santa Rita ranges in southern Arizona through the Sierra Madre Occidental to southern Durango, and on to Cerro Potosí in Nuevo León in Mexico (fig. 40). Not yet collected in Sonora but we expect it to be found there. Known elevational range: 7,100 to 9,800 feet. Specimens examined: see appendix, p. 195.

DISCUSSION: The parasitism of *Arceuthobium blumeri* and *A. apachecum* on *Pinus strobiformis* is discussed under *A. apachecum* and the two taxa compared in table 18.

Unusual features of *A. blumeri* include its gray shoots, 4- to 6-merous staminate flowers, and rare formation of witches' brooms.

ARCEUTHOBIUM CALIFORNICUM
SUGAR PINE DWARF MISTLETOE

7. *Arceuthobium californicum* Hawksworth & Wiens, Brittonia 22: 266, 1970. TYPE: CALIFORNIA: MARIPOSA CO.: Fish Camp, 0.25 mi. W of State Route 41 on Summit Camp rd., on *Pinus lambertiana, Hawksworth & Hawksworth 1147,* November 6, 1968 (US, Isotypes ARIZ, COLO, DS, FPF, MO, RM, UC, UT). *Arceuthobium campylopodum* Engelm. var. *crytopodum* (Engelm.) Jepson, Man. Fl. Pl. Calif. 284. 1925.

DESCRIPTION: Mean shoot height ca. 8 cm., but up to 12 cm. (fig. 41). Shoots greenish to bright yellow, turning brown at base of older shoots, flabellately branched. Basal diameter of dominant shoots 1.5–4 mm. (mean 2 mm.). Third internode 6–16 mm. (mean 10.5 ± 2.9 mm.) long and 1–2 mm. (mean 1.5 mm.) wide (8 collections), length/width ratio 7.0:1. Flowers axillary. Staminate flowers 3.3 mm. in diameter; perianth 3- or 4-merous, segments ca. 1.5 mm. long and 1.1 mm. wide. Mean anther diameter 0.5 mm., centered 0.7 mm. from tip of segment. Pollen polar diameter 18–23 (mean 20μ); equatorial diameter 19–25 (mean 23μ); polar/equatorial diameter ratio 1:1.12; spine height ca. 1.6μ approximately twice wall thickness—ca. 0.8μ (4 collections). Mature fruit 4 mm. long and 2.5 mm. wide; proximal portion ca. 2.0 mm. long. Seeds 3.2 × 1.2 mm. Meiosis in July. Anthesis usually in July, with extremes from late June to early August. Seeds usually mature about mid-September, with extremes from late August to early October; maturation period averages ca. 13–14 months. $n = 14$.

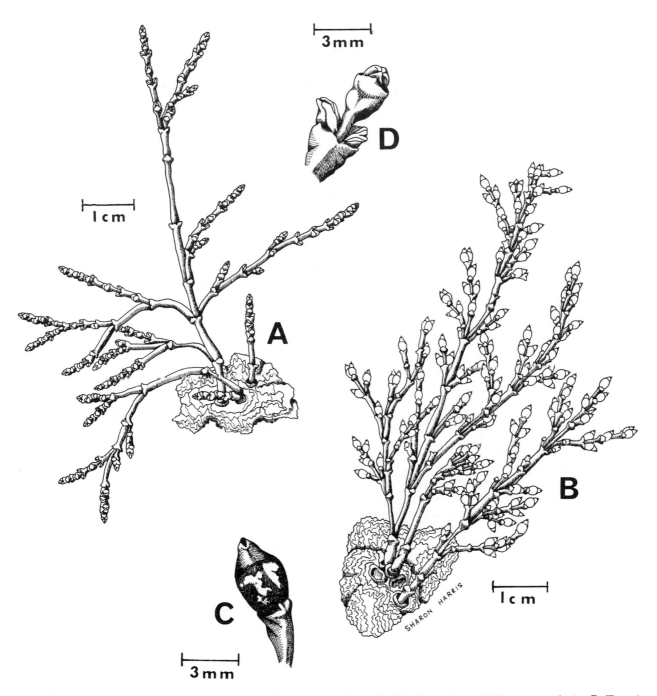

Figure 39.—*Arceuthobium blumeri* in winter: *A*, Staminate plant; *B*, Pistillate plant; *C*, Immature fruit; *D*, Terminal portion of staminate shoot.

107

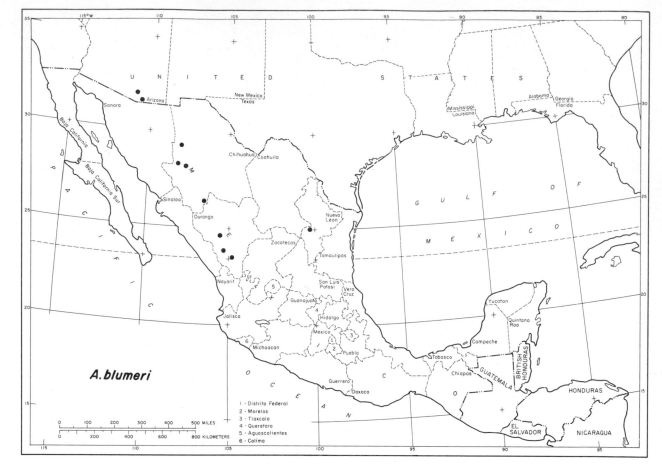

Figure 40.—Distribution of *Arceuthobium blumeri* in Mexico and Arizona (based on collections only).

HOSTS AND DISTRIBUTION: The principal host is sugar pine, *Pinus lambertiana*. The parasite ranges from southern Oregon south through the Sierra Nevada to the Cuayamaca Mountains of San Diego County and in the Coast Range south to Lake County, California (fig. 42). *A. californicum* has been reported on *Pinus monticola*, the only other common host, in the Plumas National Forest, California, and in the Siskiyou Mountains, southern Oregon. The only other known host is the rare *Picea breweriana* in southern Oregon, but in this area the distribution of sugar pine mistletoe is poorly known. Also, *A. californicum* was observed in several California localities during disease surveys[22] (Calif. Forest Pest Control Action Council 1968). Gill's (1935) report of this species on *Pinus monticola* at Rhododendron, in northern Oregon, is based on *A. tsugense*. The known eleva-

tional range of this mistletoe is from 2,000 to 6,500 feet. Specimens examined: see appendix, p. 196.

DISCUSSION: Jepson's (1925) variety *cryptopodum*, which was intended for the parasites of *Pinus lambertiana* and *Abies grandis*, is invalid because it is based on a misapplied name *A. cryptopodum* Engelm., a Rocky Mountain parasite of *Pinus ponderosa*.

As discussed under *A. apachecum*, Gill's *A. campylopodum* f. *blumeri* includes three distinct species: *A. apachecum*, *A. blumeri*, and *A. californicum*. *A. californicum* differs from *A. blumeri* and *A. apachecum* in its larger size, earlier meiosis and anthesis, distinct hosts, and a more westerly range. *A. californicum* is distinguished from *A. cyanocarpum*, the only other western dwarf mistletoe that parasitizes the white pines, by its much larger size, shoots not densely clustered, earlier meiosis and flowering, larger staminate spikes, and its parasitism of *P. lambertiana*. *Arceuthobium*

---

[22] Personal communication, D. R. Miller, U.S. Forest Service, 1968.

108

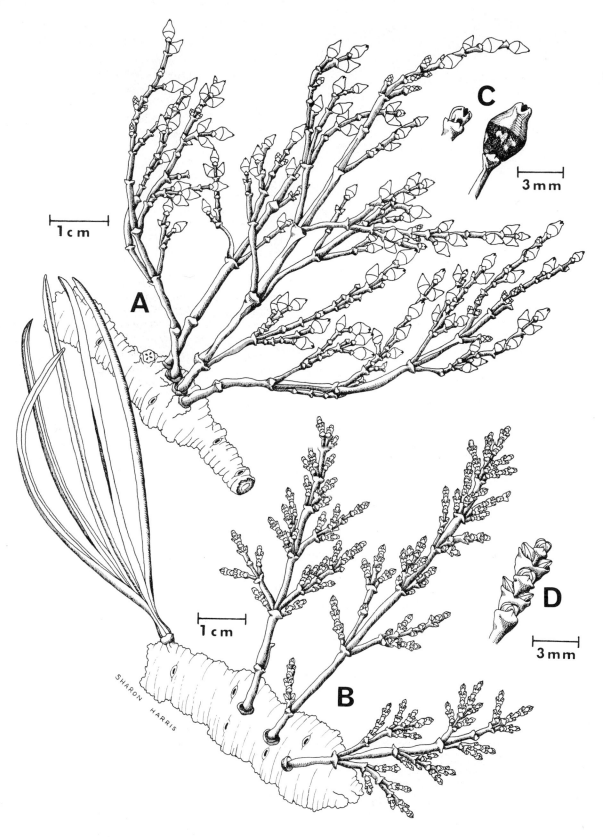

Figure 41.—*Arceuthobium californicum* in summer: *A*, Pistillate plant; *B*, Staminate plant; *C*, Pistillate flower (left) and nearly mature fruit (right); *D*, Terminal portion of staminate shoot.

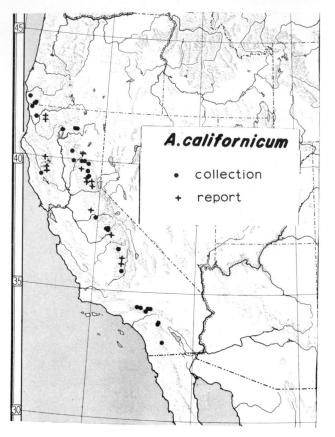

A.californicum

• collection

+ report

Figure 42.—Distribution of *Arceuthobium californi-cum*. Outline map copyrighted by Denoyer-Geppert Co., Chicago (used by permission).

8. *Arceuthobium campylopodum* Engelmann in Gray, Boston, J. Natur. Hist. 6: 214, 1850. TYPE: "Oregon," on *Pinus ponderosa*, Geyer 577 in 1843 (GH! Isotype US). *Arceuthobium campylopodum* Engelm. var. *macrarthron* Engelm. loc. cit. *Razoumofskya campylopoda* (Engelm.) Kuntze, Rev. Gen. Pl. 2:587, 1891. *Arceuthobium campylopodum* Engelm. forma *typicum* Gill, Trans. Conn. Acad. Arts & Sci. 32:185, 1935 (in part).

DESCRIPTION: Mean shoot height ca. 8 cm., but up to 13 cm. (fig. 43). Shoot olive-green to yellow, flabellately branched. Staminate plants brownish, and pistillate plants greenish, particularly in northern populations. Basal diameter of dominant shoots 1.5–5 mm. (mean 3 mm.). Third internode 7–22 mm. (mean 11.3 ± 3.8 mm.) long and 1.5–2.5 mm. (mean 2.0 mm.) wide (27 collections), length/width ratio 5.6:1. Staminate flowers 3.0 mm. in diameter; perianth 3- (occasionally 4-) merous, segments ca. 1.4 mm. long and 1.0 mm. wide. Mean anther diameter 0.5 mm., centered 0.8 mm. from tip of segment. Pollen polar diameter 18–25 (mean 20μ); equatorial diameter 20–27 (mean 24μ); polar/equatorial diameter ratio 1:1.18; spine height ca. 2.2μ about 2.5 times wall thickness—ca. 0.8μ (5 collections). Mature fruit 5.0 mm. long and 3.0 mm. wide. Meiosis in July. Peak anthesis usually during mid-September, with extremes from early August to late October. Seeds usually mature in late September, with extremes from late August to late November; maturation period averages about 13 months. $n = 14$.

HOSTS: The principal and commonly infected hosts are *Pinus ponderosa* var. *ponderosa* and *P. jeffreyi*. Other trees frequently infected, particularly when associated with the above hosts, are *P. coulteri* and *P. attenuata*. In the Charleston Mountains, Nevada, *Pinus ponderosa* var. *scopulorum* is a common host, but this is the only record where *A. campylopodum* occurs naturally on this tree. In Oregon, however, Roth (1967) inoculated varieties *scopulorum* and *ponderosa* with *A. campylopodum*, and found both to be equally susceptible.

Occasional hosts for *A. campylopodum* are *Pinus contorta* vars. *latifolia* and *murrayana*. Dr. T. W. Childs[23] informs us that *Pinus lambertiana* is very rarely infected by this mistletoe in the vicinity of Hammer Butte in the Deschutes National Forest in northern Klamath County, Oregon.

Weir (1918a) successfully inoculated seedlings of *Pinus sylvestris*, *P. montana*, *P. resinosa*, *Picea abies*, *Abies concolor*, *A. grandis*, and *Larix occidentalis*. The latter three trees are commonly asso-

---

cyanocarpum did not attack *P. lambertiana* in the only case we have seen where the mistletoe was associated with this pine (in the San Jacinto Mountains of southern California).

Gill (1935) reported that "infected trees are infrequent and were found only in presence of other infected species." Our studies indicate that neither statement is applicable to *A. californicum*, because this dwarf mistletoe is very damaging in California (Scharpf and Hawksworth 1968). Results of surveys show that the parasite was present on 22 percent of 274 *Pinus lambertiana* plots in California (Calif. Forest Pest Control Action Council 1968). We have seen many instances where *A. californicum* was the only dwarf mistletoe present in a stand. Sometimes it is sympatric with *A. campylopodum*, however, and this may have been the basis for Gill's statement.

This mistletoe induces large compact witches' brooms in *Pinus lambertiana* (see fig. 10).

[23] Personal communication, U.S. Forest Service, 1964.

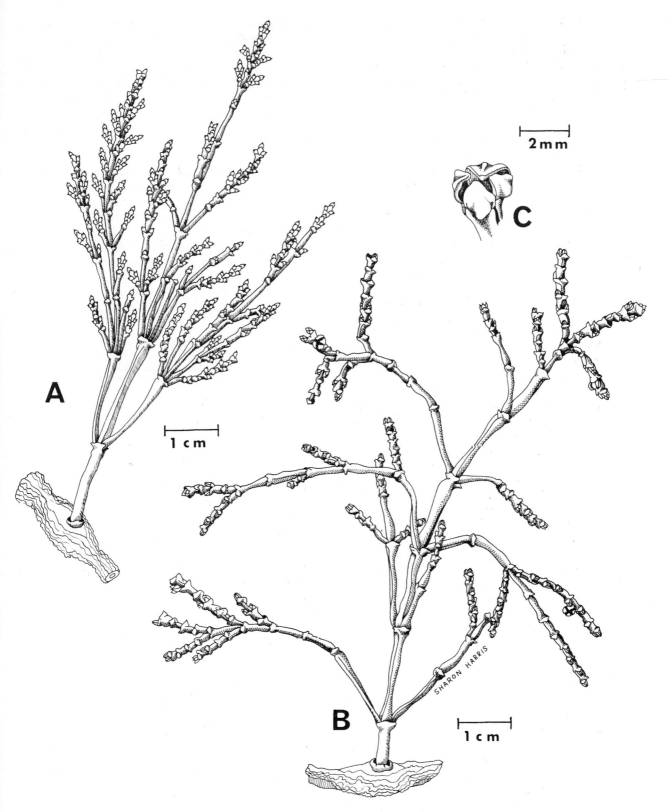

Figure 43.—*Arceuthobium campylopodum* in winter: *A*, Pistillate plant with young fruits; *B*, Staminate plant with remnants of flowers; *C*, Old flower.

111

ciated with *A. campylopodum* on *Pinus ponderosa*, but we have never seen the parasite on any of the three. Kuijt (1960b) found the European *Pinus pinaster* infected naturally at the Institute of Forest Genetics Arboretum at Placerville, California. J. R. Weir collected *A. campylopodum* on *Pinus sylvestris* near Hayden Lake, Idaho (see specimens cited).

Pinus washoensis is probably susceptible to *A. campylopodum*, but we know of no collections on this host. We found none on the extensive populations of *P. washoensis* in the vicinity of Patterson Guard Station in the southern end of the Warner Mountains, Modoc County, California. Similarly, Dr. R. S. Peterson[24] reports no *A. campylopodum* in the type locality for *P. washoensis* on Mount Rose, near Reno, Nevada.

DISTRIBUTION: This dwarf mistletoe occurs from northern Washington and eastern Idaho, south through Oregon and California (but not known in the southern coast range) to the Sierra de San Pedro Mártir in Baja California, Mexico. In Nevada, it is found in the vicinity of Lake Tahoe and in the Charleston Mountains of Clark County (fig. 44). Not known from British Columbia, *A. campylopodum* occurs within about 20 miles of the International Boundary near Kettle Falls, Washington. Gill's (1935) reports of this species in western Montana are based on occasional parasitism of *P. ponderosa* by the larch dwarf mistletoe, *A. laricis*. The wide elevational distribution of *A. campylopodum* ranges from about 100 feet along the Columbia River near the mouth of the Hood River in Oregon to 7,800 feet in the Charleston Mountains of southern Nevada. Specimens examined: see appendix, p. 196.

DISCUSSION: The type locality is listed as "Oregon," although Piper (1906) says that the specimen must have come from northern Idaho or northeastern Washington because Geyer did not collect in the area that is now Oregon.

A. campylopodum is a serious pathogen in the *Pinus ponderosa* and *P. jeffreyi* forests. According to Wagener (1965), *P. jeffreyi* is more susceptible than *P. ponderosa*, but both species suffer considerable damage and are classed here as principal hosts. Our observations suggest that damage is more severe in southern parts of the hosts' range; the most seriously damaged stands were seen in the Laguna Mountains in San Diego County, California. In the northern Sierra Nevada, damage is more conspicuous on the drier east-side than along the moister west-side forests. Roth (1966) reports that drooping-needled races of ponderosa pine in Oregon are less frequently infected by dwarf mistletoe.

[24] Personal communication, U.S. Forest Service, 1966.

Daubenmire (1961) found *A. camylopodum* in only two of the seven habitat types with ponderosa pine in eastern Washington and northern Idaho. The two habitat types with dwarf mistletoe— *Pinus/Agropyron* and *Pinus/Purshia*—were the driest of the seven recognized. The presence or absence of *Arceuthobium* was consistent enough to be used as one of the key characters to determine ponderosa pine habitat types (Daubenmire and Daubenmire 1968).

Arceuthobium campylopodum f. *typicum* of Gill (1935) is here considered to comprise two species, *A. campylopodum* and *A. occidentale*, separable on the basis of phenology, morphology, geographic distribution, and hosts (fig. 45, table 20).

G. G. Hedgcock (unpublished manuscript dated 1914) first noted some differences between these two mistletoes and, although he suggested that they warranted separate taxonomic status, he did not publish descriptions of them. In addition to the differences mentioned in table 20 the two

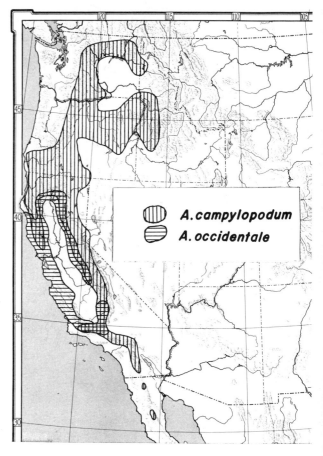

Figure 45.—**Comparative distribution of *Arceuthobium campylopodum* and *A. occidentale*. Outline map copyrighted by Denoyer-Geppert Co., Chicago (used by permission).**

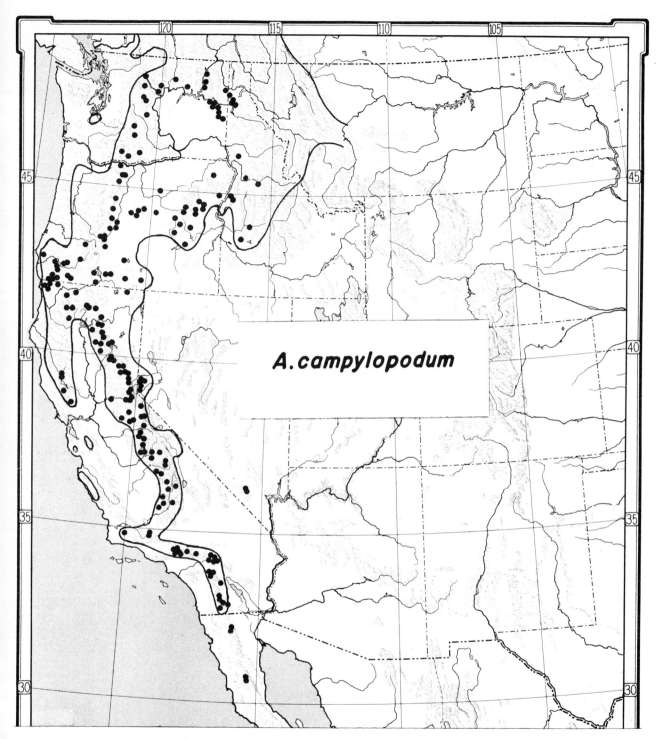

Figure 44.—Distribution of *Arceuthobium campylopodum* on all hosts and the range of *Pinus ponderosa* var. *ponderosa* (based on collections only). Localities for the mistletoe outside the range of this host are on *Pinus ponderosa* var. *scopulorum* (southern Nevada) and on *Pinus jeffreyi* (Baja California). Outline map copyrighted by Denoyer-Geppert Co., Chicago (used by permission).

113

TABLE 20.—*Comparison of* Arceuthobium campylopodum *and*
A. occidentale

Characters	A. campylopodum	A. occidentale
Principal hosts	Pinus ponderosa Pinus jeffreyi Pinus attenuata	Pinus sabiniana Pinus radiata Pinus muricata
Shoots	Glaucous; shoot clusters usually open	Nonglaucous or only slightly so; shoots in dense, globose clusters
Lateral staminate spikes in summer:		
Length	Less than 10 mm.	Over 10 mm.
Length/width ratio	Three or less	Five or more
Peak flowering time	September or earlier	October or later
Peak seed dispersal time	October or before	November or later
Distribution	Washington and Idaho to Baja California	California

dwarf mistletoes differ in germination characteristics and host reactions. The seeds of *A. campylopodum* require an afterripening period (Beckman and Roth 1968, Wicker 1965), while those of *A. occidentale* do not (Scharpf and Parmeter 1962). Witches' brooms caused by *A. campylopodum* (see fig. 14) are larger than those caused by *A. occidentale* (see fig. 8).

Host data for *A. campylopodum* and *A. occidentale*, based on observations of infection in stands where at least two species of pines occur, are given in fig. 46. The known natural hosts for *A. campylopodum* are *Pinus ponderosa*, *P. jeffreyi*, *P. attenuata*, *P. coulteri*, *P. contorta* (subsp. *latifolia, murrayana,* and *contorta*) and, very rarely, *P. lambertiana*. The hosts of *A. occidentale* are *P. sabiniana, P. radiata, P. muricata, P. attenuata, P. coulteri,* and *P. contorta* subsp. *bolanderi. Pinus attenuata* and *P. coulteri* may be attacked by either dwarf mistletoe, depending on the locality where the hosts occur.

Arceuthobium campylopodum (on *P. ponderosa*) and *A. occidentale* (on *P. sabiniana*) are sympatric in many areas of the Sierra Nevada and north Coast ranges. Despite intensive searches in several such areas, we found no evidence of cross infection between these two hosts. Neither did we observe sympatry between these two dwarf mistletoes on other hosts.

ARCEUTHOBIUM CYANOCARPUM
LIMBER PINE DWARF MISTLETOE

9. *Arceuthobium cyanocarpum* Coulter & Nelson, New Man. Bot. Cent. Rocky Mts.: 146, 1909. LECTOTYPE: WYOMING: Carbon Co.: Ferris Mountains, on *Pinus flexilis, Nelson 4959* in 1898 (RM! Isotypes NY, MO). *Razoumofskya cyanocarpa* A. Nelson in Rydberg, Colo. Agr. Exp. Sta. Bull, 100: 101, 1906 *nomen nudum. Arceuthobium cyanocarpum* (A. Nels.) Abrams, Illus. Flora Pacific Coast States I: 531, 1923. *Arceuthobium campylopodum* Engelm. forma *cyanocarpum* (A. Nels.) Gill, Trans. Conn. Acad. Arts & Sci. 32: 204, 1935.

DESCRIPTION: Mean shoot height ca. 3 cm., but up to 5 cm. (fig. 47). Shoots yellow green, flabellately branched, densely clustered. Basal diameter of dominant shoots 1–2 mm. (mean 1.4 mm.). Third internode 2–14 mm. (mean 5.2 ± 2.0 mm.) long and 1–1.5 mm. (mean 1.1 mm.) wide (15 collections); length/width ratio 4.7:1. Staminate flowers 3.0 mm. in diameter; perianth 3- (rarely 4-) merous, apex acute; same color as shoots; segments ca. 1.4 mm. long and 1.0 mm. wide. Mean anther diameter 0.4 mm., centered 0.7 mm. from tip of segment. Pollen polar diameter 15–21 (mean 19μ); equatorial diameter 20–25 (mean 22μ); polar/equatorial diameter ratio 1:1.19; spine

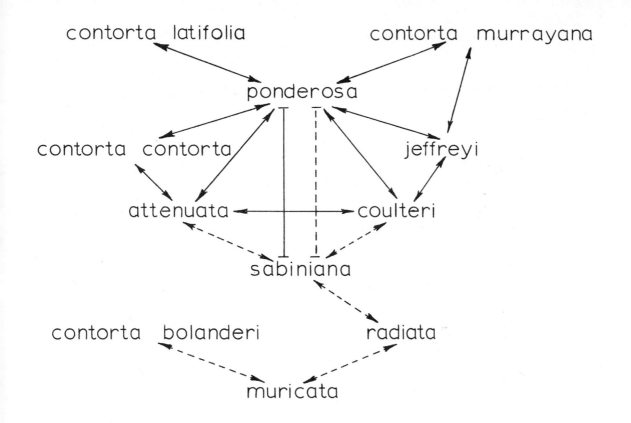

Dwarf mistletoe	Cross-infection	No cross-infection
Arceuthobium campylopodum	<--------->	|----------|
Arceuthobium occidentale	<- - - - ->	|- - - - - -|

Figure 46.—Natural hosts of *Arceuthobium campylopodum* and *A. occidentale*.

height (ca. 1.5μ) approximately twice wall thickness—ca. 0.8μ (6 collections). Mature fruit 3.5 mm. long and 2.0 mm. wide; proximal portion ca. 2.0 mm. long. Seeds 2.0 × 0.9 mm. Meiosis in July. Anthesis usually in late August, with extremes from mid-July to early September. Seed mature in late August or early September; maturation period averages ca. 12 months. Germination mostly in June. $n = 14$.

HOSTS: The principal host is *Pinus flexilis*. *Pinus aristata* and *P. albicaulis* appear to be equally susceptible, but these trees are not as common within the range of the mistletoe, and relatively few collections on them have been made. In northern California, *A. cyanocarpum* also occurs on *Pinus monticola* and rarely on *P. balfouriana* (Miller and Bynum 1965). Rare hosts include *Pinus ponderosa* var. *scopulorum* and *Pinus contorta* subsp. *latifolia* in the Rocky Mountains (Hawksworth and Peterson 1959).

Tubeuf (1919) mentions a single infection on *Picea engelmannii* from Pikes Peak, Colorado, which Hawksworth and Graham (1963) surmised was this taxon.

Inoculations of seedlings by *A. cyanocarpum* in a greenhouse have been successful on *Pinus strobus* and *P. strobiformis* (Hawksworth, unpublished data). The latter is of interest because, although

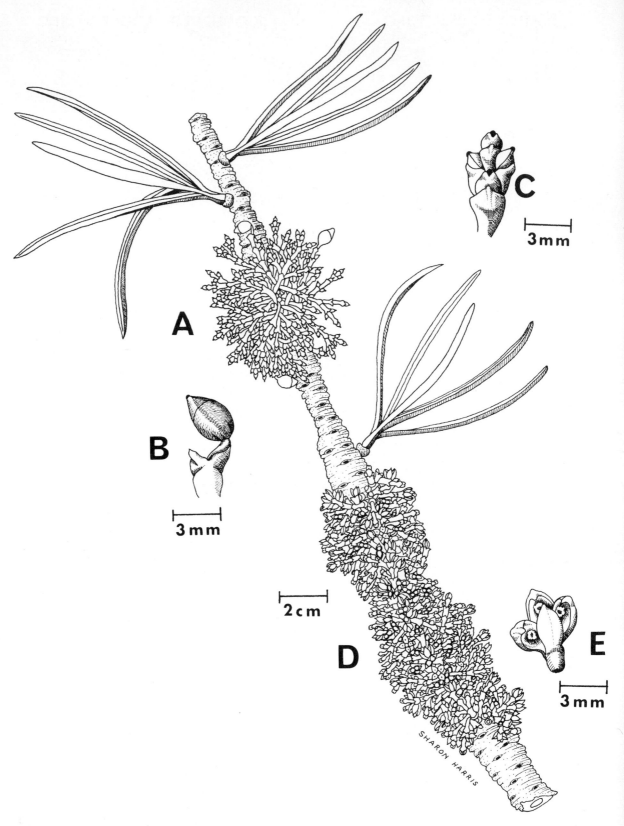

Figure 47.—*Arceuthobium cyanocarpum* in September: *A*, Pistillate plant; *B*, Detail of mature fruit; *C*, Pistillate flowers just pollinated; *D*, Staminate plants; *E*, Mature staminate flower.

116

this tree is naturally exposed to *A. cyanocarpum* on the San Francisco Peaks, Arizona, it is not infected there (Hawksworth 1965a). This emphasizes that conclusions on host relations based on inoculations under artificial conditions must be viewed with caution.

Arceuthobium cyanocarpum is not sympatric with *A. blumeri*, and the former does not attack *P. strobiformis* in the only known area where this tree and the mistletoe occur together in the San Francisco Peaks in northern Arizona (Hawksworth 1965a).

DISTRIBUTION: This dwarf mistletoe occurs from southern Montana (Brown 1970) and northern Colorado southwestward to northern California; down the east side of the Sierra Nevada and in San Bernardino and San Jacinto Mountains of southern California (fig. 48). Isolated occurrences are known from the vicinity of Pikes Peak, and in the Sangre de Cristo Mountains near Coaldale, Colorado (on *P. flexilis*), La Sal Mountains near the Utah-Colorado border (*on P. flexilis*), San Francisco Peaks, Arizona* (on *P. aristata*), and the Mount Shasta area, California (*on P. albicaulis* and *P. monticola*). Known now from only three areas in Idaho and two in Nevada, it seems likely that *A. cyanocarpum* will be found in other *P. flexilis* localities in these States. For example, Linsdale, Howell, and Linsdale (1952) illustrate a broomed *Pinus flexilis* from the Toiyabe Mountains (Nye County, Nevada) which appears to be infected by *A. cyanocarpum*. The specimens listed by Gill (1935) as *A. campylopodum* f. *cyanocarpum* on *Pinus albicaulis* from the Crater Lake region of Oregon are *A. tsugense*. This mistletoe may occur in the mountains of southern Oregon, however, and we have tentatively listed a collection on *P. albicaulis* from "Obsidian Cliff," Oregon, as this taxon.

The known elevational range of this mistletoe is from 5,200 feet in southern Montana to 9,800 feet in central Colorado. Specimens examined: see appendix, p. 201.

DISCUSSION: Weir made several collections of *A. cyanocarpum* in the vicinity of Anaconda, Montana, in 1913 and 1914, but we were unable to find it on *Pinus flexilis* in that area in 1966. Possibly the sulfur dioxide fumes that damaged the vegetation so severely there have eliminated the parasite. Scheffer and Hedgcock (1955) who studied the area in the late 1920's, noted that *Pinus*

---

* 1970 and 1971 studies of the San Francisco Peaks population on *Pinus aristata*, which we tentatively class as *A. cyanocarpum*, revealed four previously unrecorded hosts: *Picea pungens* and *P. engelmannii* are occasional hosts and *Abies lasiocarpa* var. *arizonica* and *Pinus strobiformis* rare hosts. Taxonomic studies of this population are continuing.

flexilis and dwarf mistletoe were relatively rare in the fume-damaged area.

This characteristic dwarf mistletoe of *Pinus flexilis* and associated high-altitude white pines is easily recognized by its small, densely clustered shoots. In many cases shoot mortality is excessive (cause unknown but probably a fungal disease), and only dense clusters of shoot bases about 1 mm. high remain.

Arceuthobium cyanocarpum causes heavy mortality in *Pinus flexilis* in the Rocky Mountains and in *P. albicaulis* on Mount Shasta, California. In the latter area, Cooke (1955) noted that it causes death of trees over large areas resulting in "ghost forests."

Witches' brooms induced by *A. cyanocarpum* are typically small and compact. In many instances, however, infection is so general throughout the crown of the tree that witches' brooms are not distinct.

ARCEUTHOBIUM DIVARICATUM PINYON DWARF MISTLETOE

10. *Arceuthobium divaricatum* Engelmann in U.S. Geogr. Surv. W of 100th Merid. (Wheeler Rep.) 6: 253, 1878. LECTOTYPE: ARIZONA: County unknown, Salt River Valley, on *Pinus edulis*, *Gilbert 116* in 1873 (MO! Isotype US). *Arceuthobium gracile* Engelmann in Gray, Mem. Amer. Acad. N.S. 4: 59, 1849, *nomen nudum*. *Razoumofskya divaricata* Coville, Contr. U.S. Nat. Herb. 4: 192, 1892. *Arceuthobium campylopodum* Engelmann forma *divaricatum* (Engelm.) Gill, Trans. Conn. Acad. Arts & Sci. 32: 193, 1935.

DESCRIPTION: Mean shoot height ca. 8 cm. but up to 13 cm. (fig. 49). Shoots olive green to brown, flabellately branched. Basal diameter of dominant shoots 1.5–4 mm. (mean 2 mm.). Third internode 6–15 mm. (mean 9.8 $\pm$ 2.4 mm.) long and 1–2 mm. (mean 1.6 mm.) wide (19 collections), length/width ratio 6.1:1. Staminate flowers 2.5 mm. in diameter; perianth 3-merous; segments ca. 1.1 mm. long and 0.9 mm. wide. Mean anther diameter 0.45 mm., centered 0.5 mm. from tip of segment. Pollen polar diameter 18–26 (mean 20μ); equatorial diameter 21–30 (mean 24μ); polar/equatorial diameter ratio 1:1.17; spine height 1.6μ ca. 1.5 times wall thickness—ca. 1.0μ (8 collections). Mature fruit 3.5 mm. long and 2.0 mm. wide; proximal portion ca. 2.0 mm. long. Seeds 2.0 $\times$ 0.9 mm. Meiosis in July. Peak anthesis usually in early September, with extremes from early August to late September. Seeds usually mature in late September with extremes from early September to early November in the year following pollination; maturation period average ca. 13 months. $n = 14$.

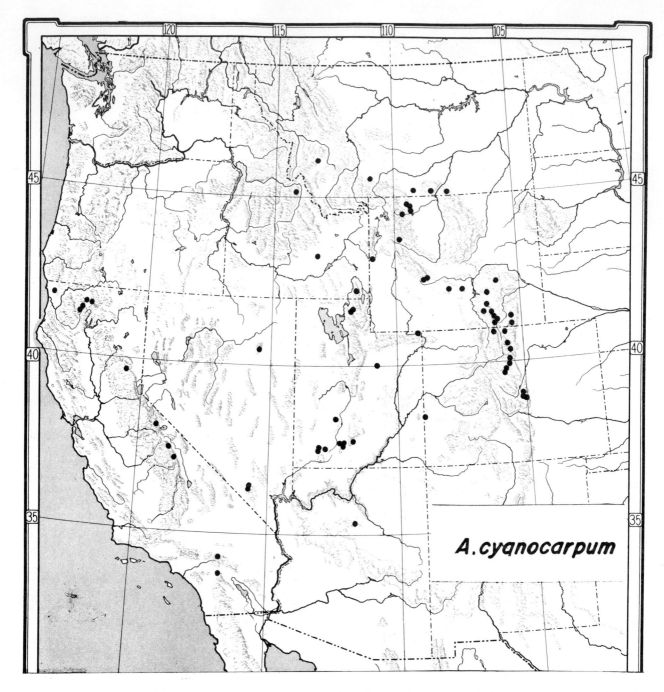

Figure 48.—Distribution of *Arceuthobium cyanocarpum* (based on collections only). Outline map copyrighted by Denoyer-Geppert Co., Chicago (used by permission).

HOSTS: This mistletoe, known only on the pinyons, is common on *Pinus edulis* and *P. monophylla*, but rare on *P. quadrifolia* and *P. cembroides*. The latter two appear to be equally susceptible, but the parasite occurs infrequently within their ranges.

Although mistletoe-infected pinyons are seldom associated with other pines, the associated pines (*P. ponderosa* and *P. jeffreyi*) were not parasitized in the few situations we observed. Thus the pinyon dwarf mistletoe is not only restricted to pinyons,

118

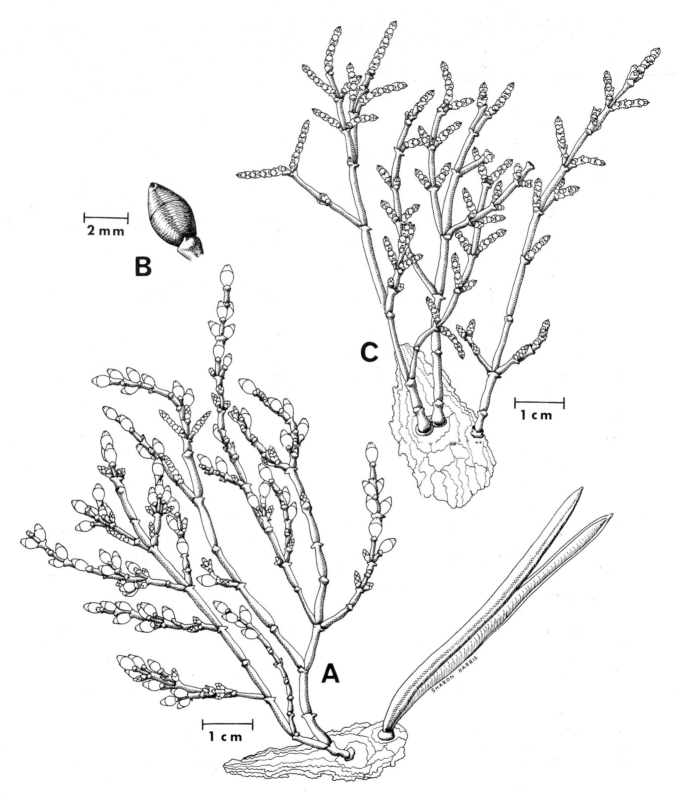

Figure 49.—*Arceuthobium divaricatum* in summer: *A*, Pistillate plant; *B*, Detail of fruit; *C*, Staminate plant.

but also is the only dwarf mistletoe that parasitizes pinyon in the United States. In a single locality in Mexico, however, we observed rare parasitism of *P. culminicola* by *A. vaginatum* subsp. *vaginatum* (Hawksworth and Wiens 1965).

DISTRIBUTION: Pinyon dwarf mistletoe occurs in eastern and southern California (east side of Sierra Nevada, Mount Pinos area, San Bernardino Mountains), the southern two-thirds of Nevada, southwestern Colorado, Arizona (except southwest), New Mexico (except northeast), and south to the Davis Mountains of western Texas (fig. 50). In Baja California, Mexico, *A. divaricatum* is known in the Sierra Juárez and is probably in the Sierra de San Pedro Mártir.[25] J. R. Weir (unpublished manuscript, 1920) reported *A. divaricatum* on *P. monophylla* in extreme southern Idaho, but we have seen no Idaho collections of this taxon.

The principal host in California and Nevada is *P. monophylla*; in Colorado, New Mexico, and Texas it is *P. edulis*; but both species are parasitized in Arizona and Utah. The distribution map (see fig. 50) suggests this mistletoe may be more abundant on *Pinus edulis* than on *P. monophylla*, but probably specimens have been more intensively collected within the range of *P. edulis*. The mistletoe has been collected on *P. quadrifolia* only in Baja California, (Hawksworth, Lightle, and Scharpf 1968) but it is to be expected on this tree in southern California. *A. divaricatum* is known on *P. cembroides* only in the extreme northern part of its range where this tree is associated with *P. edulis*. The only collections that we have seen are from the Davis Mountains, in western Texas, where Little (1966) determined the host as *P. cembroides*, but noted that it was near the range of *P. edulis* and may be intermediate. Pinyon dwarf mistletoe also occurs on "typical" *P. edulis* in this range. Elevational range of *A. divaricatum* is from 5,300 feet in Baja California to 8,900 feet in the San Mateo Mountains of New Mexico. Specimens examined: see appendix, p. 202.

DISCUSSION: The type locality for this taxon is given by Gill (1935) as Salt "Run" Valley. The original label, however, is handwritten and scarcely legible, but it appears that Salt "River" Valley was intended.

Kuijt (1960a) points out the spotty distributions of this parasite in California. We feel that *A. divaricatum* is probably more widely distributed than collections indicate, but may be less frequently collected than other species of *Arceuthobium*. Reasons for its paucity in herbaria may be that (1) it often does not form witches' brooms so it is less conspicuous than most dwarf mistletoes, and (2) its hosts are not commercial timber trees so little attention has been paid to their pathology. The pinyon dwarf mistletoe does cause witches' brooms, but they are often poorly developed and not conspicuous because of the stunted habit of healthy trees. Our observations suggest that brooming is more consistent in *P. edulis* than in *P. monophylla*.

Shoots of the pinyon dwarf mistletoe are long and slender, often divaricate. The staminate plants have relatively few flowers per shoot.

ARCEUTHOBIUM DOUGLASII
DOUGLAS-FIR DWARF MISTLETOE

11. *Arceuthobium douglasii* Engelmann in U.S. Geogr. Surv. W of 100th Merid. (Wheeler Rep.) 6: 253, 1878. LECTOTYPE: NEW MEXICO: Santa Fe Co.: Santa Fe River, on *Pseudotsuga menziesii*, *Rothrock 69* in 1874 (MO! Isotypes F, US). *Razoumofskya douglasii* (Engelm.) Kuntze, Rev. Gen. Pl. 2:587, 1891.

DESCRIPTION: Mean shoot height ca. 2 cm., but up to 7 cm. (fig. 51). Shoots olive green, flabellately branched. Basal diameter of dominant shoots 1–1.5 mm. (mean 1 mm.). Third internode 2–6 mm. (mean 3.6 ± 1.2 mm.) long and ca. 1.0 mm. wide (29 collections), length/width ratio 3.6:1. Flowers usually axillary in pairs, occasionally borne on pedicel-like segments as in *A. americanum*. Staminate flowers 2.0 mm. long and 2.3 mm. in diameter; perianth mostly 3-(occasionally 4-) merous; segments rounded at apex without a keel; inner surface reddish to purple, lower surface same color as shoots; segments ca. 1.0 mm. long and 1.0 mm. wide. Mean anther diameter 0.4 mm., centered 0.6 mm. from tip of segment. Pollen polar diameter 16–25 (mean 21μ); equatorial diameter 20–28 (mean 24μ); polar/equatorial diameter ratio 1:1.16; spine height approximately equal to wall thickness—1–1.2μ (8 collections). Pistillate flowers ca. 1.5 mm. long and 1.5 mm. in diameter. Mature fruit olive green 3.5–4.5 mm. long (mean 4 mm.) and 1.5–2 mm. wide (mean 2 mm.), obovate; proximal portion ca. 2.5 mm. long. Seeds 2.4 × 1.1 mm. Staminate meiosis in September, pistillate meiosis in April (Jones and Gordon 1965). Anthesis usually in March and April, with extremes from February to May. Seeds usually mature in September of the year following pollination; maturation period averages 17–18 months. Seeds germinate in March (Wicker 1967a). $n = 14$.

---

[25] Although we have seen no specimens from the Sierra de San Pedro Mártir, Mr. Phillipe Meling, lifelong resident of the area, informed us in 1965 that dwarf mistletoe occurs on pinyon (presumably *P. quadrifolia*) on the north slopes of this range.

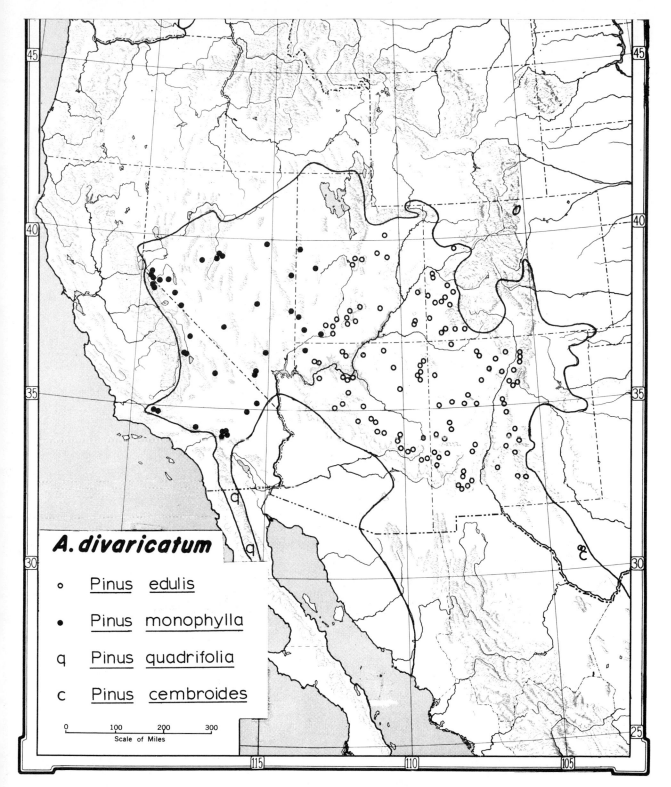

A. divaricatum

- o   <u>Pinus</u>   <u>edulis</u>

- •   <u>Pinus</u>   <u>monophylla</u>

- q   <u>Pinus</u>   <u>quadrifolia</u>

- c   <u>Pinus</u>   <u>cembroides</u>

0   100   200   300
Scale of Miles

Figure 50.—Distribution of *Arceuthobium divaricatum* within the composite range of the pinyons (based on collections only). Outline map copyrighted by Denoyer-Geppert Co., (used by permission).

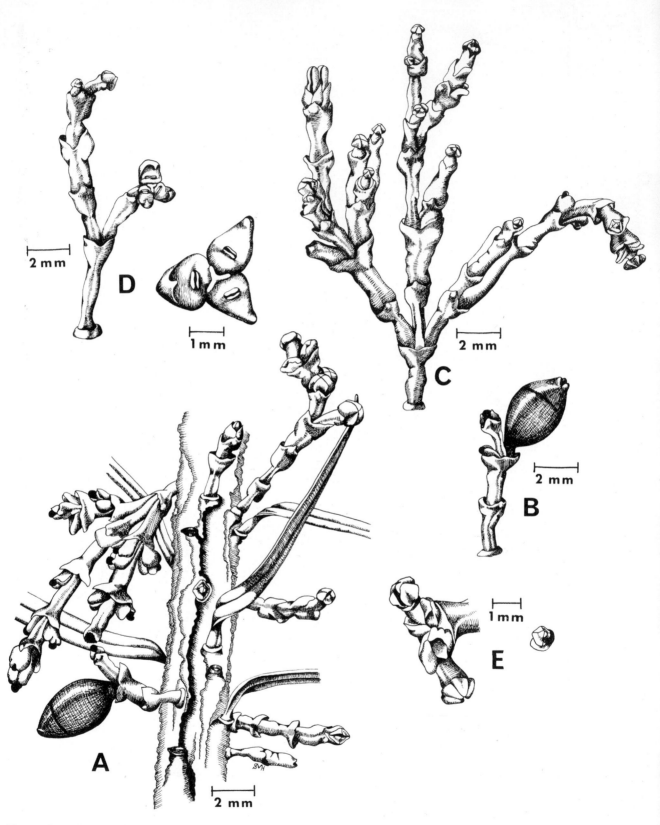

Figure 51.—*Arceuthobium douglasii* in spring: *A*, Pistillate (left) and staminate (right) plants on the same host twig; *B*, Detail of nearly mature fruit; *C*, Staminate shoot; *D*, Staminate shoot with mature buds and open flower (left) and detail of open flower (right); *E*, Staminate shoots showing characteristic rounded buds.

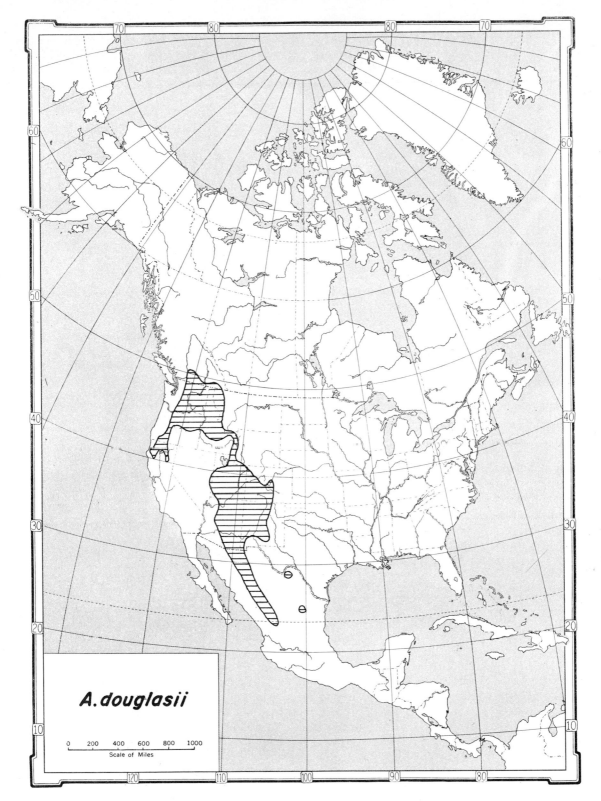

Figure 52.—General distribution of *Arceuthobium douglasii*. Outline map copyrighted by Denoyer-Geppert Co., Chicago (used by permission).

HOSTS: The principal and only commonly infected host is *Pseudotsuga menziesii*; both var. *menziesii* (in Washington, Oregon, and California) and var. *glauca* (from British Columbia to central Mexico) are parasitized. The following trees are sometimes infected when they are associated with infected Douglas-fir: *Abies concolor*, *A. grandis*, *A. lasiocarpa* vars. *lasiocarpa* and *arizonica*, *Picea engelmannii*, and *P. pungens*. Of these secondary hosts, only *A. lasiocarpa* var. *arizonica* seems to be severely parasitized. We concur with Kuijt (1960a) that reports of this mistletoe on *Pseudotsuga macrocarpa* (Jepson 1925, Munz 1935) are probably erroneous.

DISTRIBUTION: Douglas-fir dwarf mistletoe ranges as far north as Lytton and Sicamous in southern British Columbia,[26] about 130 miles north of the International Boundary. These areas are somewhat north of the distribution of the parasite given by Kuijt (1963). In Washington and Oregon, it occurs east of the crest of the Cascades, but is common on the Pacific slope from the Umpqua River drainage south to about latitude 40° N. in northern California. It is found in eastern Idaho, western Montana, western Wyoming, Utah, the southern two-thirds of Colorado, on Wheeler Peak in extreme eastern Nevada, and throughout the mountainous areas of Arizona and New Mexico (figs. 52, 53). In Mexico, it is known in only three isolated localities—Coahuila, Durango, and Nuevo León (fig. 54)—but probably occurs throughout the Sierra Madre Occidental in Chihuahua, Sonora, and Durango.

Also shown on the distribution map (see fig. 53) are several localities for the Douglas-fir dwarf mistletoe in California obtained during field work for State-wide disease surveys (Calif. Forest Pest Council 1968).

The distribution of this species shows some interesting peculiarities. It does not occur west of the Cascades in British Columbia, Washington, or northern Oregon except for a few instances where it is found within 4 to 10 miles west of the crest at White Pass, Washington (Wicker 1969) and in Clackamas and Linn Counties, Oregon.[27] However, Wicker (1969) successfully inoculated seedlings of coastal *Pseudotsuga menziesii* in western Washington with this dwarf mistletoe, and he suggests that isolational factors have precluded its occurrence on the western slope of the Cascades. This dwarf mistletoe is also absent in a number of other areas where *P. menziesii* is common, such as the central Sierra Nevada of California, central Montana, and northern Colorado. The altitudinal range of this mistletoe is correlated with latitude, and it occurs as low as 900 feet near Lytton in the Thompson River Valley in southern British Columbia to as high as 10,000 feet on Cerro Potosí in Nuevo León, Mexico. Specimens examined: see appendix, p. 205.

DISCUSSION: Although Gill (1935) questioned the validity of this species, we consider *A. douglasii* to be one of the most distinctive and stable members of the genus. It has a latitudinal range of over 2,000 miles, yet has no characteristics that warrant ecotypic or subspecific separation.

Much of the confusion in the literature on this species is due to its supposed affinities with various members of the *A. campylopodum* complex (Gill 1935). Weir (1918a) discussed the occurrence of "a small purple-flowered form on *Picea*" in the Inland Empire which he, and we, consider to be merely *A. douglasii* on an unusual host.

This dwarf mistletoe severely damages Douglas-fir (see fig. 8B).

ARCEUTHOBIUM GILLII

12. *Arceuthobium gillii* Hawksworth & Wiens, Brittonia 16: 55, 1964. HOLOTYPE: ARIZONA: Cochise Co.: Huachuca Mountains, 0.5 mi. E of Reef, on *Pinus leiophylla* var. *chihuahuana*, *Hawksworth & Lightle 236*, in 1962 (COLO., Isotypes FPF, MO, ARIZ, DS).

DESCRIPTION: Shoots up to 25 cm. long, greenish yellow or dark brown to almost black; pistillate plants usually erect, but the staminate plants often strongly divaricate; flabellately branched, internodes 0.4–1.9 cm. long and 2–8 mm. wide; staminate flower ca. 3–3.5 mm. long and up to 3.5 mm. in diameter; mostly 3-merous, perianth segments ca. 1 4 mm. long and ca. 1.0 mm. wide, apex rounded-obtuse; pistillate flower ca. 1.5 mm. long, anthers 0.7 mm. in diameter, centered 0.9 mm. from tip of segment, and ca. 1.0 mm. in diameter; fruit ca. 4–5 mm. (mean 4.5) long and 2–3 mm. (mean 2.5) wide, proximal portion 2–3 mm. long, elliptical-obovate, conspicuously whitish-blue glaucous on proximal portion; anthesis from approximately mid-February through April and possibly May.

Parasitic on pines of the section *Leiophylla* and *P. teocote*. This species comprises two subspecies differentiated by shoot color, internode thickness, geographic ranges, time of anthesis, and host affinities (Hawksworth and Wiens 1965).

---

[26] Personal communication, Dr. R. B. Smith, Canada Dep. Fisheries and Forestry, 1966.

[27] Personal communications, J. L. Stewart and D. M. Knutson, U.S. Forest Service, 1969–70.

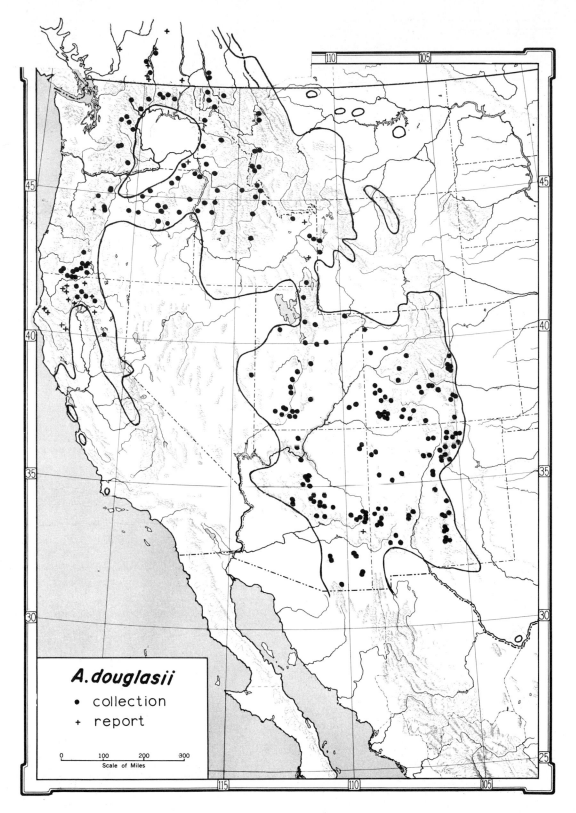

Figure 53.—Distribution of *Arceuthobium douglasii* on all hosts in the United States and in British Columbia, Canada (based on collections and reports). The range of *Pseudotsuga menziesii* is shown by the solid line. Outline map copyrighted by Denoyer-Geppert Co., Chicago (used by permission).

125

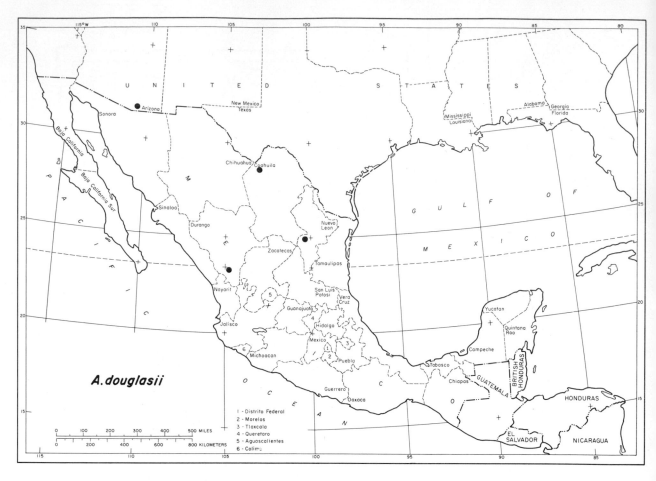

Figure 54.—Distribution of *Arceuthobium douglasii* in Mexico (based on collections only).

Key to the Subspecies

1. Plant greenish to brownish yellow; parasitic almost exclusively on *Pinus leiophyila* var. *chihuahuana*; anthesis from mid-February through mid-April; fruit maturity in November; Sierra Madre Occidental of Sonora and Chihuahua, Mexico north to southern Arizona.

12a. A. gillii subsp. gillii.

1. Plants dark brown to almost black; parasitic on *Pinus leiophylla* vars. *leiophylla* and *chihuahuana*, *P. lumholtzii* and *P. teocote*; anthesis from mid-March through mid-April or later; fruit maturity in September; Sierra Madre Occidental of Durango to Hidalgo, Oaxaca, and Veracruz, Mexico.

12b. A. gillii subsp. nigrum.

ARCEUTHOBIUM GILLII SUBSP. GILLII
CHIHUAHUA PINE DWARF MISTLETOE

12a. *Arceuthobium gillii* Hawksworth & Wiens subsp. *gillii*.

DESCRIPTION: Mean shoot height ca. 11 cm. but up to 25 cm. (fig. 55). Shoots greenish brown. Basal diameter of dominant shoots 2.5–8 mm. (mean 4 mm.). Third internode 5–18 mm. (mean 10.7 ± 3.4 mm.) long and 2–4.5 mm. (mean 2.8 mm.) wide (9 collections), length/width ratio 3.8:1. Staminate flowers 3.5 mm. long and 2.5–4 mm. (mean 3.2 mm.) in diameter; pollen polar diameter 19–25 (mean 22μ); equatorial diameter 24–28 mean 26μ); polar/equatorial diameter ratio 1:1.19; spine height (1.7μ) slightly greater than wall thickness—1.3μ (4 collections). Pistillate flowers ca. 1.5 mm. long and 1 mm. in diameter. Proximal portion of fruit conspicuously glaucous. Seeds 3.1 $\times$ 1.4 mm. Meiosis in September. Anthesis usually in March and April. Seeds mature in October[28] of the year following pollination; maturation period averages ca. 19 months, the longest in the genus. $n = 14$.

[28] Dr. R. L. Gilbertson of the University of Arizona found that seed dispersal in 1967 occurred between October 13 and November 5 in the Santa Catalina Mountains near Tucson.

126

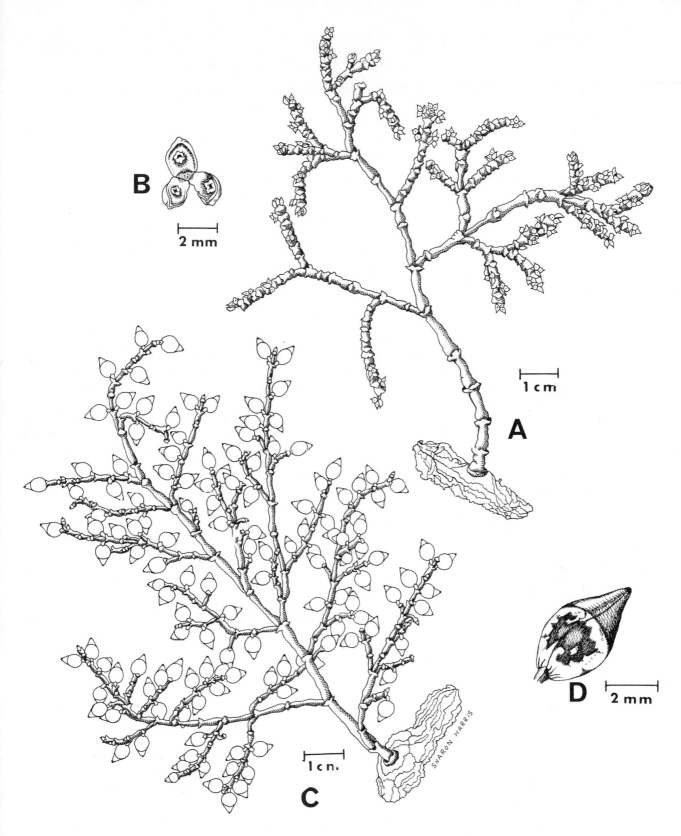

Figure 55.—*Arceuthobium gillii* subsp. *gillii* in spring: *A*, Staminate plant in anthesis; *B*, Detail of a mature staminate flower; *C*, Pistillate plant; *D*, Detail of fruit showing characteristic glaucousness of the proximal portion.

HOSTS: The principal and only commonly infected host is *Pinus leiophylla* var. *chihuahuana*. *Pinus lumholtzii* and *P. leiophylla* var. *leiophylla* seem to be equally susceptible to the parasite, but are not common in the areas where *A. gillii* occurs. In western Chihuahua we found this mistletoe rarely on *Pinus ponderosa* vars. *scopulorum* and *arizonica*, but we have not found these trees to be infected in Arizona although both are exposed to *A. gillii* there.

DISTRIBUTION: This dwarf mistletoe occurs in southeastern Arizona (Santa Catalina, Rincon, Santa Rita, Huachuca, and Chiricahua Mountains), eastern Sonora, western Chihuahua, and Sinaloa (fig. 56). It is to be expected in the Animas Mountains in extreme southwestern New Mexico. We have examined several other *Pinus leiophylla* var. *chihuahuana* stands in New Mexico (on Bear Mountain near Silver City, Mule Mountains, and Peloncillo Mountains) without finding the parasite. Also the following Arizona localities of this pine have been examined and found to be free of *A. gillii*: Graham Mountains, the Pinal Mountains, and below the Mogollon Rim near Colcord Mountain, Gila County.[29]

Arceuthobium gillii ranges from 5,600 feet in Arizona to 8,700 feet in southern Chihuahua. Specimens examined: see appendix, p. 210.

DISCUSSION: This subspecies had long been confused with *A. vaginatum* subsp. *cryptopodum* but it differs in several respects (Hawksworth and Wiens 1964), some of which are summarized in table 21.

---

[29] Personal communication, Dr. P. C. Lightle, U.S. Forest Service, 1969.

In Arizona, the two species are not sympatric because they are usually separated by at least 1,000 feet in elevation. In an area about 36 miles southwest of La Junta in Chihuahua, Mexico, however, we found these two taxa growing together, but intermediates between them were not evident.

This dwarf mistletoe causes open, nonsystemic brooms similar to those induced by *A. gillii* subsp. *nigrum* (see fig. 10).

ARCEUTHOBIUM GILLII SUBSP. NIGRUM

12b. *Arceuthobium gillii* subsp. *nigrum* Hawksworth & Wiens, Brittonia 17: 233, 1965. HOLOTYPE: MEXICO: Durango, 32 mi. E of El Salto on Route 40, on *P. teocote, Hawksworth & Wiens 304* in 1963 (COLO. Isotypes FPF, MEXU, MO, US).

DESCRIPTION: Mean shoot height ca. 15–20 cm., but up to 45 cm. (fig. 57). Shoots dark brown to black. Basal diameter of dominant shoots 3–8 mm. (mean 5 mm.). Third internode 5–19 mm. (mean 10.8 ± 3.8 mm.) long and 2.5–6 mm. (mean 3.7 mm.) wide (6 collections), length/width ratio 2.9:1. Staminate flowers ca. 3 mm. long and 3.5 mm. in diameter. Pollen poorly known and only a few grains available for study in one collection: polar diameter ca. 20μ, equatorial diameter ca. 23μ; spine height ca. 2.0μ, ca. twice wall thickness—1.0μ. Mature fruit 6–9 mm. (mean 7 mm.) long and ca. 3.5 mm. wide, proximal portion ca. 2–3 mm. Seeds 3.5×1.3 mm. Meiosis in August and September. Anthesis usually in March or April. Seeds mature in September of the year following pollination; maturation period averages 17–18 months. $n = 14$.

TABLE 21.—*Comparison of* Arceuthobium gillii *and* A. vaginatum *subsp.* cryptopodum

Characters	A. *gillii*	A. *vaginatum* subsp. *cryptopodum*
Principal hosts	*Pinus leiophylla* var. *chihuahuana*	*Pinus ponderosa* vars. *arizonica* and *scopulorum*, *P. engelmannii*
Shoot color	Greenish yellow	Yellow to orange
Fruits	Proximal portion of fruit bluish-white glaucous; distal portion (including perianth segments) accounting for ca. 40 percent of fruit length	Fruit essentially nonglaucous; distal portion (including perianth segments) accounting for ca. 30 percent of fruit length
Peak flowering time	February to early April	May to June
Seed maturation period	ca. 19 months	14–15 months

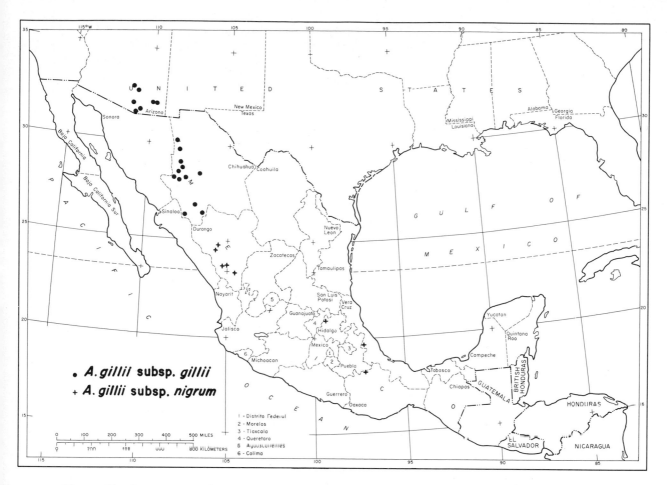

Figure 56.—Distribution of the two subspecies of *Arceuthobium gillii* (based on collections only).

HOSTS: Principally on pines of section *Leiophyllae* (*Pinus leiophylla* vars. *leiophylla* and *chihuahuana* and *P. lumholtzii*) and *Teocote* (*P. teocote*). Rare on *P. montezumae*.

DISTRIBUTION: Presently known from the Mexican States of Durango, Hidalgo, Veracruz, and northern Oaxca, but is to be expected in other adjacent States (see fig. 56). Known elevational range is 7,400 to 8,800 feet. Specimens examined: see appendix, p. 210.

DISCUSSION: This subspecies is distinguished from subsp. *gillii* by its darker color, more southerly range, markedly divaricate staminate shoots, and larger plants. Plants from Cofre de Perote in Veracruz, tentatively referred to this subspecies, are morphologically similar to subsp. *nigrum* from other localities but somewhat lighter in color. Witches' brooms caused by subsp. *nigrum* are illustrated in figure 10.

ARCEUTHOBIUM GLOBOSUM

13. *Arceuthobium globosum* Hawksworth & Wiens, Brittonia 17: 223, 1965. HOLOTYPE: MEXICO: DURANGO: 1.5 mi. E of El Salto on Route 40, on *Pinus cooperi, Hawksworth & Wiens 3414* in 1963 (COLO, Isotypes DS, F, FPF, INIF, MEXU, MO, US).

DESCRIPTION: Mean shoot height ca. 20–30 cm., but up to 70 cm. in Guatemala (fig. 58). Shoots yellow to greenish, flabellately branched. Basal diameter of dominant shoots 3–44 mm. (mean 12 mm.). Third internode 4–35 mm. (mean 20.5 ± 8.4 mm.) long and 2–23 mm. (mean 5.5 mm.) wide (6 collections), length/width ratio 3.7:1. Staminate flowers ca. 3.5 mm. long and 3–3.5 mm. in diameter; perianth 3- or 4-merous; same color as shoots; segments ca. 1.3 mm. long and 1.0 mm. wide. Mean anther diameter 0.6 mm.,

129

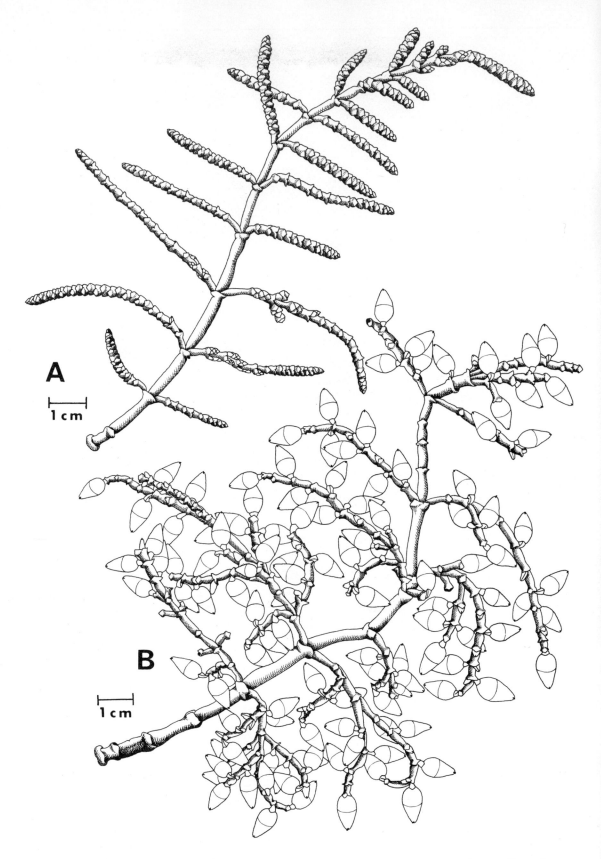

A

1 cm

B

1 cm

Figure 57. *Arceuthobium gillii* subsp. *nigrum* in spring: *A*, Staminate shoot; *B*, Pistillate shoot.

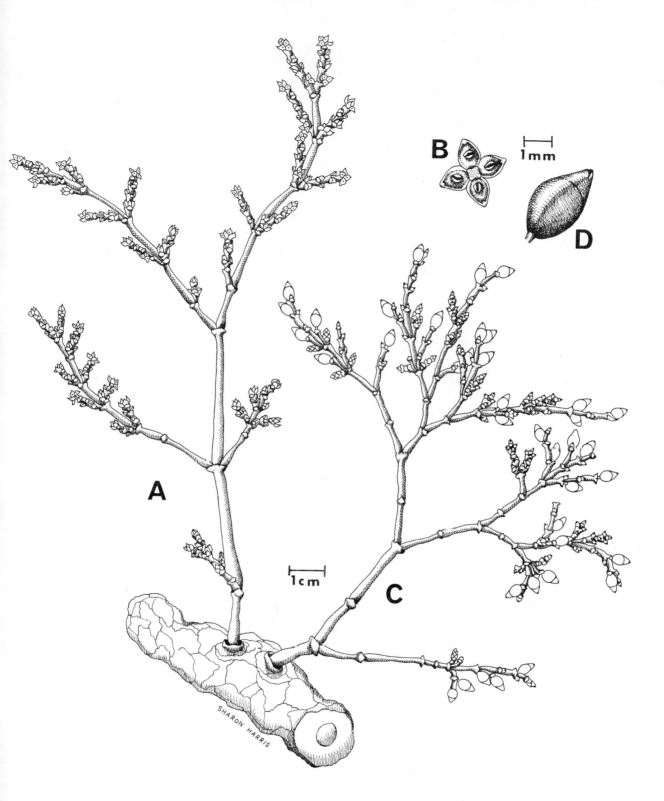

Figure 58.—*Arceuthobium globosum* in March: *A*, Staminate shoot; *B*, Detail of staminate flower; *C*, Pistillate shoot; *D*, Detail of fruit.

1mm

1cm

131

centered 0.9 mm. from tip of segment. Pollen polar diameter 19–23 (mean 22μ); equatorial diameter 24–28 (mean 26μ); polar/equatorial diameter ratio 1:1.18; spine height (ca. 1.9μ) approx. twice wall thickness—ca. 1.0μ (4 collections). Pistillate flowers ca. 1.5 mm. long and 1.5 mm. in diameter; 2-merous. Mature fruit ca. 6–7 mm. long, and ca. 4 mm. wide; proximal portion ca. 3.5 mm. long. Seeds 5 × 2 mm. Pedicels 4–5 mm. long. Time of meiosis unknown. Anthesis usually in March-April. Seeds mature in June-July in northern and central Mexico and September in Guatemala; maturation period averages 15–16 months. n = unknown.

HOSTS: This species has the broadest known host range of any of the dwarf mistletoes; it occurs on at least 14 pines as well as *Cupressus*. Hawksworth and Wiens (1965), in the original description of the species, listed 11 hosts: *Pinus cooperi*, *P. durangensis*, *P. engelmannii*, *P. hartwegii*, *P. lawsonii*, *P. michoacana*, *P. montezumae*, *P. ponderosa* var. *arizonica*, *P. pseudostrobus*, *P. rudis*, and *P. tenuifolia*, all from Mexico. Three additional hosts have been noted in Michoacán, Mexico: *Pinus douglasiana*, *P. pringlei*, and *P. teocote*, but the dwarf mistletoe was not identified (Valdivia 1964). We believe the parasite is *A. globosum* because: (1) we have examined many of Valdivia's specimens, (2) his description fits that of this species, and (3) this is the only species known from Michoacán. Valdivia (1964) gives the hosts in northeastern Michoacán, in decreasing order of susceptibility, as: *Pinus tenuifolia*, *P. pseudostrobus*, *P. pseudostrobus* f. *protuberans*, *P. montezumae*, *P. michoacana*, *P. durangensis*, *P. douglasiana*, *P. lawsonii*, *P. pringlei*, *P. teocote*, and *P. rudis*. *Pinus leiophylla* and *Abies religiosa* were recorded as immune.

Hunt (1962) reported a dwarf mistletoe (as "*A. vaginatum*") on *Pinus caribaea* from Mountain Pine Ridge, British Honduras; we have examined his specimens and determined that they are *A. globosum*. Etheridge (1968) noted that *A. globosum* was damaging in two localities on Mountain Pine Ridge.

The hosts of *A. globosum* in Guatemala are poorly known because many collections recorded the host only as *Pinus* sp. However, at least *P. pseudostrobus*, *P. tenuifolia*, *P. rudis*, and *Cupressus* are infected there. This is the only known instance of *Arceuthobium* on *Cupressus* in the Western Hemisphere (Standley and Steyermark 1946). Parasitism of *Cupressus* is apparently rare, however, because we did not observe infection of this tree where it was associated with *A. globosum* on *Pinus rudis* in the Sierra Cuchumatanes of Guatemala.

DISTRIBUTION: This is one of the most widely distributed dwarf mistletoes in Mexico and Guatemala, and is the only species known from British Honduras (fig. 59). In Mexico it occurs from western Chihuahua and eastern Sonora south through the Sierra Madre Occidental to Michoacán; east to Veracruz and south through Oaxaca and Chiapas, where it crosses the border into the highlands of Guatemala. It is known from a single area in west-central British Honduras.

Arceuthobium globosum is usually a high-altitude species; in central Mexico it ranges from 10,000 feet to as high as 13,000 feet in Nevado de Toluca. It occurs as low as about 3,000 feet in the Maya Mountains in British Honduras. Specimens examined: see appendix, p. 210.

DISCUSSION: One of the most distinctive dwarf mistletoes, *A. globosum* is characterized by globose masses, 30–100 cm. in diameter, of bright yellow to greenish shoots. The shoots on older plants may exceed 4 cm. in diameter and 70 cm. in height.

The form of the species in the Sierra Cuchumatanes of Guatemala differs from the populations in northern and central Mexico. For example, in Guatemala the plants are larger and consistently dark greenish yellow, while those in Mexico are smaller and yellow. Guatemalan plants produce witches' brooms; the Mexican populations do not. In Mexico, the peak seed dispersal period is apparently in June and early July, but in Guatemala, the fruits were just maturing in mid-September. In view of the differences between the two population systems, subspecific separation might be desirable if the differences are further confirmed. Detailed field studies are also needed in southern Mexico to determine whether the differences between central Mexican and Guatemalan populations are discontinuous.

Valdivia (1964), who surveyed a million acres of pine forest in northeastern Michoacán, Mexico, found *A. globosum* on nearly 40 percent of the forest area.

ARCEUTHOBIUM GUATEMALENSE

14. *Arceuthobium guatemalense* Hawksworth & Weins, Brittonia 22: 267, 1970. HOLOTYPE: GUATEMALA: DEPT. HUEHUETENANGO, Sierra Cuchumatanes, on road from Huehuetenango to Santa Eulalia at Km 142; 54 km north of Huehuetenango or 10 km south of San Juan Ixcoy, on *Pinus ayacahuite, Hawksworth & Weins 1221*, Sept. 11, 1969. (US, Isotypes COLO, DS, EAP, FPF, MO, UT).

DESCRIPTION: Mean shoot height ca. 1–3 cm. on systemic brooms, but shoots on nonsystemic infections up to ca. 7 cm. high (fig. 60); shoots

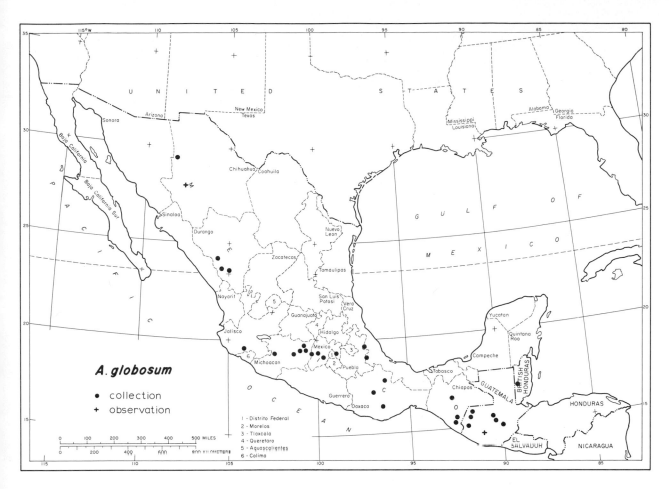

Figure 59.—Distribution of *Arceuthobium globosum* in Mexico, Guatemala, and British Honduras.

greenish to purple, yellow to brown when dried, flabellately branched; basal diameter of dominant shoots 2–2.5 mm. Third internode 8–15 (mean 11.4 ± 2.8 mm.) long and 1.5–2 (mean 1.7) mm. wide; length/width ratio 6.7:1 (3 collections). Staminate flowers ca. 2 mm. in diameter; perianth 2- or 3-merous, segments 0.9 mm. long and 0.7 mm. wide. Mean anther diameter 0.5 mm. Few pollen grains available for study; mean polar diameter 21μ and mean equatorial diameter 24μ; polar/equatorial diameter ratio 1:1.14; spine height—ca. 1.5μ, wall thickness—ca. 1.0μ (1 collection). Mature fruit ca. 3.7 mm. long and 1.8 mm. wide; distal portion ca. 1.2 mm. long; dark green, nonglaucous, with a slightly swollen ring at the base of the fruit where it joins the receptacle of the pedicel (fig. 60). Seed 2.0 × 0.8 mm. Time of meiosis unknown. Anthesis apparently in August and early September. Fruits mature in September so the fruit maturation period is from 12–13 months. Germination in September. n = unknown.

HOSTS AND DISTRIBUTION: This parasite of *Pinus ayacahuite* is known only from the high mountains of Guatemala (Departments of Huehuetenango and Totonicipán), but it probably also occurs on *P. ayacahuite* in southern Mexico. We collected it in the Sierra Cuchumatanes, and along the Pan American Highway between Nahualá and Quetzaltenango. It is quite common in the vicinity of Santa Eulalia, north of Huehuetenango. The elevational distribution of this species is poorly known, but we observed it between 8,300 and 10,100 feet. No range map was prepared for this species because its distribution is too poorly known. Specimens cited: see appendix, p. 212.

DISCUSSION: The consistent formation of systemic witches' brooms is a distinctive characteristic of this species. The brooms are sometimes 10 to 15 feet in diameter. An unusual feature of the brooms is that mistletoe shoots are consistently formed on host twigs as young as 1 year old and, in some cases, we found buds on the current year's growth (in September).

133

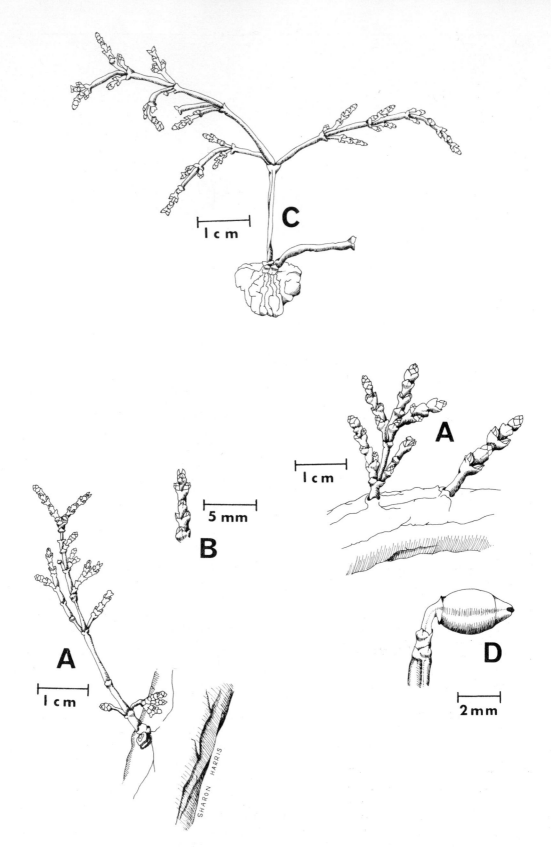

Figure 60.—*Arceuthobium guatemalense* in September: *A*, Staminate shoots; *B*, Detail of staminate shoot; *C*, Pistillate shoot; *D*, Detail of mature fruit showing typical enlargement at base.

This species is quite damaging and causes considerable mortality (see fig. 11D).

ARCEUTHOBIUM HONDURENSE

15. *Arceuthobium hondurense* Hawksworth & Wiens, Brittonia 22: 267, 1970. HOLOTYPE: HONDURAS: DEPT. FRANCISCO MORAZAN, Piedra Herrada, 22 km. southeast of Tegucigalpa on road to Escuela Agrícola Panamericana, on *Pinus oocarpa, Hawksworth, Wiens, and Molina 1203,* Sept. 4, 1969 (US, Isotypes EAP, COLO, DS, F, FPF, MO, UT).

DESCRIPTION: Mean shoot height ca. 14 cm., but up to 21 cm. (fig. 61); shoots olive brown to grayish green, markedly glaucous; flabellately branched; basal diameter of dominant shoots 3–9 (mean 5) mm.; nodes of older shoots swollen; lateral branches of staminate plants at nearly right angle to axis of the main shoot; third internode 7–12 (mean 9.1 ± 1.5 mm.) long and 2.5–4 (mean 3.2 mm.) wide; length/width ratio 6.1:1 (2 collections). Staminate flowers ca. 2.5 mm. in diameter; inner surface reddish, lower surface the same color as shoots; perianth usually 3- (sometimes 2- or 4-) merous, segments ca. 1.2 mm. long or 0.8 mm. wide; nectary with 2 large lobes and 1 small lobe. Pollen polar diameter 18–23 (mean 20μ); equatorial diameter 21–25 (mean 24μ); polar/equatorial diameter ratio 1:1.21; spine height (ca. 2.5μ) about twice wall thickness—1.1μ (2 collections). Pistillate flowers with stigmas exserted ca. 0.5 mm., copious nectar secretion. Mature fruit ca. 5.5 mm. long and 3.0 mm. wide, greenish glaucous; proximal portion ca. 4.0 mm. long; stigma exserted. Seeds ca. 3.1 × 1.5 mm. Meiosis in August or early September. Anthesis and seed maturation in September so the seed maturation period averages ca. 12 months. $n = 14$.

HOSTS AND DISTRIBUTION: This species has been collected only on *Pinus oocarpa,* although it has been seen on *Pinus pseudostrobus.*[30] The distribution of this species is poorly known, and the only three collections that have been made are from the same general area near Piedra Herrada, southeast of Tegucigalpa, Honduras, on the road to Escuela Agrícola Panamericana. Roadside surveys totaling 140 miles through *P. oocarpa* stands, mainly in the Departments of Francisco Morazán, El Paraiso, and Comayagua, failed to reveal additional populations of the parasite. The indiscriminate cutting of the original forests has apparently reduced the occurrence of *A. hondurense* in these areas, which are now either agricultural lands or

second-growth forests. Unless the species occurs in areas less subject to severe disturbance, *A. hondurense* faces extinction. No range map was prepared for this species because its distribution is so poorly known. The few populations observed were between 4,000 and 5,300 feet in elevation. Specimens cited: see appendix, p. 212.

DISCUSSION: Originally we believed *A. hondurense* (see fig. 12) to be conspecific with *A. bicarinatum,* a species endemic to Hispaniola. Observations of living plants of both dwarf mistletoes, however, demonstrated discontinuities in many characters (see table 19). *A. hondurense* appears most closely related to *A. rubrum* and *A. bicarinatum,* which are slender, dark-colored species in the southern range of the genus. In fact, *A. bicarinatum* and *A. hondurense,* occupy the distributional limits of the genus in the southeastern and southern parts of the New World, respectively.

ARCEUTHOBIUM LARICIS
LARCH DWARF MISTLETOE

16. *Arceuthobium laricis* (Piper) St. John, Flora SE Wash. & Adj. Idaho: 115, 1937. LECTOTYPE: WASHINGTON: Kittitas Co.: N of Ellensburg, on *Larix occidentalis, Brandegee 1071* in 1883 (US! Isotypes GH, PH, UC). *Razoumofskya douglasii* (Engelm.) Kuntze subsp. *laricis* Piper, Contr. U. S. Nat. Herb. 11: 223, 1906, *nomen nudum. Arceuthobium douglasii* Engelm. var. *laricis* M. E. Jones, Univ. Mont. Bull. 61 (Biol. Ser. 15): 25, 1910, *nomen nudum. Razoumofskya laricis* Piper, in Piper and Beattie, Flora SE Wash. & Adj. Idaho: 80, 1914. *Arceuthobium campylopodum* Engelm. forma *laricis* (Piper) Gill, Trans. Conn. Acad. Arts & Sci. 32: 202, 1935.

DESCRIPTION: Mean shoot height ca. 4 cm. but up to 6 cm. (fig. 62). Shoots mostly dark purple, flabellately branched. Basal diameter of dominant shoots 1.5–3 mm. (mean 2 mm.). Third internode 5–14 mm. (mean 8.0 ± 2.0 mm.) long and 1–2.5 mm. (mean 1.3 mm.) wide (12 collections), length/width ratio 6.1:1. Staminate flowers 2.7 mm. in diameter; perianth mostly 3- (sometimes 4-) merous; segments ca. 1.4 mm. long and 1.1 mm. wide. Mean anther diameter 0.5 mm., centered 0.5 mm. from tip of segment. Pollen polar diameter 18–25 (mean 20μ); equatorial diameter 21–27 (mean 23μ); polar/equatorial diameter ratio 1:1.16; spine height (ca. 2μ) about twice wall thickness—ca. 1.0μ (3 collections). Pistillate flowers ca. 1 mm. long and 1 mm. in diameter. Mature fruit 4.5 mm. long and 2.5 mm. wide; proximal portion ca. 2.5 mm. long. Meiosis in June. Peak anthesis usually in early August, with extremes from late July to early September. Seeds

---

[30] Personal communication, Antonio Molina R., Escuela Agrícola Panamericana, Tegucigalpa, Honduras, 1969.

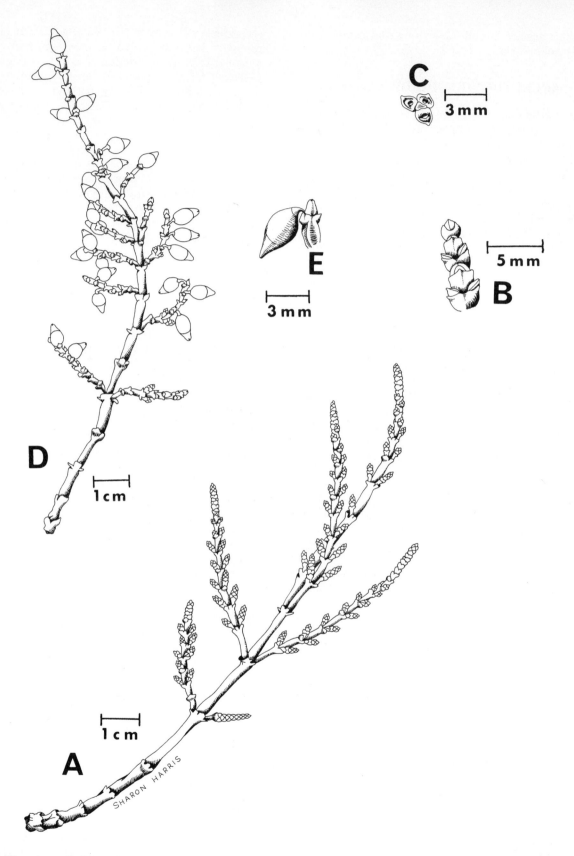

Figure 61.—*Arceuthobium hondurense* in September: *A*, Staminate shoot; *B*, Detail of terminal portion of staminate shoot showing unopen flowers; *C*, Open staminate flower; *D*, Pistillate shoot; *E*, Detail of mature fruit.

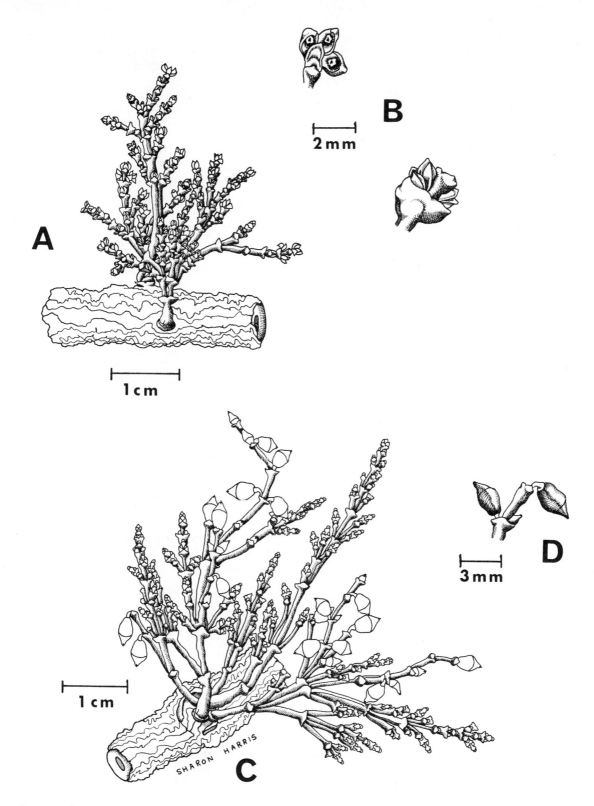

Figure 62.—*Arceuthobium laricis* in August: *A*, Staminate shoot in anthesis; *B*, Detail of staminate flowers; *C*, Pistillate shoot; *D*, Nearly mature fruit.

usually mature in September, with extremes from early August to early October. Maturation period averages 13–14 months. $n = 14$.

HOSTS: The principal and only commonly infected host is *Larix occidentalis*. Other trees that are sometimes infected when they grow in association with infected *L. occidentalis* are: *Abies lasiocarpa, A. grandis, Picea engelmannii, Pinus albicaulis, P. contorta, P. monticola, P. ponderosa,* and *Tsuga mertensiana.* The status of this mistletoe on subalpine larch, *Larix lyallii,* is poorly known, and only two early collections are available from this host (by J. R. Weir, from the Bitterroot and Cabinet Mountains of Montana). Exotic trees infected naturally include *Pinus banksiana* (Graham 1959a), *P. resinosa* (U. S. Department of Agriculture 1962), *P. sylvestris* (Graham and Leaphart 1961), and *Picea abies* (U. S. Department of Agriculture 1963).

Weir (1918a) has shown that, on the basis of seedling inoculations, the European larch, *Larix europaea,* and Japanese larch, *L. leptolepis,* are susceptible to the larch dwarf mistletoe.

The occurrence of *A. laricis* on *Tsuga mertensiana* in Idaho and Montana (see fig. 13B) is of interest, because this mistletoe will not infect *T. heterophylla.* Our observations in many mixed *Larix-Tsuga* stands in the Cascades in Oregon and Washington, and in Idaho and Montana confirm that *T. heterophylla* is not susceptible to *A. laricis.* In mixed *Tsuga heterophylla-T. mertensiana* stands in the the Coeur d' Alene National Forest, Idaho, only the latter was infected. We do not know whether *A. laricis* is associated with *T. mertensiana* in the Cascades.

DISTRIBUTION: The larch dwarf mistletoe occurs generally throughout the range of its principal host, *Larix occidentalis,* in southern British Columbia, east of the Cascades in Washington and northern Oregon, north and central Idaho, and western Montana (fig. 63). Known elevational range is 2,300 to 6,500 feet.

Arceuthobium laricis extends to Salmon Arm and north to Kootenay Lake,[31] which is somewhat farther north than the range Kuijt (1963) gives for this taxon. Specimens examined: see appendix, p. 212.

DISCUSSION: *A. laricis* is a serious pathogen of *Larix occidentalis* (Weir 1916a). For example, surveys show that about two-thirds of the western larch stands are infested on the Coeur d'Alene National Forest, Idaho, and in the Kootenai National Forest, Montana (Graham 1959b, 1959c). On the Colville National Forest and adjacent private lands in northeastern Washington, infestation was 86 percent (Graham and Frazier 1962).

In nature, selective parasitism is the easiest diagnostic feature that separates *A. laricis* from *A. tsugense*: *A. laricis* infects *Larix occidentalis* but not *Tsuga heterophylla*; *A. tsugense* attacks *T. heterophylla* but not *L. occidentalis.* In greenhouse and plantation inoculations, however, R. B. Smith has infected *Larix occidentalis* with *A. tsugense.*[31] *Arceuthobium tsugense* is generally larger and more profusely branched than *A. laricis* (Kuijt 1970). Table 22 gives some other distinguishing features for these two Northwestern taxa (see fig. 13).

ARCEUTHOBIUM MICROCARPUM
WESTERN SPRUCE DWARF MISTLETOE

17. *Arceuthobium microcarpum* (Engelmann) Hawksworth & Wiens, Brittonia 22: 268, 1970. LECTOTYPE: ARIZONA: Apache Co.: Sierra Blanca,

---

[31] Personal communication, Dr. R. B. Smith, Canadian Dep. Fisheries and Forestry, 1967.

TABLE 22.—*Comparison of* Arceuthobium laricis *and* A. tsugense

Characters	*A. laricis*	*A. tsugense*
Principal hosts	*Larix*	*Tsuga*
Shoots:		
Base of older shoots	Angular	Rounded
Terminal internodes on main axis of staminate shoots	Ca. 2 mm. long	Over 3 mm. long
Length of lateral staminate spikes in summer	2–3 mm.	5–6 mm.
Staminate flowers	Rarely 4-merous	Sometimes 4-merous
Peak flowering time	August	September
Peak seed dispersal time	September	October

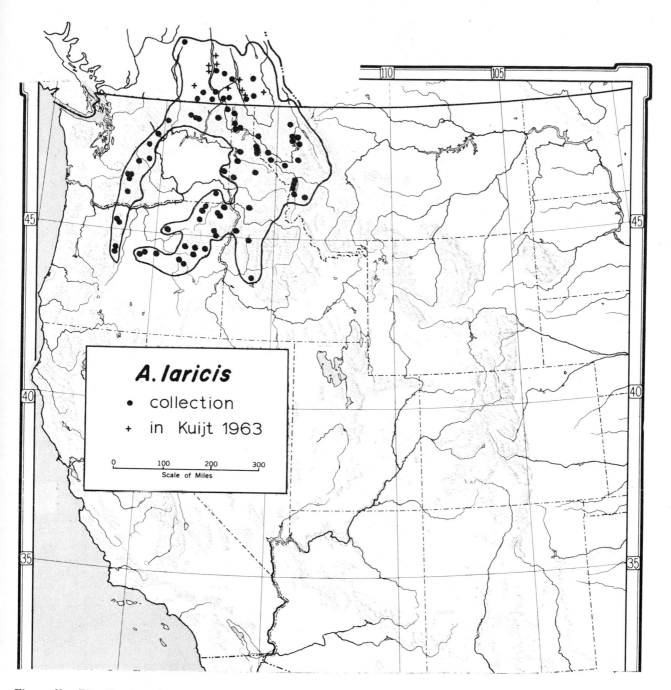

Figure 63.—Distribution of *Arceuthobium laricis* on all hosts in the United States and in British Columbia, Canada (based on collections and reports). Also shown is the range of *Larix occidentalis*. Outline map copyrighted by Denoyer-Geppert Co., Chicago (used by permission).

on *Picea engelmannii, Gilbert 112* in 1873 (MO! Isotype ILL, US). *Arceuthobium douglasii* Engelm. var.? *microcarpum* Engelm. in U.S. Geogr. Surv. W of 100th Meridian (Wheeler Rep.) 6: 253, 1878. *Razoumofskya microcarpa* (Engelm.) Wooton & Standley, Contr. U.S. Nat. Herb. 19: 179, 1915. *Razoumofskya douglasii* (Engelm.) Kuntze var.

microcarpa (Engelm.) Tubeuf, Naturw. Zeitschr. Forst. u. Landw. 17: 216, 1919. *Arceuthobium campylopodum* Engelm. forma *microcarpum* (Engelm.) Gill, Trans. Conn. Acad. Arts & Sci. 32: 209, 1935.

DESCRIPTION: Mean shoot height ca. 5 cm., but up to 10 cm. (fig. 64). Shoots green to purple,

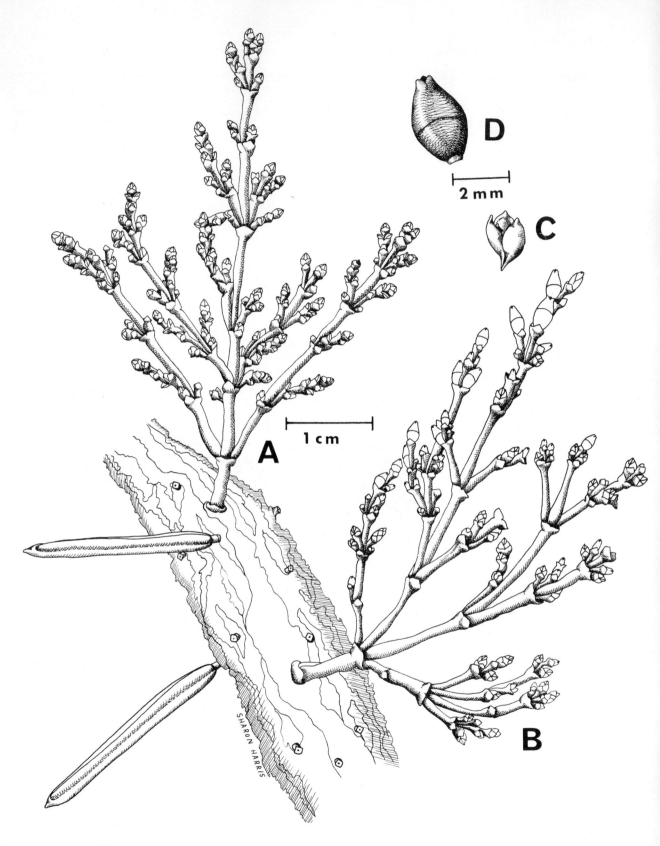

Figure 64.—*Arceuthobium microcarpum* in August: *A*, Staminate shoot; *B*, Pistillate shoot; *C*, Detail of young pistillate flower; *D*, Nearly mature fruit.

flabellately branched. Basal diameter of dominant shoots 1.5–3 mm. (mean 2 mm.). Third internode 5–16 mm. (mean 9.3 ± 2.2 mm.) long and 1–2 mm. (mean 1.5 mm.) wide (9 collections), length/width ratio 6.2:1. Staminate flowers 2.3 mm. in diameter; perianth mostly 3-, rarely 4-merous; segments ca. 1.2 mm. long and 1.0 mm. wide. Mean anther diameter 0.4 mm., centered 0.6 mm. from tip of segment. Pollen polar diameter 18–21 (mean 19μ); equatorial diameter 21–23 (mean 22μ); polar/equatorial diameter ratio 1:1.16; spine height (1.2μ) approximately equal to wall thickness—1.4μ (1 collection). Pistillate flowers ca. 1 mm. long and 1 mm. in diameter. Mature fruit 3.5 mm. long and 2.0 mm. wide; proximal portion ca. 2.5 mm. long. Seeds 2.4 × 1.0 mm. Meiosis in July. Anthesis usually in late August or early September. Seeds mature in September. Maturation period averages 12 to 13 months. n = 14.

HOSTS: Common and serious only on *Picea engelmannii* and *P. pungens*. Gill (1935), who collected one specimen on *Abies lasiocarpa* var. *arizonica* near Columbine Ranger Station in the Graham Mountains of Arizona, noted that *A. microcarpum* rarely infected this host; our searches in the same area failed to reveal any infection on *Abies*, although the parasite was common on *Picea*. Also, we have examined *Abies* in many other stands where *A. microcarpum* is abundant, but have found no infection on it.

DISTRIBUTION: This dwarf mistletoe, which has been found only in Arizona and New Mexico (fig. 65), has one of the smallest ranges of any species of *Arceuthobium*. In Arizona, the parasite has been observed in the Apache National Forest, the Graham Mountains, the North Rim of Grand Canyon, and the San Francisco Peaks and nearby Kendrick Peak,[32] but not in the Chiricahua Mountains.[32] In New Mexico, the only infested area known is in the Mogollon Mountains, although we suspect the parasite is more widely distributed in the mountains of southwestern New Mexico. We found no spruce dwarf mistletoe, however, in northern, central, and south-central New Mexico, or in the commercially valuable spruce forests from southern Utah and Colorado northward. Known elevational range is 7,900 to 10,000 feet. Specimens examined: see appendix, p. 213.

Apparently, the rare *Picea chihuahuana* is not parasitized, because no infections have been reported from the Sierra Madre Occidental of Chihuahua or Durango, Mexico. Gordon (1968) did not observe the parasite in his ecological study of the tree near El Salto, Durango.[33] If *P. chihuahuana* is parasitized by dwarf mistletoe, *A. microcarpum* would be the most likely taxon.

DISCUSSION: The original specimens cited by Engelmann are *Gilbert 100* and *102*. The only specimen now at the Missouri Botanic Garden is *Gilbert 112* which is labeled in Engelmann's handwriting as the type. The original label for specimen *100* is in the same packet. Presumably, *Gilbert 102* in the original citation should have been *112*. In any case, the collections are now combined so *Gilbert 112* is our choice for a lectotype.

This localized southwestern species is characterized by its almost exclusive occurrence on *Picea*. Gill (1935) gave a much larger distribution for this taxon (to California, Idaho, and Montana). Hawksworth and Graham (1963), however, have shown that Gill's records are based on occasional parasitism of spruce by other dwarf mistletoes (*A. laricis*. *A. douglasii*, *A. americanum*, and possibly *A. tsugense* and *A. cyanocarpum*).

This species induces small, dense witches' brooms (see fig. 9). Heavily infected trees may bear hundreds of brooms. Although this dwarf mistletoe causes heavy mortality in *Picea engelmannii* and *P. pungens* in Arizona and New Mexico, the spruces constitute only a minor part of the total forest volume. The dwarf mistletoe is not found in the main commercial range of *P. engelmannii*.

ARCEUTHOBIUM OCCIDENTALE
DIGGER PINE DWARF MISTLETOE

18. *Arceuthobium occidentale* Engelmann, U.S. Geogr. Surv. W of 100th Meridian (Wheeler Rep.) 6: 375, 1878 and Bot. Calif. 2: 107, 1880. LECTOTYPE: CALIFORNIA: Kern Co.; Walker's Basin, on *Pinus sabiniana*, *Rothrock 429* in 1875 (MO! Isotype US). *Razoumofskya occidentale* (Engelm.) Kuntze, Rev. Gen. Pl. 2: 587, 1891.

DESCRIPTION: Mean shoot height ca. 8 cm., but up to 17 cm. (fig. 66). Shoots yellowish, glaucous, flabellately branched. Basal diameter of dominant shoots 1.5–5 mm. (mean 2 mm.). Third internode 7–18 mm. (mean 12.7 ± 2.0 mm.) long and 1.5–3.5 mm. (mean 1.8 mm.) wide (11 collections), length/width ratio 7.1:1. Staminate flowers 3.0 mm. in diameter; perianth 3- or 4-merous; segments ca. 1.5 mm. long and 1.0 mm. wide. Mean anther diameter 0.5 mm., centered 0.6 mm. from tip of segment. Pollen polar diameter 18–23 (mean 20μ); equatorial diameter 21–25

---

[32] Personal communication, Dr. John R. Jones, U.S. Forest Service, 1968.

[33] Personal communication, Dr. A. G. Gordon, Canada Dep. Fisheries and Forestry, 1969.

141

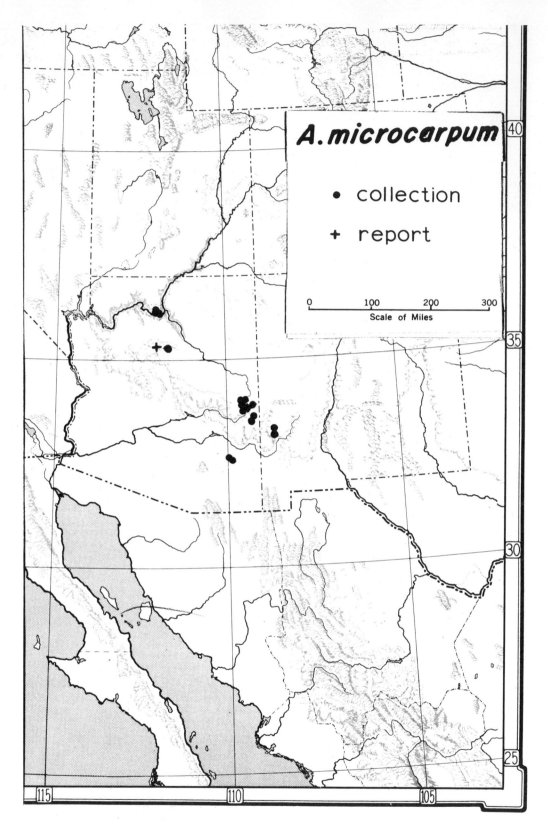

Figure 65.—Distribution of *Arceuthobium microcarpum*. Outline map copyrighted by Denoyer-Geppert Co., Chicago (used by permission).

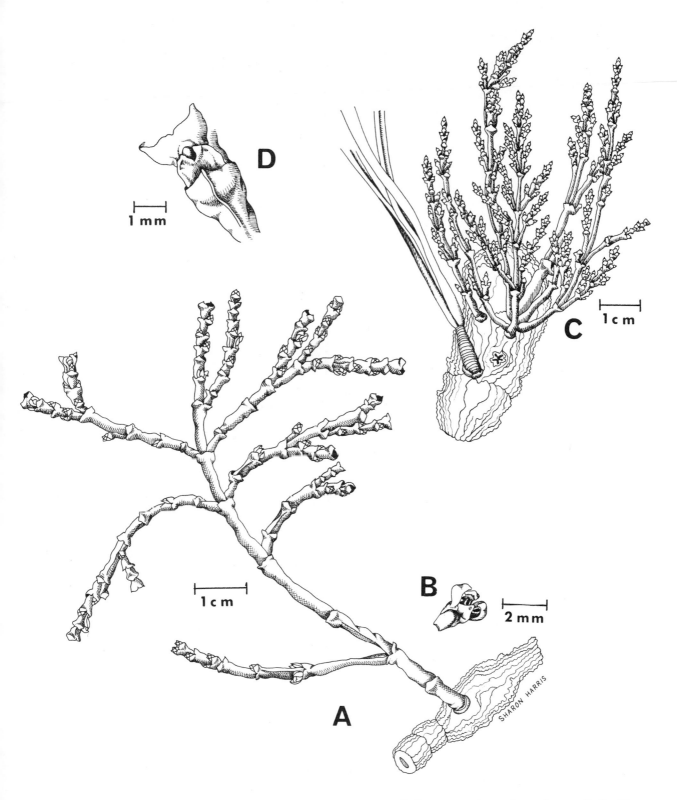

Figure 66.—*Arceuthobium occidentale* in March: *A*, Staminate shoot; *B*, Remnant of staminate flower; *C*, Pistillate shoot; *D*, Young fertilized fruit.

143

(mean 23μ); polar/equatorial diameter ratio 1:1.16; spine height (ca. 2μ) approximately twice wall thickness—1.1μ (3 collections). Mature fruit 4.5 mm. long and 3.0 mm. wide; proximal portion ca. 3.0 mm. long. Seeds 2.6 × 1.0 mm. Meiosis in August. Peak anthesis usually during late October, with extremes from early September to late November. Seeds usually mature in November, with extremes from early October to January; maturation period averages ca. 13 months. *n* = 14.

HOSTS: Principal hosts are *Pinus sabiniana, P. radiata,* and *P. muricata. Pinus coulteri* and *P. attenuata* are sometimes infected in the coastal mountains of central California. *Pinus contorta* var. *bolanderi* is occasionally attacked where this tree is associated with infected *P. muricata. A. occidentale* will not infect *P. ponderosa,* although it is commonly associated with this tree on *P. sabiniana* in the Sierra Nevada.

Hedgcock and Hunt (1917) successfully inoculated *A. occidentale* on seedlings of *Pinus banksiana, P. bungeana, P. caribaea, P. pinea,* and *P. virginiana* as did Kuijt (1960a) for *P. torreyana.*

DISTRIBUTION: This dwarf mistletoe occurs throughout the foothills and low mountains surrounding the Central Valley of California and along the coastal mountains from the Mount Pinos area (Ventura County) north to Mendocino County (fig. 67). It is found in two of the three populations of *Pinus radiata:* Monterey and Cambria but not Swanton (Offord 1964a). One of the few dwarf mistletoes to become established outside its natural range, *A. occidentale* has been collected on *P. radiata* at Stanford University (Peirce 1905) and at Berkeley, California (Offord 1964b). In both cases, the source of infection presumably was diseased trees transplanted from the Monterey area.

This mistletoe ranges from near sea level on *P. radiata* and *P. muricata* to an elevation of about 4,700 feet in the southern Sierra Nevada on *P. sabiniana.* Specimens examined: see appendix, p. 214.

DISCUSSION: Engelmann's 1878 report specifically lists only the specimen *Rothrock 429* on *Pinus sabiniana,* but also mentions that it occurs on *P. ponderosa.* No specimens are cited in Engelmann's 1880 report. Engelmann thus considered *A. occidentale* to include both the parasite on *Pinus ponderosa* (our *A. campylopodum*) and *P. sabiniana* (our *A. occidentale*). Engelmann's writings are not clear as to what he considered to be the relationship of *A. occidentale* to his previously described *A. campylopodum* (*in* Gray 1850). Traditionally, the name *A. campylopodum* has been associated with

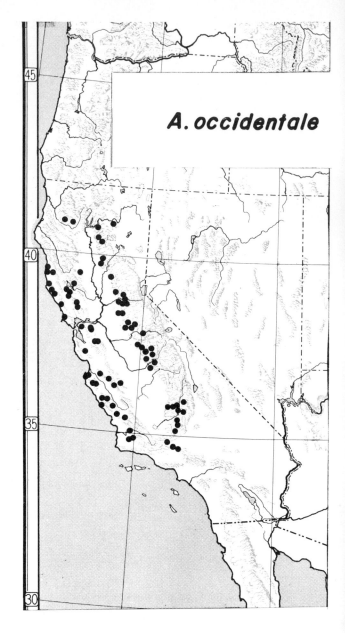

Figure 67.—**Distribution of *Arceuthobium occidentale* in California. Outline map copyrighted by Denoyer-Geppert Co., Chicago (used by permission).**

the ponderosa pine parasite, and we maintain this usage.

Several characteristics that distinguish *A. occidentale* from *A. campylopodum* (see table 20) are discussed under the latter taxon. Also, the type of witches' brooms formed differs considerably. Frequently, *A. occidentale* does not form witches' brooms in *Pinus sabiniana* (see fig. 8c), but those that are formed are small and open compared with the large, dense brooms that *A. campylopodum* causes on *P. ponderosa.* Witches' brooms are more frequent in *Pinus radiata* (Offord 1964a) and *P. muricata* than in *P. sabiniana*. Swellings at the point of infection are particularly conspicuous on *P. radiata*.

Shoot color in *A. occidentale* varies with the species of host parasitized: shoots are light brown to straw colored on *P. sabiniana*, olive green on *P. radiata*, and dark brown on *P. muricata*. These color differences may be due to hosts, or to local populations of the parasite in areas where the three main hosts occur.

Populations of *A. occidentale* on its three principal hosts (*Pinus sabiniana, P. radiata,* and *P. muricata*) are usually geographically separated, although there are a few instances of cross infection between them (see fig. 46). *Pinus muricata* is attacked by *A. occidentale* on Huckleberry Hill near Monterey where the parasite is common on *P. radiata*. However, infection in *P. muricata* is most common in the north coastal area of California where *P. contorta* var. *bolanderi* is the only other infected tree. *Pinus radiata* and *P. sabiniana* do not occur together naturally, but *P. radiata* has been planted within the range of *P. sabiniana*. An example is at Mount Hamilton Observatory where planted *P. radiata* near mistletoe-infected *P. sabiniana* was also generally infected. Apparently *Pinus muricata* and *P. sabiniana* are not sympatric.

Scharpf (1969a) successfully inoculated *A. occidentale* from *Pinus sabiniana* on *P. radiata*; Parmeter and Cobb (1967) grew this mistletoe from *P. muricata* on *P. radiata*.

Even though *Pinus sabiniana* typically occurs in very open forests, *A. occidentale* is widely distributed in these stands. The distribution pattern suggests that vectors (possibly birds), in addition to explosive seed dispersal, are important in disseminating this mistletoe.

ARCEUTHOBIUM PUSILLUM
EASTERN DWARF MISTLETOE

19. *Arceuthobium pusillum* Peck, Trans. Albany Inst. 7: 191, 1872. HOLOTYPE: NEW YORK: Rensselaer Co.: Sandlake, on *Picea mariana*, Peck in 1871 (Isotype MO!) *Arceuthobium minutum* Engelmann, Bull. Torrey Bot. Club 2: 43, 1871, *nomen nudum. Arceuthobium oxycedri* (DC.) M. Bieb. var. *abigenium* Wood, Amer. Botanist and Florist: 446, 1871. *Arceuthobium abigenium* Wood, Class-Book of Botany: 832, 1881. *Razoumofskya pusilla* (Peck) Kuntze, Rev. Gen. Pl. 2: 587, 1891. *Razoumofskya minuta* (Engelm.) Kuntze, Loc. Cit.

DESCRIPTION: Mean shoot height ca. 1 cm., but up to 3 cm. (fig. 68). Shoots green to brown, without secondary branching. Basal diameter of dominant shoots ca. 1.0 mm. Third internode 1–4 mm. (mean 1.9 ± 0.8 mm.) long and 0.5–1.5 mm. (mean 1.0 mm.) wide (17 collections), length/width ratio 1.9:1; segments often markedly wider at top than at base. Pistillate shoots often longer than staminate. Staminate flowers 1.7–2.2 mm. (mean 1.8 mm.) in diameter; perianth mostly 3-merous, sometimes 2- or 4-; segments ca. 0.8 mm. long and 0.7 mm. wide. Mean anther diameter 0.4 mm., centered 0.5 mm. from tip of segment. Pollen polar diameter 19–25 (mean 22μ); equatorial diameter 23–28 (mean 26μ) polar/equatorial diameter ratio 1:1.16; spine height (ca. 2.2μ) ca. 1.5 times wall thickness—1.4μ (4 collections). Mature fruit ca. 3.0 mm. long and 1.25–1.75 mm. wide (mean 1.5 mm.); proximal portion ca. 2.0 mm. long. Seeds 2.0 × 0.9 mm. Staminate meiosis in September and pistillate meiosis in May (Tainter 1968). Anthesis usually in April or May, with extremes from late March to June (Fernald 1950, Tainter 1968). Seeds mature in September or early October of the same year as pollination; maturation period averages about 5 months. Germination mostly in May and June (Tainter 1968). $n = 14$.

HOSTS: *Arceuthobium pusillum* is mainly parasitic on *Picea mariana*, and to a somewhat lesser extent on *P. glauca*; its occurrence on *P. glauca* is somewhat variable. This tree is heavily attacked along the Maine Coast (Nash 1955), and in the pure *P. glauca* stands near Glenboro, Manitoba.[34] Occasional hosts are *Picea rubens* and *Larix laricina* (Kliejunas 1969; Tainter and French 1967, 1968). Rare hosts are *Picea pungens* (U.S. Department of Agriculture 1960), *Pinus banksiana* (Laut 1967; Pomerleau 1942; Sippell, Rose, and Larsen 1968), *Pinus resinosa* (Krotkov 1940, Kuijt 1955), and *Pinus strobus* (House 1935).

DISTRIBUTION: Eastern dwarf mistletoe occurs in Canada from the Hudson Bay and Cumberland areas in eastern Saskatchewan to southern Manitoba, southern Ontario, Quebec, the Maritime Provinces and Newfoundland. In the United States it is found in the northern parts of Minnesota, Wisconsin, and Michigan, northeastern Pennsylvania, extreme northwestern New Jersey and all six New England States (figs. 69, 70, 71). Distribution maps for *A. pusillum* have been prepared for New England (Eaton 1931, Eaton and Dow 1940); Maine (Brower 1960); Minnesota (Tainter and French 1969a); New Brunswick, Nova Scotia, and Prince Edward Island (Forbes, Underwood, and Van Sickle 1968); and for Manitoba and Saskatchewan (Kuijt 1963, Zalasky 1956). In Ontario and Quebec the northern limits of this mistletoe are

---

[34] Personal communication, J. G. Laut, Canada Dep. of Fisheries and Forestry, 1968.

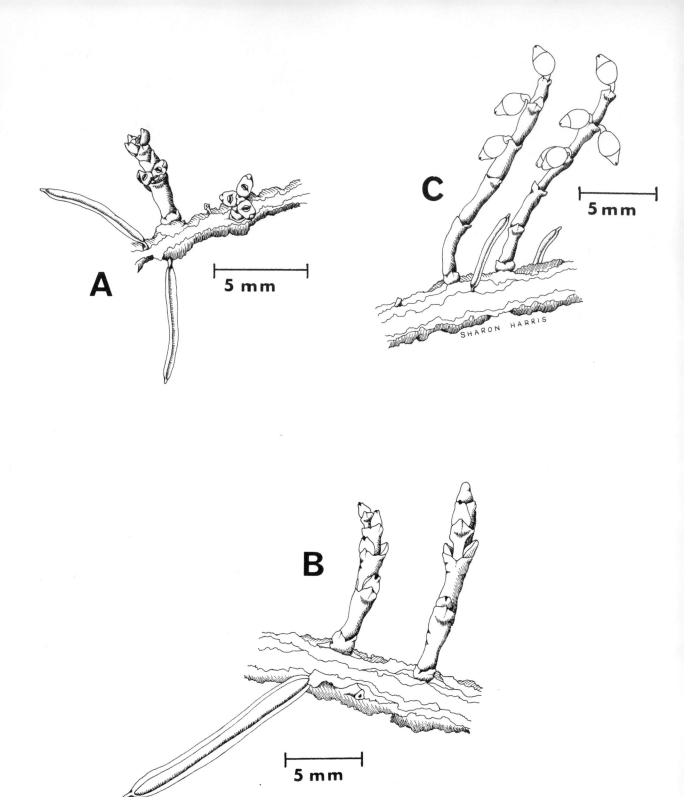

Figure 68.—*Arceuthobium pusillum: A*, Staminate plant with mature flowers, May; *B*, Pistillate plant with immature fruit, midsummer; *C*, Pistillate plant with mature fruit, September. Drawn from photographs provided by F. H. Tainter, University of Minnesota.

146

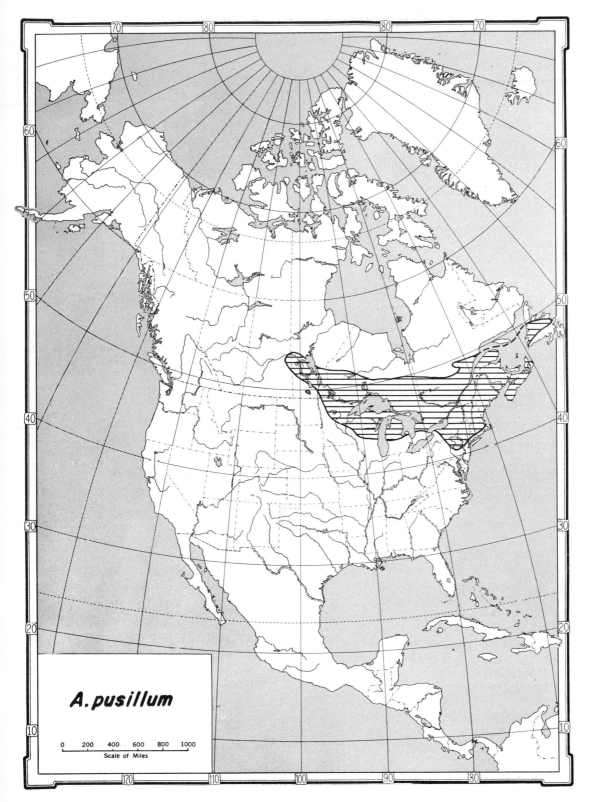

Figure 69.—General distribution of *Arceuthobium pusillum*. Outline map copyrighted by Denoyer-Geppert Co., Chicago (used by permission).

147

poorly known; also, the report from White Cloud in West Central Michigan (Martin 1926) should be verified, because no other collections are known within about 50 miles of this locality. This dwarf mistletoe ranges from sea level in Maine and the Maritime Provinces to 2,700 feet on Mount Katahdin, Maine (Brower 1960). Specimens examined: see appendix, p. 216.

DISCUSSION: Wood's (1871) variety *abigenium* was based on Peck's specimen from Sandlake, New York. Since it was proposed as a variety, it cannot replace Peck's (1872) validly published specific name *pusillum*.

The discovery of *A. pusillum* at Warrensburg, New York, in 1871 triggered a flurry of activity which eventually showed the parasite to be widely distributed in the spruce forests of the Lake States, New England, and southern Canada. The plant, no longer considered a curiosity, is recognized as an important damaging agent of spruce in many parts of its range. For example, mortality is severe in *Picea glauca* along the Maine Coast (Nash 1955), and the parasite is considered to be the most serious disease agent of *Picea mariana* in the Lake States (Beckwith and Anderson 1956).

Eastern dwarf mistletoe shoots average about 1 cm. high. Only *A. minutissimum* of the Himalayas has smaller shoots.

The witches' brooms induced by *A. pusillum* have been the subject of several investigations.[35] Witches' brooms appear to be mostly of the systemic type (see fig. 14); thus shoot formation is regular and progressive. Shoots usually first appear in late summer or autumn as small eruptions in the bark of twigs two seasons old; during the third season the shoots mature; they flower the following spring; the fruits mature the next autumn. Thus, shoots with mature fruits usually occur only on 4-year-old host growth. Thomas (1954) stated that the type of brooms formed on *Picea mariana* is dense and dark, while that on *P. glauca* is light and loose. The brooms he observed possibly were in different stages of development, because Anderson and Kaufert (1959), in a study of the parasite on *P. mariana* showed that brooms grow rapidly for the first 5 to 10 years and then abruptly decline in vigor.

Brower (1960) and Nash (1955) suggest that the dwarf mistletoe on *Picea glauca* along the Maine Coast is distinct from the inland mistletoe characteristically found in spruce bogs. We have not studied this possibility in the field, but the herbarium specimens we examined from hosts on the two sites showed no morphological differences.

---

[35] Von Schrenk 1900, Gill 1935, Pomerleau 1942, Anderson and Kaufert 1959, Kuijt 1960b.

Although *P. glauca* appears to be more severely infested along the Maine Coast, the occurrence of *A. pusillum* on this host is not unique to this area. It occurs commonly on *P. glauca* in the Mackinac Straits area of Michigan and in the Sprucewoods area of southwestern Manitoba, and sporadically on this host throughout the range of the parasite (see specimens cited).

That *A. pusillum* occurs in *P. mariana* bogs is well known, but ecology of the parasite has not been adequately investigated. Only complete studies will help explain the unusual distribution patterns reported for *A. pusillum:* In Quebec, it is restricted to within 1 mile of lakes or rivers (Bernard 1957); in Maine on *P. glauca* to within ¼ mile of the Coast (Nash 1955). If, as Bonga (1969a) suggests on the basis of New Brunswick studies, *A. pusillum* requires an uninterrupted period of high atmospheric humidity in the spring, its absence in inland-upland sites except bogs might be explained.

When Eaton (1931) noted an 80- to 100-mile gap in the distribution of *A. pusillum* in southern New England, only one collection was known between central Vermont and New Hampshire and central Massachusetts. Later, *A. pusillum* was recorded from two other localities, and, since the mistletoe also occurs in New York just west of the Massachusetts-Vermont boundary (fig. 70), the gap is probably more apparent than real (Eaton and Dow 1940).

Several islands where *A. pusillum* infections occur are isolated 20 miles or more from the parasite's main range; for example, Monhegan Island off the Maine Coast and Beaver Island in Lake Michigan.

ARCEUTHOBIUM RUBRUM

20. *Arceuthobium rubrum* Hawksworth & Wiens, Brittonia 17: 233, 1965. HOLOTYPE: MEXICO: DURANGO: 29 mi. E of El Salto on Route 40, on *Pinus teocote, Hawksworth & Wiens 3490* in 1963. (COLO, Isotypes FPF, INIF, MEXU, MO, US).

DESCRIPTION: Mean shoot height ca. 10 cm., but up to 15 cm. (fig. 72). Shoots reddish brown, flabellately branched. Staminate plants usually taller than pistillate plants. Basal diameter of dominant shoots 2–4 mm. (mean 2.4 mm.). Third internode 4–12 mm. (mean 6.9 ± 2.7 mm.) long and 2–3 mm. (mean ca. 2.0 mm.) wide (5 collections), length/width ratio 3.4:1. Staminate flowers 1.0–1.5 mm. in diameter; mostly 3-merous; segments ca. 0.6 mm. long and 0.6 mm. wide. Pollen polar diameter 23–26 (mean 24μ); equatorial diameter ratio 1:1.05; spine height (ca. 1.0μ) slightly

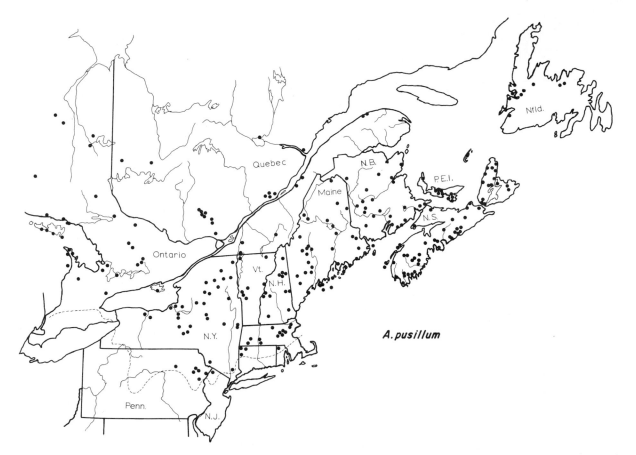

Figure 70.—Distribution of *Arceuthobium pusillum* in Eastern North America (based on collections and reports). The dashed line shows the approximate southern limits of *Picea mariana*.

greater than wall thickness—0.8μ (1 collection). Mature fruit ca. 3.5 mm. long and 2.0 mm. wide. Seeds 2.0 × 1.0 mm. Meiosis in June? Anthesis usually in July. Seeds mature in mid-July to August of the year following pollination; maturation period averages 12-13 months. n = unknown.

HOSTS: Known on *Pinus teocote*, *P. cooperi*, *P. engelmannii*, *P. herrerai* and *P. durangensis*, all of which appear to be highly susceptible.

DISTRIBUTION: This rare species is known only from the Sierra Madre Occidental in Durango and Sinaloa, Mexico. No range map was prepared for this taxon because its distribution is so poorly known. Known elevational range is 8,200 to 8,900 feet. Specimens examined: see appendix, p. 219.

DISCUSSION: This distinctive slender, red mistletoe is apparently widespread in the mountains of Durango (see fig. 10 B). As the plants dry, red turns to dull brown, and the apical portion of each segment becomes golden yellow, which gives dried specimens a characteristic banded appearance. The shiny fruits, a unique character that readily distinguishes this species from all other dwarf mistletoes, remain shiny when dried but the bright red color turns dark brown.

Another distinctive characteristic of this taxon is the very small, scarcely opened staminate flowers. In all July collections examined, the staminate flowers were still not expanded, although they were past maturity and nearly all pollen had been shed. Instead, the perianth segments formed a nearly closed cup with only a slight separation between the segments. The plants must be examined closely to tell whether they are undergoing anthesis.

ARCEUTHOBIUM STRICTUM

21. *Arceuthobium strictum* Hawksworth & Wiens, Brittonia 17: 234, 1965. HOLOTYPE: MEXICO: DURANGO: 16 mi. S of city of Durango on road to La Flor, on *Pinus leiophylla* var. *chihuahuana*, *Hawksworth & Wiens 3465* in 1963 (COLO, Isotypes DS, FPF, INIF, MEXU, MO, US).

DESCRIPTION: Mean shoot height ca. 7 cm., but up to 13 cm. (fig. 73). Pistillate shoots generally a

149

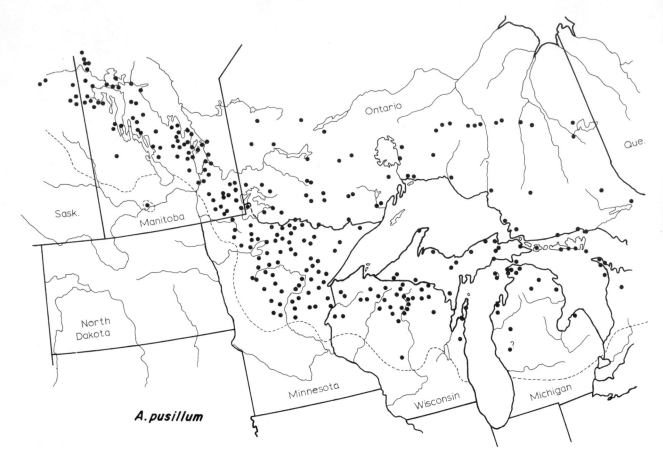

Figure 71.—Distribution of *Arceuthobium pusillum* in central Canada and the Lake States (based on collections and reports). The dashed line indicates the approximate southern limits of spruce.

greenish yellow brown, flabellately branched. Staminate shoots brownish, seldom branching. Pistillate plants usually taller than staminate plants. Basal diameter of dominant shoots 2.5–4 mm. (mean 3.1 mm.). Third internode 1–8 mm. (mean 3.6 ± 2.0 mm.) long and 1.5–3.5 mm. (mean 2.3 mm.) wide (5 collections), length/width ratio 1.6:1. Staminate flowers ca. 3 mm. in diameter, perianth 3-, 4- or 5-, rarely 6- or 7-merous (Kuijt 1970); segments ca. 1.5 mm. long and 1 mm. wide. Pollen polar diameter 18–19 (mean 18μ); equatorial diameter 20–25 (mean 22μ); polar/equatorial diameter ratio 1:1.19; spine height ca. 1μ, approximately equal to wall thickness (1 collection). Mature fruit ca. 4 mm. long and ca. 2.5 mm. wide. Seeds 2.5 mm. × 1.0 mm. Meiosis in July. Anthesis from late July to October, with peak in September. Seeds mature from mid-September to October of the year following pollination; maturation period averages ca. 13 months. *n* = 14.

HOSTS: Chihuahua pine, *Pinus leiophylla* var. *chihuahuana* is the principal host, *P. teocote* an occasional host, and *P. engelmannii* a rare host.

DISTRIBUTION: This rare dwarf mistletoe is known only in the Sierra Madre Occidental south and west of Durango, State of Durango, Mexico. No range map for this species was prepared because its distribution is too poorly known. Elevational range is 7,300 to 8,200 feet. Specimens examined: see appendix, p. 219.

DISCUSSION: The most distinctive feature of this mistletoe is its branching pattern (Hawksworth and Wiens 1965, Kuijt 1970). The staminate shoots seldom branch; instead they may become single spikes 4 to 6 cm. long (see fig. 73). The pistillate plants, however, have abundant secondary branching with dense clusters of small, yellow-green fruits. This species is damaging to *Pinus leiophylla* var. *chihuahuana* (see fig. 10).

150

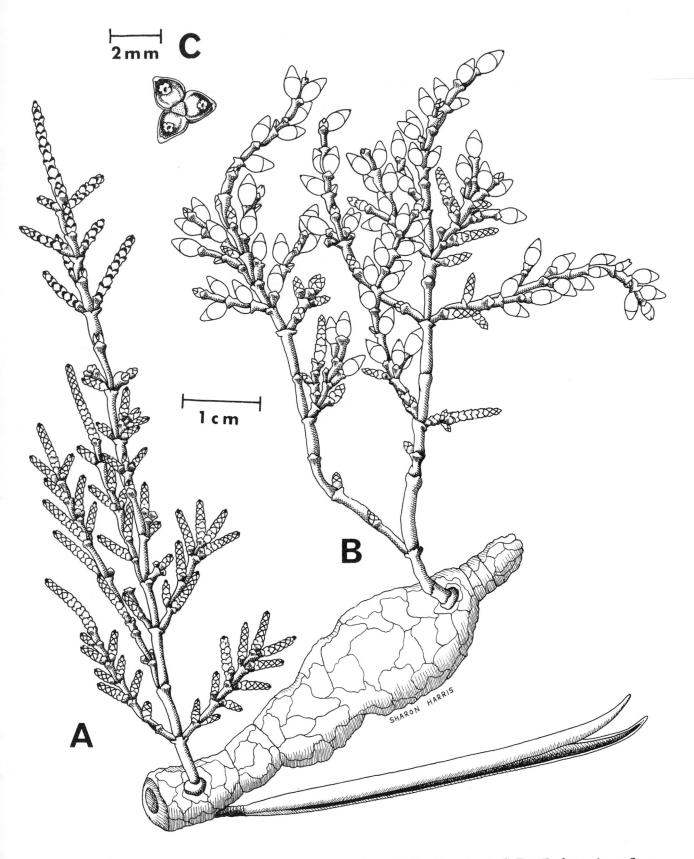

Figure 72.—*Arceuthobium rubrum* in July: *A*, Staminate shoot; *B*, Pistillate shoot; *C*, Detail of staminate flower.

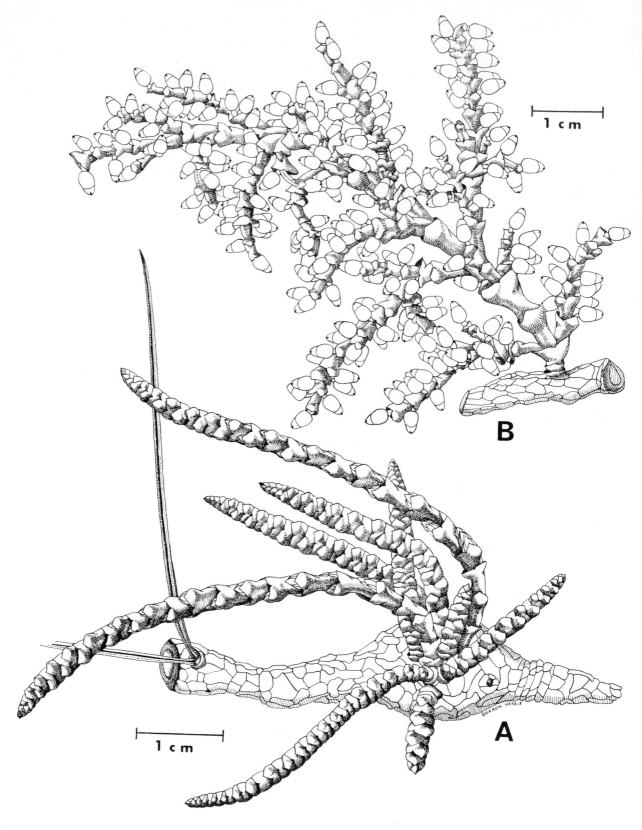

Figure 73.—*Arceuthobium strictum* in July: *A*, Staminate plant showing characteristic lack of branching in the annual growth segments; *B*, Pistillate plant.

ARCEUTHOBIUM TSUGENSE
HEMLOCK DWARF MISTLETOE

22. *Arceuthobium tsugense* (Rosendahl) G. N. Jones, Univ. Wash. Publ. Biol. 5: 139, 1936 (as *A. tsugensis*). HOLOTYPE: CANADA: BRITISH COLUMBIA: Vancouver Island, Port Renfrew on *Tsuga heterophylla, Rosendahl 826* in 1902, (MIN. Isotypes COLO, DS, FPF, ILL, MO, RM). *Razoumofskya tsugensis* Rosendahl, Minn. Bot. Stud. 3: 272, 1903. *Razoumofskya douglasii tsugensis* (Rosendahl) Piper, Contr. U.S. Nat. Herb. 11: 222, 1906. *Arceuthobium douglasii* Engelm. var. *tsugensis* (Rosendahl) M. E. Jones, Univ. Mont. Bull. 61 (Biol. Ser. 15): 25, 1910. *Arceuthobium camplyopodum* Engelm. forma *tsugensis* (Rosendahl) Gill, Trans. Conn. Acad. Arts & Sci. 32: 200, 1935.

DESCRIPTION: Mean shoot height ca. 5 cm., but up to 13 cm. (fig. 74). Shoots greenish to reddish, darker in winter, flabellately branched. Basal diameter of dominant shoots 1.5–4 mm. (mean 2.0 mm.). Third internode 4–16 mm. (mean 9.2 ± 2.5 mm.) long and 1–2 mm. (mean 1.5 mm.) wide (15 collections), length/width ratio 6.1:1. Staminate flowers 2.8 mm. in diameter; perianth 3- or 4-merous, segments ca. 1.2 mm. long and 1.0 mm. wide. Mean anther diamter 0.5 mm., centered 0.6 mm. from tip of segment. Pollen polar diameter 19–21 (mean 20μ); equatorial diameter 23–25 (mean 24μ); polar/equatorial diameter ratio 1:1.19; spine height (2.4μ) approximately 3 times wall thickness—0.8μ (4 collections). Pistillate flowers ca. 1 mm. long and 1 mm. in diameter. Mature fruit 3 mm. long and 2 mm. wide; proximal portion ca. 2.0 mm. long. Meiosis in July. Peak anthesis usually in late August, with extremes from early August to late September, or even December in British Columbia (Baranyay 1962). Seeds mature from late September to early November (Smith 1966a). Maturation period averages ca. 13–14 months. Germination usually from February to May in British Columbia (Smith 1966b). *n* = 14.

HOSTS: The hemlocks, *Tsuga heterophylla* and *T. mertensiana*, are the principal hosts, although several other trees are attacked, particularly when they grow in association with infected hemlocks: *Abies lasiocarpa, A. amabilis, A. grandis, A. procera, Pinus contorta* subsp. *contorta, P. albicaulis,* and *P. monticola. A. tsugense* is fairly common on *Abies amabilis;* many reports from Washington should show *A. tsugense* as the parasite on this host rather than *A. abietinum.* Very rarely *A. tsugense* is found on *Picea sitchensis* in Alaska (Laurent 1966) and in British Columbia (Molnar, Harris, Ross, and Ginns 1968). Also, we found it on *P. engelmannii* in the Oregon Cascades.

Arceuthobium tsugense rarely occurs on *Picea breweriana* in northern California.

Along the south coastal areas of British Columbia and on Orcas Island, Washington, a dwarf mistletoe is common on *Pinus contorta* subsp. *contorta* and on *P. monticola.* We classify this as *A. tsugense* although, as mentioned by Kuijt (1956), the pines are often infected in areas where there is little or no current infection on *Tsuga.*

Eastern hemlock, *Tsuga canadensis,* was shown to be susceptible on the basis of seedling inoculations (Weir 1918a). *Larix europea* became infected when planted under infected *Tsuga heterophylla* on Vancouver Island, British Columbia (Kuijt 1964), but it apparently was not a compatible host because swellings formed but no shoots developed. On the basis of artificial inoculations of potted seedlings, Smith (1965) showed the following as susceptible to *A. tsugense; Tsuga heterophylla* from south coastal and interior British Columbia, *Pinus contorta* subsp. *latifolia* from Montana, *Picea glauca* from central British Columbia, and *Picea abies* from Europe. Smith has also successfully infected *Picea engelmannii* (1970b) and, with difficulty, *Larix occidentalis* (1970a). In the latter host-parasite combination, most infections resulted only in swellings, but in one instance a few short-lived shoots were produced. Of the several mixed *Larix occidentalis-Tsuga heterophylla* stands in the Oregon Cascades we examined, where *Tsuga* grew in close association with *A. laricis* on *Larix,* we found no infected *Tsuga.* Based on greenhouse and plantation inoculations in British Columbia, *Pinus ponderosa, P. radiata,* and *P. sylvestris* were susceptible to *A. tsugense* (Smith and Craig 1968).

DISTRIBUTION: This dwarf mistletoe ranges from near Haines, Alaska[36] to central California (figs. 75, 76, 77). It is found throughout the coastal hemlock forests of Alaska, British Columbia[37] (Kuijt 1963), and Washington. In Oregon, *A. tsugense* is common on the west slope of the Cascades and in the coastal mountains, and occurs in California at least as far south as Alpine County in the Sierra Nevada and along the coast to Mendocino County. This taxon apparently is widespread in the coastal mountains of Oregon and California, although few specimens have been collected in these areas.

Hultén (1968) mentions that this plant is "much overlooked;" this observation is emphasized by his distribution map of *A. tsugense* in southeastern Alaska, which indicates only two Alaska localities.

---

[36] Personal communication, T. W. Laurent, U.S. Forest Service, 1965.

[37] Personal communication, Dr. R. B. Smith, Canadian Dep. Fisheries and Forestry, 1969.

153

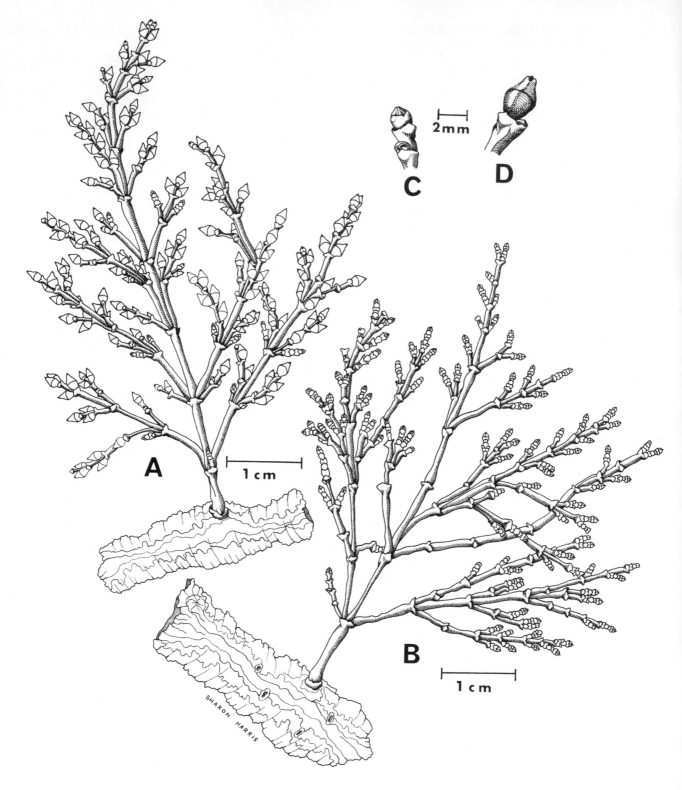

Figure 74.—*Arceuthobium tsugense* in August: *A*, Pistillate plant; *B*, Staminate plant; *C*, Immature staminate flower; *D*, Nearly mature fruit.

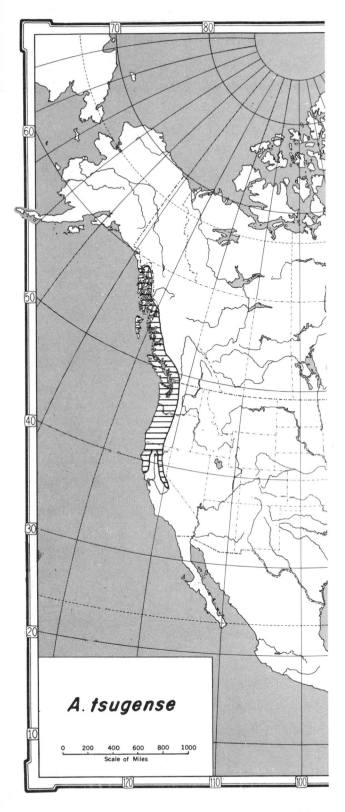

A. tsugense

| 0 | 200 | 400 | 600 | 800 | 1000 |
Scale of Miles

Our field investigations did not confirm the reports of *A. tsugense* in Idaho. Although Weir (1916c) reports and illustrates infected *Tsuga heterophylla* on Marble Creek on the St. Joe National Forest, the host probably is *T. mertensiana*.[38] In intensive mistletoe surveys in northern Idaho, western Montana, and eastern Washington, D. P. Graham[39] found no infection on *T. heterophylla* in Marble Creek or elsewhere in this region. Graham (1959b) reports mistletoe on *Tsuga mertensiana* on the Coeur d'Alene National Forest and our studies there in 1966 identified the parasite involved as *A. laricis* (see fig. 13c). *Tsuga heterophylla* was not infected even though several individuals grew in close association with infected *T. mertensiana, Larix occidentalis*, and *Abies lasiocarpa*.

The specimens that Weir collected in Idaho, reportedly on *Tsuga heterophylla* (see specimens cited), are so fragmentary that specific identification of the mistletoe is impossible. Thus, whether *A. tsugense* does attack *T. heterophylla* in Idaho will be in doubt until populations of the parasite can be rediscovered and studied. Marble Creek and nearby areas have been extensively logged during the 50 years since Weir recorded his observations, and it is remotely possible that the parasite has been eradicated. Although cutting the timber might be expected to reduce the amount of mistletoe in a stand, we know of no instances where logging has eliminated a species.

The known elevational range of *A. tsugense* is from sea level in Alaska, British Columbia, and Washington, to 8,100 feet in the central Sierra Nevada of California. Specimens examined: see appendix, p. 220.

DISCUSSION: The name *tsugensis* was published as a species of *Razoumofskya;* however, the Botanical Rules of Nomenclature require that the gender of generic and specific names agree, so with the transfer to *Arceuthobium* the correct name became *tsugense*. This mistletoe has been variously treated as a distinct species, or as allied to *A. douglasii* or *A. campylopodum* (Gill 1935). Its phenology and general appearance certainly relate it to the *campylopodum* group. *A. tsugense* and *A. laricis* are compared in table 22.

We have not observed *A. tsugense* growing with other summer-flowering dwarf mistletoes. However, it occurs within about ¼ mile of *A. abietinum* f. sp. *concoloris* and *A. occidentale* near Fort

Figure 75.—**General distribution of *Arceuthobium tsugense* in Canada and the United States. Outline map copyrighted by Denoyer-Geppert Co., Chicago (used by permission).**

---

[38] Personal communication, Dr. E. F. Wicker, U.S. Forest Service, 1967.

[39] Personal communication, U.S. Forest Service, 1965.

155

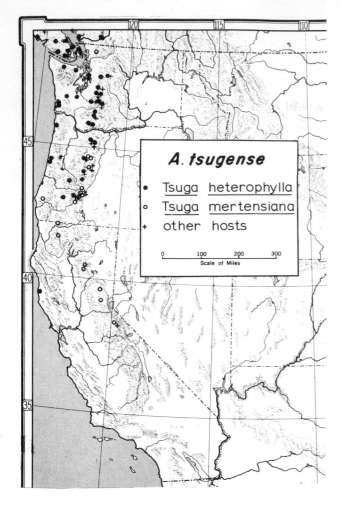

Figure 76.—Distribution of *Arceuthobium tsugense* in the United States (based on collections only). Outline map copyrighted by Denoyer-Geppert Co., Chicago (used by permission).

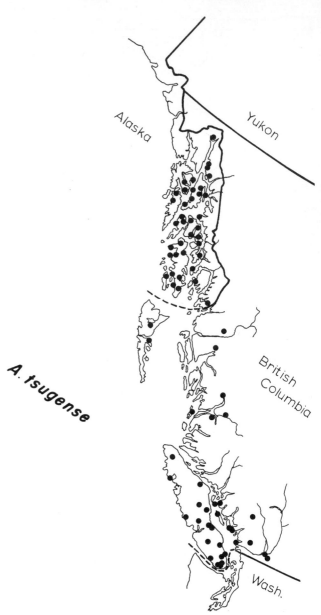

Figure 77.—Distribution of *Arceuthobium tsugense* in British Columbia and Alaska (based on collections and reports).

Bragg, California, and within a few miles of *A. abietinum* f. sp. *concoloris* and *A. laricis* in the Oregon and Washington Cascades.

Since the dwarf mistletoes are sensitive to light, this may account for the scarcity of shoots on most lower infections under the dense shade of coastal hemlock forests (Smith 1969). In such situations vigorous shoots are often found only along margins of stands, on young trees in openings, or in higher branches of older trees. Witches' brooms caused by this taxon in *Tsuga mertensiana* are illustrated in figure 13D.

ARCEUTHOBIUM VAGINATUM

23. *Arceuthobium vaginatum* (Willdenow) Presl in Berchtold, O Přirozenosti Rostlin aneb Rostlinář 2: 28, 1825.

DESCRIPTION: Shoots up to approximately 30 cm. long, but rarely reaching 50 cm., bright orange to dark brown or black, usually densely branched and erect, but large older plants sometimes become pendulous; flabellately branched; internodes ca. 1–3 cm. long, 0.2–0.4 cm. wide; staminate flower up to 3.5 mm. long and up to 3.5 mm. in diameter, mostly 3-, sometimes 4-merous, perianth segments up to 2.0 mm. long and up to 1.5 mm. wide, apex acute to obtuse, pistillate flower up to 2.5 mm. long and up to 1.5 mm. in diameter; fruit 4–6 mm. long and 2–3 mm. wide,

156

elliptical to obovate; anthesis from approximately late March through May. Parasitic on *Dipoxylon* pines.

Our studies in Mexico (Hawksworth and Wiens 1965) and the United States show that *A. vaginatum* is composed of three subspecies distinguishable on the basis of shoot color, size, staminate flowers, fruit, time of anthesis, and geographic distribution (figs. 78, 79).

Usually the three subspecies are distinct, although some intermediates were found in a transition zone between subsp. *cryptopodum* and *vaginatum* southwest of Matachic, in western Chihuahua (Hawksworth and Wiens 1965).

Key to the Subspecies

1. Plants dark brown to black; staminate flowers usually greater than 3.0 mm. long and wide; anthesis from approximately March through April; Sierra Madre Occidental from central Chihuahua southward to the Central Cordillera, the Sierra Madre Oriental, and the mountains of Nuevo León and Coahuilla.
  23a. *A. vaginatum* subsp. *vaginatum*
1. Plants dull orange to bright reddish orange; staminate flowers usually less than 3.0 mm. long and wide; anthesis from approximately April through May; Sierra Madre Occidental of northern Chihuahua and Sonora, or central Durango; southwestern and central Rocky Mountain States.
  2. Mature plants generally bright reddish orange, often greater than 20 cm. long; mature internodes usually greater than 1.5 cm. long; fruit ca. 5 mm. long, the proximal portion ca. 4 mm. long; the stigmas of mature fruit usually slightly exceeding the perianth segments (under magnification); staminate flowering peduncles 1 to 1.5 cm. long, unbranched; known only from several localities near the crest of the Sierra Madre Occidental in Durango and Sinaloa on the road between Mazatlán and Durango.
    23c. *A. vaginatum* subsp. *durangense*
  2. Mature plant generally orange to dull orange, not bright, usually less than 20 cm. long, internodes usually less than 1.5 cm. long, fruit ca. 4 mm. long, the proximal portion ca. 3 mm. long; the stigmas on mature fruit generally about equal to the perianth segments (under magnification); staminate flowering peduncles usually under 0.5 cm. long, branched; Sierra Madre Occidental of northern Chihuahua and Sonora; central Coahuila and west Texas north to central Utah and northern Colorado.
    23b. *A. vaginatum* subsp. *cryptopodum*

ARCEUTHOBIUM VAGINATUM SUBSP. VAGINATUM

23a. *Arceuthobium vaginatum* (Willdenow) Presl subsp. *vaginatum* in Berchtold, O Přirozenosti Rostlin aneb Rostlinář 2: 28, 1825. TYPE: MEXICO: VERACRUZ: Cofre de Perote, on *Pinus* sp., *Humboldt & Bonpland* in 1804 (Isotype MO!). *Viscum vaginatum* Willdenow, Sp. Pl. ed. 4, 4: 740, 1806. *Razoumofskya mexicana* Hoffman, Hort. Mosquensis (unpaged), 1808. *Viscum vaginatum* (Willd.) Kunth. Nov. Gen. et Spec. 3: 445, 1820. *Arceuthobium vaginatum* (H.B.K.) Eichler, in Mart. Fl. Bras. 5(2); 105, 1868. *Razoumofskya vaginata* (Willd.) Kuntze, Rev. Gen. Pl. 2: 587, 1891.

DESCRIPTION: Mean shoot height ca. 20 cm., but up to 50 cm. (fig. 80). Shoots dark brown to black. Basal diameter of dominant shoots 4–20 mm. (mean 7 mm.). Third internode 5–30 mm. (mean 14.4 ± 6.0 mm.) long and 2.5–8.5 mm. (mean 5.0 mm.) wide (11 collections), length/width ratio 2.9:1. Staminate flower segments ca. 1.6 mm. long and 1.1 mm. wide. Mean anther diameter 0.6 mm. centered 0.8 mm. from tip of segment. Pollen polar diameter 19–23 (mean 21μ); equatorial diameter 22–26 (mean 25μ); polar/equatorial diameter ratio 1:1.17; spine height 1.7μ ca. 1.5 times wall thickness—1.2μ (3 collections). Mature fruit ca. 5.5 mm. long and 3.5 mm. wide. Meiosis in February. Anthesis usually in March–April. Seeds mature in August of the year following pollination; maturation period averages 16–17 months. $n =$ unknown.

HOSTS: This dwarf mistletoe is common on *Pinus montezumae*, *P. hartwegii*, *P. herrerai*, *P. lawsonii*, *P. rudis*, *P. cooperi*. *P. ponderosa* vars. *scopulorum* and *arizonica*, *P. durangensis* and *P. engelmannii*, all of which appear to be highly susceptible. It rarely infects *Pinus culminicola* on Cerro Potosí, Nuevo León (Hawksworth and Wiens 1965).

DISTRIBUTION: This subspecies, one of the most widely distributed dwarf mistletoes in Mexico, occurs in the Sierra Madre Occidental from western Chihuahua south through Durango, Jalisco, and into the Central Cordillera of Mexico and Puebla; southeastward in the Sierra Madre Oriental from Coahuila and Nuevo León to Veracruz (see fig. 79). Known elevational range is from 7,000 feet in Nuevo León to 12,800 feet on Nevado de Toluca near Mexico City. Specimens examined: see appendix, p. 222.

DISCUSSION: The shoots of *A. vaginatum* subsp. *vaginatum* range up to 50 cm. high in the vicinity of Mexico City.

The hosts and ecological requirements of *A. vaginatum* subsp. *vaginatum* and *A. globosum* are similar; the two mistletoes frequently occur to-

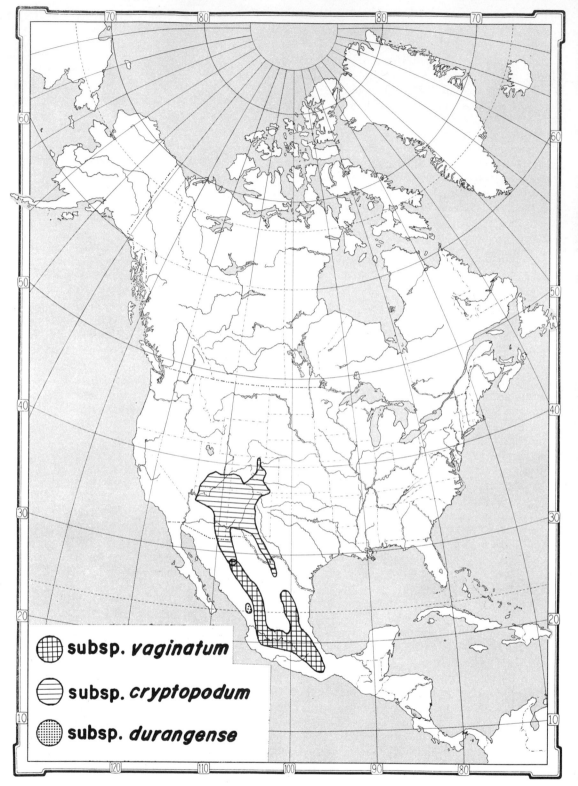

Figure 78.—General distribution of the three subspecies of *Arceuthobium vaginatum*. Outline map copyrighted by Denoyer-Geppert Co., Chicago (used by permission).

158

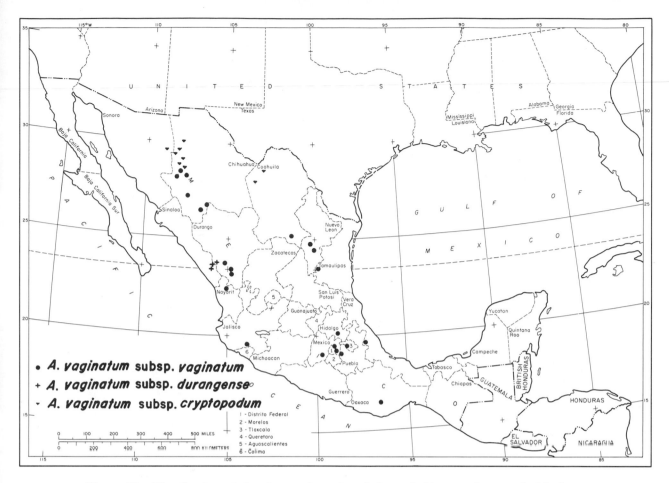

Figure 79.—Distribution of the three subspecies of *Arceuthobium vaginatum* in Mexico.

gether, sometimes on the same trees (Hawksworth and Wiens 1965).

ARCEUTHOBIUM VAGINATUM SUBSP. CRYPTOPODUM SOUTHWESTERN DWARF MISTLETOE

23b. *Arceuthobium vaginatum* subsp. *cryptopodum* (Engelm.) Hawksworth & Wiens, Brittonia 17: 230, 1965. HOLOTYPE: NEW MEXICO: Santa Fe Co., Santa Fe, on *Pinus ponderosa, Fendler 283* in 1847 (MO! Isotypes GH, K, NY). *Arceuthobium robustum* Engelmann in Gray, Mem. Amer. Acad. N.S. 4: 59, 1849, *nomen nudum. Arceuthobium cryptopodum* Engelmann *in* Gray, Bost. J. Nat. Hist. 6: 214, 1850. *Razoumofskya robusta* (Engelm.) Kuntze, Rev. Gen. Pl. 2: 587, 1891. *Razoumofskya cryptopoda* (Engelm.) Coville, Contr. U.S. Nat. Herb. 4: 192, 1893. *Arceuthobium vaginatum* (Willd.) Presl forma *cryptopodum* (Engelm.) Gill, Trans. Conn. Acad. Arts & Sci. 32: 178, 1935.

DESCRIPTION: Mean shoot height ca. 10 cm., but up to 27 cm. (fig. 81). Shoots orange to reddish brown. Basal diameter of dominant shoots 2–10 mm. (mean 4 mm.). Third internode 4–16 mm. (mean 7.8 ± 3.2 mm.) long and 2–4.5 mm. (mean 3.1 mm.) wide (25 collections), length/width ratio 2.5:1. Staminate flowers 2.5–3.0 mm. (mean 2.7 mm.) in diameter; perianth segments ca. 1.3 mm. long and 1.0 mm. wide. Mean anther diameter 0.5 mm., centered 0.5 mm. from tip of segment. Pollen polar diameter 18–28 (mean 22μ); equatorial diameter 23–30 (mean 26μ); polar/equatorial diameter ratio 1:1.15; spine height (ca. 1.5μ) or 1.5 times wall thickness—1.0μ (5 collections). Mature fruit 4.5–5.5 mm. long (mean 5.0 mm.) and 2.0–3.0 mm. wide (mean 2.5 mm.); proximal portion ca. 3.5 mm. long. Seeds 2.7×1.1 mm. Meiosis in April. Anthesis usually in May–June. Seeds mature in late July or early August of the year following pollination; maturation period averages 14–15 months. Germination in August to September. $n = 14$.

HOSTS: Principal hosts are *Pinus ponderosa* vars. *scopulorum* and *arizonica, P. engelmannii,* and the

159

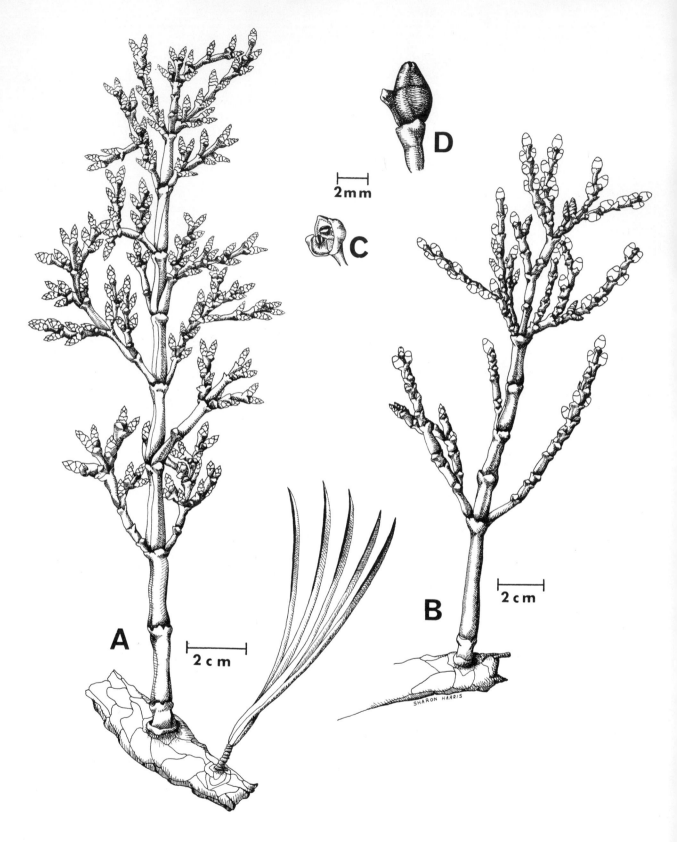

Figure 80.—*Arceuthobium vaginatum* subsp. *vaginatum* in March: *A*, Staminate plant; *B*, Pistillate plant; *C*, Staminate flower; *D*, Immature fruit.

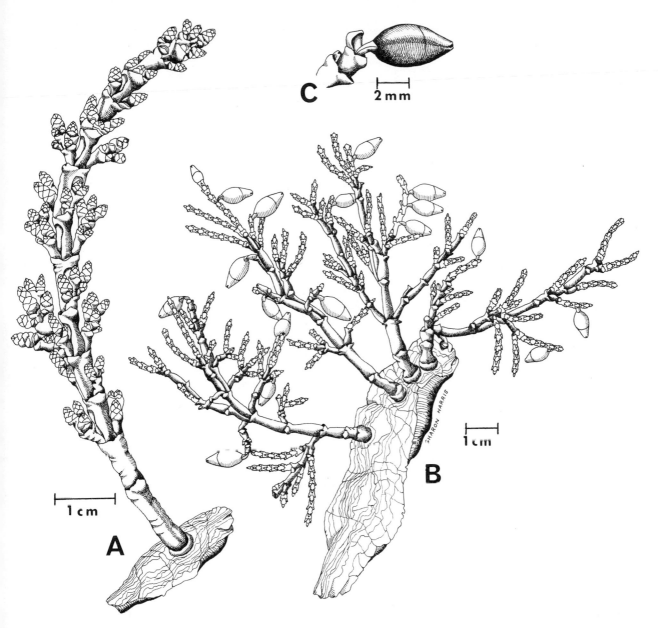

Figure 81.—*Arceuthobium vaginatum* subsp. *cryptopodum* in July: *A*, Staminate plant; *B*, Pistillate plants; *C*, Detail of nearly mature fruit.

tree known as *P. arizonica* var. *stormiae* Martínez in the Sierra del Carmen, Coahuila, Mexico; occasional hosts are *P. contorta* var. *latifolia* (Hawksworth 1956a) and *P. aristata* (Hawksworth 1965a); rare hosts are *Pinus flexilis* and *P. strobiformis*.

DISTRIBUTION: Southwestern dwarf mistletoe is widely distributed throughout the *Pinus ponderosa* forests from central Utah* (Sevier County) and

northern Colorado (Larimer County) to Arizona, New Mexico, west Texas (Guadalupe and Davis, but not Chisos Mountains),[40] at least as far south as the Sierra del Pino in central Coahuila and into the Sierra Madre Occidental in Sonora and Chihuahua (figs. 79, 82).

Found as far west as the Hualapai Mountains near Kingman, Arizona, this taxon occurs in nearly every southwestern mountain range where *P. ponderosa* grows. Andrews and Daniels (1960)

* Robert C. Loomis (Personal communication, 1971) of the Southwestern Region of the U.S. Forest Service, reports that *A. vaginatum* subsp. *cryptopodum* is common on Navajo Mountain, San Juan County, Utah.

[40] Personal communication, Dr. P. C. Lightle, U.S. Forest Service, 1966.

161

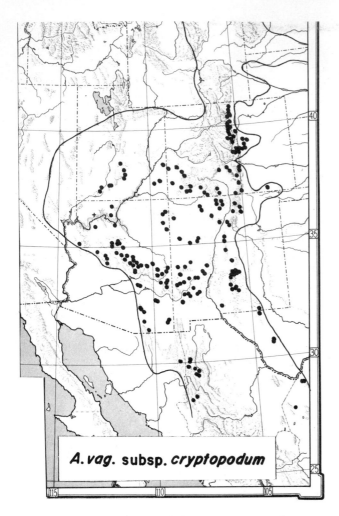

recorded the parasite on 36 percent of some 3,000 *P. ponderosa* plots in Arizona and New Mexico. In 1969, when we examined several *P. ponderosa* localities in northwestern Arizona (Mount Dellenbaugh, Black Rock Mountain, and Mount Trumbull) we found no dwarf mistletoe, although an infection has previously been reported from Mount Trumbull.[41] Known elevational range is 5,500 to 9,700 feet although this species is found mainly between 6,600 and 8,500 feet in southwestern United States. Specimens examined: see appendix, p. 222.

DISCUSSION: This mistletoe, common on *P. ponderosa* pine in the central Rocky Mountains and Southwestern States, is characterized by thick, orange-colored shoots. While the shoots are usually some shade of orange, certain populations show various gradations from yellow to red, and rarely may be purple or nearly black. Plants growing in deep shade tend to be greenish, as do those on *Pinus contorta* subsp. *latifolia*.

Some writers (for example, Kuijt 1955) have questioned whether this taxon is distinct from *A. campylopodum*, the parasite of *Pinus ponderosa* along the Pacific Coast. Some additional features that distinguish these two taxa are summarized in table 23.

Southwestern dwarf mistletoe is particularly damaging to *P. ponderosa* in south central New Mexico (Lincoln National Forest, Mescalero Apache Reservation), central Arizona, and along the Front Range in Colorado. For reasons yet to be explained, the parasite, although common, is not as damaging to *P. ponderosa* in southwestern Colorado or southeastern Utah.

Figure 82.—Distribution of *Arceuthobium vaginatum* subsp. *cryptopodum* in the United States and northern Mexico and the range of *Pinus ponderosa* var. *scopulorum*. Outline map copyrighted by Denoyer-Geppert Co., Chicago (used by permission).

[41] Personal communication, John Churches, U.S. Forest Service, 1956.

TABLE 23.—*Comparison of* Arceuthobium vaginatum *subsp.* cryptopodum *and* A. campylopodum

Characters	*A. vaginatum* subsp. *cryptopodum*	*A. campylopodum*
Shoots:		
Third segment	Ca. 8 mm. long and 3 mm. wide; length/width ratio ca. 2–3	Ca. 11 mm. long and 2 mm. wide; length/width ratio ca. 5–6
Basal diameter	Up to 10 mm.	Under 5 mm.
Color	Usually orange	Olive green to brownish
Fruits	Orange, nonglaucous	Greenish
Meiosis	April	July
Peak flowering time	May–June	August–September
Peak seed dispersal time	Late July–August	September
Seed germination	Late summer or fall of year of dispersal	Spring following year of dispersal

The witches' brooms induced by this taxon (Hawksworth 1961a; see fig. 11A,B,C) are similar on all hosts except *Pinus contorta* subsp. *latifolia*. On this species, witches' brooms are smaller and swellings at the point of infection more pronounced (often two to three times the diameter of healthy parts of the branch) than in *P. ponderosa*.

ARCEUTHOBIUM VAGINATUM SUBSP. DURANGENSE

23c. *Arceuthobium vaginatum* subsp. *durangense* Hawksworth & Wiens, Brittonia 17: 230, 1965. HOLOTYPE: MEXICO: DURANGO: 36 mi. W of El Salto on Route 40, on *Pinus durangensis*, *Hawksworth & Wiens 3507* in 1963 (COLO. Isotypes DS, F, FPF, INIF, MEXU, MO, US).

DESCRIPTION: Mean shoot height ca. 20–30 cm. but up to 50 cm. (fig. 83). Shoots bright orange. Longer shoots becoming pendulous. Basal diameter of dominant shoots 4–8 mm. (mean 6 mm.). Third internode 9–22 mm. (mean 14.9 ± 4.1 mm.) long and 3.5–6 mm. (mean 4.5 mm.) wide (3 collections), length/width ratio 3.3:1. Internodes often slightly swollen at base. Staminate flowers ca. 2.5 mm. long and 2.5 mm. in diameter, segments ca. 1 mm. long and 1 mm. wide. Pollen polar diameter 18–19 (mean 18μ); equatorial diameter 20–21 (mean 21μ); polar/equatorial diameter ratio 1:1.15; spine height 1.5μ about 1.5 times wall thickness—1.0μ (1 collection). Mature fruit ca. 7 mm. long and 3.5 mm. wide, bluish; proximal portion ca. 4 mm. long. Seeds 4×1.5 mm. Time of meiosis unknown, probably February. Anthesis usually in April. Seeds mature from mid-July to September of the year following pollination; maturation period averages 15–18 months. $n =$ unknown.

HOSTS: *Pinus durangensis*, *P. montezumae*, and *P. herrerai*.

DISTRIBUTION: This rare dwarf mistletoe, known only in extreme western Durango and adjacent Sinaloa on the western edge of the escarpment near the crest of the Sierra Madre Occidental on Highway 40 between Durango and Mazatlán (see figs. 78, 79), probably occurs in other areas along the west side of this mountain range. Known elevational range is 5,900 to 8,900 feet. Specimens examined: see appendix, p. 227.

DISCUSSION: Although its distribution is poorly known, this taxon is distinct and readily recognizable. It differs from subsp. *vaginatum* by its bright orange shoot color and from subsp. *cryptopodum* by its larger size, brighter color, branching pattern of the staminate spikes, and geographical distribution.

The branching pattern of the staminate plants on the populations on *Pinus herrerai* in extreme western Durango near the Sinaloa boundary seem to differ slightly from nearby populations on *P. montezumae*. We believe that both populations are the same taxon, but we will need further field studies to confirm this.

ARCEUTHOBIUM VERTICILLIFLORUM

24. *Arceuthobium verticilliflorum* Engelmann, Bot. Calif. 2: 107, 1880. TYPE: MEXICO: DURANGO: Sierra Madre, (on *Pinus sp.?*), *Seemann 2138* in 1852 (MO! Isotype K, ILL). *Razoumofskya verticillata* (Engelm.) Kuntze, Rev. Gen. Pl. 2:587, 1891.

DESCRIPTION: Mean height ca. 7 cm., but up to 11 cm. (fig. 84). Shoots mostly yellowish green to purple, without secondary branching, shoots lightly glaucous when young. Basal diameter of dominant shoots 2.5–5 mm. (mean 3.6 mm.). Third internode 2–7 mm. (mean 3.0 ± 1.2 mm.) long and 2.5–4.5 mm. (mean 3.2 mm.) wide (4 collections), length/width ratio 0.9:1. Staminate flowers 3.5–4.5 mm. (mean 4.0 mm.) in diameter; perianth mostly 4-, sometimes 3-merous; verticillate, with 5–6 flowers per whorl; segments 1.8 mm. long and 1.2 mm. wide. Mean anther diameter 1.0 mm., centered 0.8 mm. from tip of segment. Pollen polar diameter 21–25 (mean 24μ); equatorial diameter 26–30 (mean 28μ); polar/equatorial diameter ratio 1:1.18; spine height (ca. 1.0μ) or ca. ⅔ the wall thickness 1.5μ (2 collections). Mature fruit ca. 15 mm. long and 10 mm. wide. Seeds ca. 11×6 mm., embryos 4×1 mm. Meiosis in September–October. Anthesis usually in March–April. Fruits mature in September and October of the year following pollination; maturation period averages 18–19 months. $n = 14$.

HOSTS: This dwarf mistletoe is known only on *Pinus engelmannii* and *P. cooperi*; *Pinus leiophylla* vars. *leiophylla* and *chihuahuana* and *P. teocote* associated with these infected pines were not parasitized.

DISTRIBUTION: This poorly known species has been collected only west of Durango along the Durango-El Salto highway at elevations between 7,900 and 8,900 feet. The location of Seemann's type collection is uncertain but it is presumably somewhat south of the above area. Specimens examined: see appendix, p. 227.

DISCUSSION: This species, although first described by Engelmann in 1880, had received no serious consideration until we showed that it was indeed a valid, and very distinctive, species (Hawksworth and Wiens 1965). The staminate shoots are characterized by the thick spikes (4–6 mm. in diameter) with verticillate 4-merous flowers, mostly 6 in a whorl; the staminate spikes

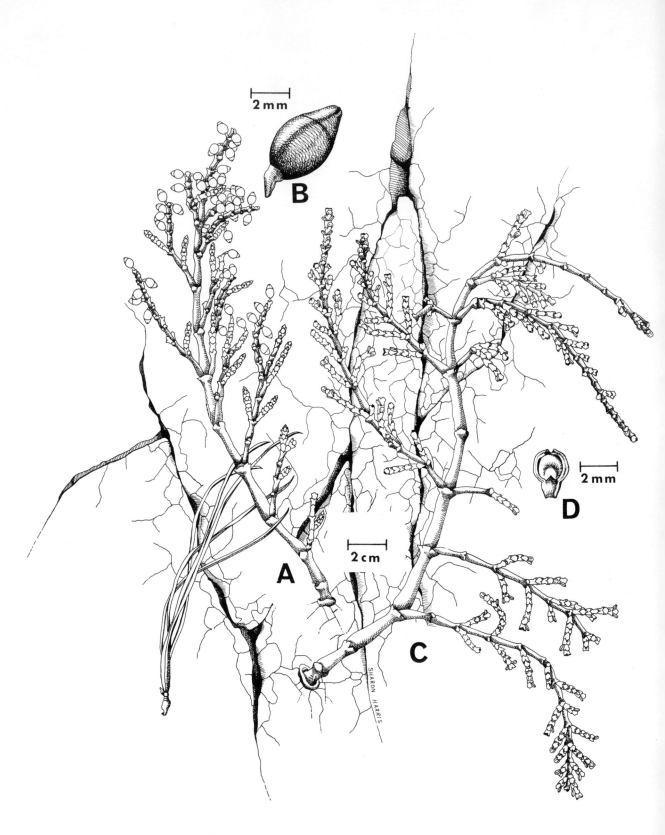

Figure 83.—*Arceuthobium vaginatum* subsp. *durangense* in July: *A*, Pistillate shoot; *B*, Detail of nearly mature fruit; *C*, Staminate shoot; *D*, Detail of staminate floral remnant.

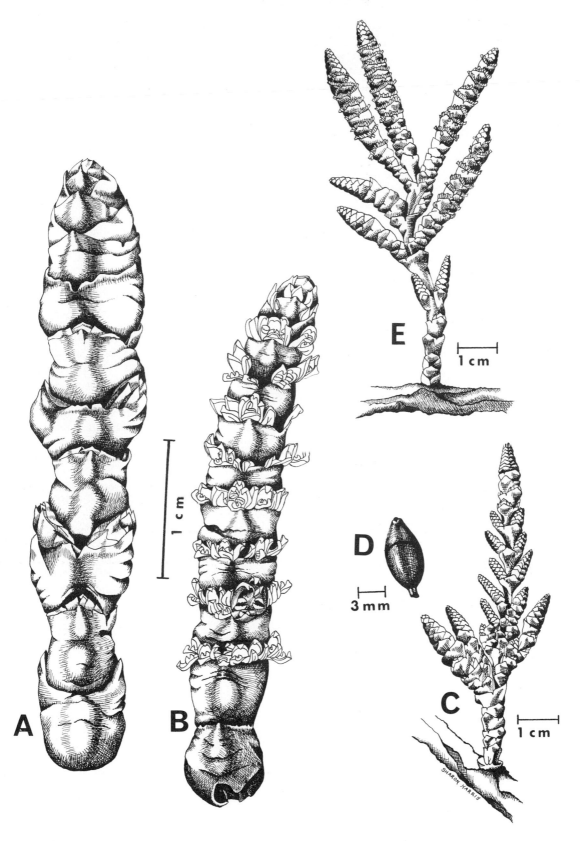

Figure 84.—*Arceuthobium verticilliflorum* in March: *A*, Distal portion of pistillate shoot; *B*, Distal portion of staminate shoot; *C*, Pistillate shoot; *D*, Immature fruit; *E*, Staminate shoot.

are deciduous after flowering. The species has fruits larger than any other dwarf mistletoe. These averaged 3 × 6 mm. in March, 7 × 14 mm. in July, and 10 × 15 mm. in September, when they were nearly mature. A few fruits were expelled in early September, but the peak period of seed dispersal is presumably in October.

In all taxa except this one, the pedicels elongate so that the distal ends of the fruits are oriented downward, and the seeds at maturity are expelled upward. By contrast, an apparently unique feature of *A. verticilliflorum* is that the pedicels do not elongate at maturity and the seeds seem to be expelled more or less at random. This feature, plus apparent evidence of bird feeding, suggests that the taxon may be evolving away from explosive seed dispersal, perhaps in favor of bird dispersal. Other observations that also suggest bird dispersal are the common occurrence of the mistletoe in very open stands and the almost random distribution of infection in tree crowns. All other dwarf mistletoes are concentrated in the lower portions of the tree crowns during the early stages of infection.

Kuijt (1970) concluded that the branching pattern of *A. verticilliflorum* was basically verticillate. This dwarf mistletoe causes massive witches' brooms (see fig. 10A).

Old World Taxa

ARCEUTHOBIUM CHINENSE

25. *Arceuthobium chinense* Lecomte, Notulae Systematicae 3: 170, 1915. TYPE: CHINA: YUNNAN: Bois audessus de Ta pin tze; parasite on *Abies, Delavay* s. n., not dated.

DESCRIPTION: Plants 2–5 cm. high, color of living plants unknown; secondary branching verticillate (Kuijt 1970). Basal diameter of dominant shoots ca. 1.5 mm. Third internode 4–6 mm. (mean 5 mm.) long and 1–1.5 mm. (mean 1.1 mm.) wide (4 collections); length/width ratio 4.4:1. Staminate flowers ca. 2 mm. in diameter, 4-, rarely 3-merous; segments ca. 1 mm. long and 1 mm. wide; perianth segments tapered to tip, widest at base. Pollen polar diameter 14–18 (mean 16μ); equatorial diameter 16–19 (mean 17μ); polar/equatorial diameter ratio 1:1.09; spine height and wall thickness ca. 1.0μ (2 collections). Mature fruit ca. 3–3.5 mm. long and 1.5–2 mm. wide, distal portion ca. 2 mm. long, proximal portion nonglaucous (?). Time of meiosis unknown. Anthesis usually in September but beginning in July in one specimen, fruits mature in September, so fruit maturation period is ca. 11–12 months. n = unknown.

HOSTS AND DISTRIBUTION: On *Abies* and *Keteleeria* in Yunnan and Szechwan Provinces in southwestern China at 8,200 to 13,000 feet in elevation. Handel-Mazzetti (1929) gives the lower elevational range of "*A. chinense*" as 1,600 meters (5,250 feet) but it is uncertain whether this refers to *A. chinense sensu stricto* or *A. pini*. The dwarf mistletoe reported on *Abies pindrow* in India may be this taxon (Rajagopaliengar 1955). Specimens examined: see appendix, p. 227.

DISCUSSION: Information on this very poorly known taxon is available only from a few reports (Anonymous 1939, Danser 1936, Handel-Mazzetti 1929, and Lecomte 1915) but these papers do not distinguish *A. chinense* from the recently described *A. pini*. Some features of these two parasites are compared in table 24.

Type of witches' brooms formed by *A. chinense* has not been reported, but the specimen *Schneider 2951* (at Kew) on *Keteleeria* exhibits a systemic type of parasitism. Handel-Mazzetti (1929) reports a young *Keteleeria* stand in Yunnan Province that was completely killed, presumably by *A. chinense*.

TABLE 24.—*Comparison of* Arceuthobium chinense *and* A. pini

Characters	A. chinense	A. pini
Hosts	*Abies, Keteleeria*	*Pinus tabulaeformis*
Mean plant height	2–5 cm.	10–20 cm.
Shoots:		
Third internode	5 × 1 mm.	12 × 2 mm.
Basal diameter of dominant shoots	Ca. 1.5 mm.	2.5–3 mm.
Staminate flowers:		
Lobes	Mostly 4-merous	Mostly 3-merous
Perianth segments	Rounded; widest near middle	Tapered to tip; widest at base
Peak time of flowering	August–September	May–June

ARCEUTHOBIUM MINUTISSIMUM
HIMALAYAN DWARF MISTLETOE

26. *Arceuthobium minutissimum* J. D. Hooker, Fl. Brit. India 5: 227, 1886. TYPE: KUMAON HIMALAYA, alt. 10,700 feet, on *Pinus griffithii* (as *P. excelsa*), *Duthie* s.n., not dated. *Razoumofskya minutissima* (Hook.) Tubeuf, Naturw. Zeitschr. Forst. u. Landw. 17: 195, 1919.

DESCRIPTION: Plants ca. 5 mm. high, but up to 10 mm. (fig. 85), yellow to yellow green; primary branching multiple from basal cups, but without secondary branching (Kuijt 1970). Basal diameter of dominant shoots ca. 1 mm. Third internode 0.5–1.4 mm. long (mean 0.8 ± 0.3 mm.) and 0.3–1.0 mm. (mean 0.4 mm.) wide (3 collections); length/width ratio 1.5:1. Staminate flowers 2–2.5 mm. in diameter; perianth mostly 4-, sometimes 3-merous; segments ca. 0.8 mm. long and 0.8 mm. wide. Anther diameter ca. 0.5 mm. centered ca. 0.4 mm. from tip of segment. Pollen polar diameter 16–19 (mean 18μ); equatorial diameter 19–21 (mean 21μ); polar/equatorial diameter ratio 1:1.16; spine height about the same as wall thickness—0.8μ (3 collections). Mature fruit 2–2.5 mm. long and 1–1.5 mm. wide. Time of meiosis unknown. Anthesis, reported to be from August to October (Datta 1956), was in September in all flowering specimens that we examined. Seed dispersal also in September, so fruit maturation period averages ca. 12 months. n = unknown.

HOSTS: The only certain host is *Pinus griffithii* (syn. *P. excelsa* Wall., *P. wallichiana* A. B. Jacks), but reported indirectly on *Abies pindrow* in a description of a land shell said to occur in basal cups of *A. minutissimum* on this host in the Simla Hills, East Punjab, India (Rajagopaliengar 1955).

DISTRIBUTION: This dwarf mistletoe is known only from the western Himalayas in West Pakistan, Kashmir, India, and Nepal. Brandis (1907) reports it at elevations of from 8,000 to 11,000 feet. Bagchee (1952) gives its distribution in India as the dry zone of the Himalayas in Upper and Lower Bashahr in Himachal Pradesh, Kulu in East Punjab, and the four divisions of Kashmir. Specimens examined: see appendix, p. 227.

DISCUSSION: Hooker (1886) described *A. minutissimum* as the smallest known dicotyledonous plant. While it does have very small aerial shoots, which average less than 5 mm. high, the plant is much more extensive because of its endophytic system within the host tissues. Thus, it is difficult to compare the size of the mistletoes with that of autotrophic plants.

Whether *A. minutissimum* is dioecious (as are all the other members of the genus) or monecious has not been resolved (Danser 1931, Datta 1951, and Hooker 1886), because intermixed pistillate and staminate shoots frequently occur. This does not mean, however, that this species is monecious. Perhaps mixed infections occur more frequently in *A. minutissimum* than in the North American dwarf mistletoes. Datta (1951) described a single hermaphroditic flower in *A. minutissimum*, and Bhandari and Nanda (1968) discuss the embryology and morphology of this distinctive taxon.

Kuijt (1960b) suggests that fruits of *A. minutissimum*, as in the North American *A. pusillum*, may mature in a single growing season (ca. 5 months). However, the specimens that we have examined and our field studies in Kashmir clearly indicate that peak periods for both anthesis and seed dispersal occur in September; thus, a maturation period of abour 12 months is indicated.

The parasite is a serious pathogen of *P. griffithii*, particularly on the drier sites where it causes severe mortality (Gorrie 1929). *A. minutissimum* induces systemic witches' brooms (Gorrie 1929, Kuijt 1960b; see fig. 14C).

ARCEUTHOBIUM OXYCEDRI
JUNIPER DWARF MISTLETOE

27. *Arceuthobium oxycedri* (DC.) M. Bieb., Flora Taurico-Caucasia III: 629, 1819. TYPE: details of type unknown but Komarov (1936) says that it is in Paris. *Viscum oxycedri* DC., Fl. Fr. 4: 274, 1805. *Razoumofskya caucasica* Hoffman, Hort. Mosqu. (unpaged), 1808. *Razoumofskya oxycedri* (DC.) Schultz, ex Nym. Consp.: 320, 1853. *Viscum caucasicum* Steud. No. ed 1: 888, 1891. *Arceuthobium juniperi* Bubani, Flora Pyrenacea: 131, 1897. *Arceuthobium juniperi-procerae* Chiovenda, Ann. di Botanica (Rome) IX (fasc. 2): 134, 1911. *Arceuthobium juniperorum* Reynier, Bull. Soc. Bot. France 66: 97, 1919. *Arceuthobium oxycedri* (DC.) M. Bieb. var *cupressii* Zefirov, Akad. Nauk SSSR. Bot. Inst. 17: 110, 1955.

DESCRIPTION: Shoots mostly 5–10 cm. high, but up to 20 cm.; yellow green; verticillately branched (Kuijt 1970). Basal shoots 1.5–2 mm. in diameter. Third internode 5–9 mm. long and ca. 1 mm. in diameter; shoots terete; segments often markedly wider at the top than at the base. Staminate flowers 1.5–2.5 mm. in diameter, perianth mostly 3-, but sometimes 2- or 4-merous. Pollen polar diameter 17–19 (mean 18μ), equatorial diameter 19–22 (mean 21μ); polar/equatorial diameter ratio 1:1.17; spine height (1.5μ) slightly greater than wall thickness—1.0μ (2 collections). Mature fruit ca. 3 mm. long and 1.5–2 mm. wide. Anthesis in September and October (Heinricher 1915a). Seed dispersal in autumn (Heinricher 1915a). n = reported to be 13 or 14 (Pisek 1924) but

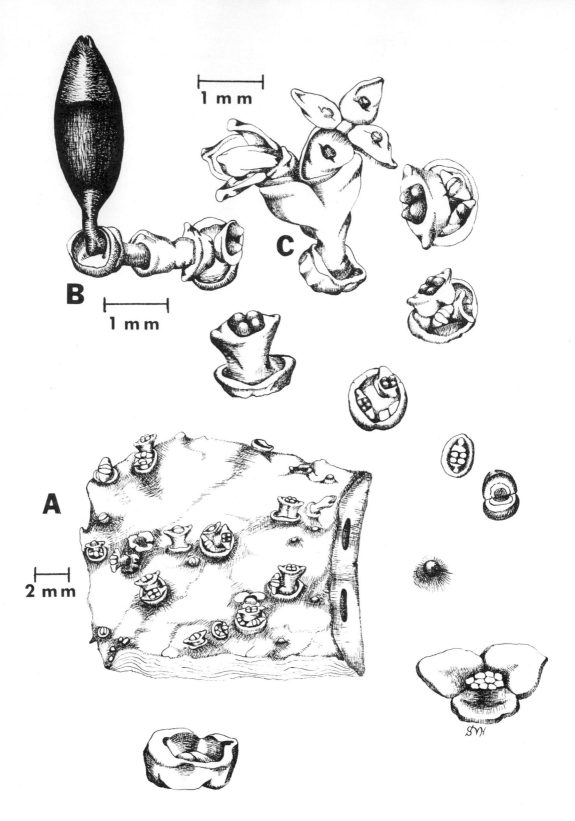

Figure 85.—*Arceuthobium minutissimum* in September: *A*, General habit of shoots on a piece of host bark; *B*, Pistillate shoot; *C*, Staminate shoot with two flowers. Other drawings illustrate various shoot details (same scale as *B* and *C*).

Wiens (1968) suggests that it is probably $n = 14$, as are all North American taxa of the genus counted to date.

HOSTS: Parasitic mainly on *Juniperus oxycedrus*, but also on several other species of *Juniperus* (table 25).

DISTRIBUTION: Described as "very local" (Tutin, Heywood, Burges, and others 1964), *Arceuthobium oxycedri* is the most widely distributed dwarf mistletoe. The most comprehensive accounts of its distribution (Turrill 1920, 1926) give a 6,000-mile range from the Azores, throughout the Mediterranean area of Europe and Africa, Asia Minor, and east to India, in addition to the Aberdare Mountains of Kenya, the only known locality for *Arceuthobium* in the southern hemisphere.

Turrill (1920), and others as noted, have reported *A. oxycedri* from the following countries: EUROPE: Azores, Portugal (Palhinha 1942), Spain, France, Corsica (specimen at US), Italy? (Tutin, Heywood, Burges, and others 1964), Yugoslavia, Hungary, Albania, Greece, Bulgaria, U.S.S.R. (Crimea); AFRICA: Algeria, Ethiopia, Kenya; ASIA: Turkey, Lebanon, Syria, Iran, U.S.S.R. (Armenia, Georgia, Turkmen S.S.R., Tadzhik S.S.R.) (Komarov 1936) and India.

DISCUSSION: The occurrence of *A. oxycedri* over such an extremely wide geographical area suggests that detailed field study may reveal segregates of the species (Wiens 1968). For example, the apparent outlier in east central Africa has been accorded specific rank as *A. juniperi-procerae* (Chiovenda 1911). Also Zefirov (1955), who described a new variety (var. *cupressi*) on an introduced tree (*Cuppressus macrocarpa*), said the variety could be distinguished from the typical form on *Juniperus* by its longer, thinner, greenish shoots. We consider such erection of taxonomic entities based on their occurrence on introduced hosts as spurious.

ARCEUTHOBIUM PINI

28. *Arceuthobium pini* Hawksworth & Wiens, Brittonia 22:267, 1970. HOLOTYPE: CHINA: YUNNAN Prov, E flank of Lichiang Range, Lat. 27° 35′ N, elevation 12,000 feet, on *Pinus*, *Forrest 10169* in 1913 (BM, Isotype K).

DESCRIPTION: Plants 10–22 cm. high, olive to dull green; no secondary branching observed in 5 specimens examined. Basal diameter of dominant shoots 2.5–3 mm. Third internode 5–14 mm. (mean 12) mm. long and 1.5–2.5 (mean 2 mm.) wide (5 collections); length/width ratio 6.2:1. Staminate flowers ca. 2 mm. in diameter; perianth mostly 3-, rarely 4-merous; segments ca. 1 mm. long and 1 mm. wide; perianth segments rounded, widest near the middle. Pollen polar diameter 15–18 (mean 16μ); equatorial diameter 16–18 (mean 18μ); polar/equatorial diameter ratio

TABLE 25.—*Hosts of* Arceuthobium oxycedri

Host	Locality	Reference
Juniperus oxycedrus (including *J. rufescens*)	General	Turrill 1920
J. communis	do.	do.
J. drupacea	do.	do.
J. sabina	do.	do.
J. brevifolia	Azores	do.
J. procera	Kenya	do.
Do.	Eritrea	Chiovenda 1911
J. phoenicia	France	Leveillé 1904
J. macropoda	India	Brandis 1907
J. excelsa	U.S.S.R.	Komarov 1936
J. semiglobosa	do.	do.
J. seravschanica	do.	do.
J. turcomanica	do.	do.
Cupressus macrocarpa	do.	Zefirov 1955
Chamaecyparis thyoides[1]	Inoculations	Heinricher 1930
Thuja orientalis	[2]	Beer 1951

[1] Heinricher (1930) listed this tree as *Chamaecyparis sphaeroides* var. *pendula*, although it is now known as *C. thyoides*. The same tree was erroneously recorded earlier as *Cupressus pendula* (Heinricher 1920).

[2] Transmitted vegetatively to *Thuja orientalis* scions on infected *Juniperus communis* stock.

1:1.13; spine height 1.5μ, wall thickness—ca. 1.0μ (3 collections). Mature fruit ca. 3–3.5 mm. long and ca. 2 mm. wide, distal portion probably glaucous. Time of meiosis unknown. Anthesis usually in April–June, but one specimen collected in July had a few flowers still with pollen. Fruit maturation time not precisely known, but apparently in August or September; fruit maturation period presumably averages ca. 16 months. n = unknown.

HOST: Known only on *Pinus tabulaeformis*.

DISTRIBUTION: This dwarf mistletoe is known only from Yunnan and Szechwan Provinces in Southwestern China and in Tibet. Known elevational range is from 9,000 to 12,000 feet. Handel-Mazzetti (1929) gives the lower altitudinal range range of "*A. chinense*" as 1,600 meters (5,250 feet), but it is not known whether this refers to this species or *A. chinense sensu stricto*. Specimens examined: see appendix, p. 227.

DISCUSSION: Some characteristics that serve to distinguish this little-known taxon from the equally poorly known *A. chinense* were given in table 24.

Nothing has been published on the witches' brooms formed by this dwarf mistletoe. The type specimen (*Forrest 10169*) at Kew has one branch that is systemically infected. This specimen, which was collected in June 1913, is described below:

1913 and 1912 growth:	no shoots
1911 growth:	dwarf mistletoe buds ca. 1 mm. high at proximal and distal ends of segment.
1910 and 1909 growth:	shoot bases throughout segment, shoots broken off.

We do not know whether *A. pini* consistently forms this type of broom. The British Museum specimen of Forrest's same collection and four other specimens examined did not show systemic brooming. Handel-Mazzetti (1929) discusses swellings associated with the parasite on pines, but he does not mention witches' brooms.

Rejected Species

1. *Arceuthobium bonaniae* Grisebach, Cat. Plant. Cuben.: 121, 1866 = *Dendrophthora bonaniae* (Griseb.) Eichler, Flora Brasil. 5 (2): 103, 1868.
2. *Arceuthobium cupressoides* (Macf.) Grisebach, Flora Brit. West Indies: 315, 1864. *Razoumofskya cupressoides* (Macf.) Kuntze, Rev. Gen. 2: 587, 1891 = *Dendrophthora cupressoides* (Macf.) Eichler, Flora Brasil. 5 (2): 103, 1868.
3. *Arceuthobium dacrydii* Ridley, J. Fed. Malay States Mus. 6: 170, 1915 = *Korthalsella dacrydii* (Ridley) Danser, Rec. Trav. Bot. Neer. 31: 759, 1934.
4. *Arceuthobium domingensis* (Spreng.) Grisebach, Cat. Plant. Cuben: 121, 1866 = *Dendrophthora domingensis* (Spreng.) Eichler, Flora Brasil. 5 (2): 103, 1868.
5. *Arceuthobium epiviscum* Grisebach, Mem. Amer. Acad. Arts and Sci. N.S., 8: 192, 1861 = *Dendrophthora epiviscum* (Griseb.) Eichler, Flora Brasil. 5 (2): 103, 1868.
6. *Arceuthobium glauca* Grisebach, Cat. Plant. Cuben.: 121, 1866 = *Dendrophthora glauca* (Griseb.) Eichler, Flora Brasil. 5 (2): 103, 1868.
7. *Arceuthobium gracile* (DC.) Grisebach, Flora Brit. West Indies: 315, 1864 (non Engelmann, Mem. Amer. Acad. Arts. and Sci., N.S., 4 (4): 59, 1849). *Razoumofskya gracilis* (DC.) Kuntze, Rev. Gen. 2: 587, 1891 = *Dendrophthora flagelliformis* (Lam.) Krug & Urban, Ber. Deutsch Bot. Ges. 14: 287, 1896.
8. *Arceuthobium mancinellae* Grisebach, Cat. Plant. Cuben.: 121, 1866 = *Dendrophthora mancinellae* (Griseb.) Eichler, Flora Brasil. 5 (2): 103, 1868.
9. *Arceuthobium opuntioides* (L.) Grisebach, Flora Brit. West Indies: 315, 1864. *Razoumofskya jamaicensis* Hoffman, Hortus Mosquensis (unpaged), 1808. *Razoumofskya opuntioides* (L.) Kuntze, Rev. Gen. 2: 587, 1891 = *Dendrophthora opuntioides* (L.) Eichler, Flora Brasil. 5 (2): 102, 1868.

MAJOR CONCLUSIONS

Some of the major conclusions of this work are:

1. *Arceuthobium* is a well-defined genus of the Viscaceae parasitic on conifers. The genus is probably of early Tertiary origin in Eastern Asia. *Korthalsella*, which occurs from Hawaii throughout the South Pacific area, is probably the closest related genus.

2. *Arceuthobium* presumably migrated to the New World in pre-Miocene times. An intensive adaptive radiation occurred into the Pinaceae of the New World, and this area is now the center of species diversification. Of the 32 taxa recognized in this paper, 28 are in the New World, and 4 in the Old World.

3. Most of the Pinaceae of western North America and Mexico have been colonized by *Arceuthobium*. In the western United States, all the species of *Abies*, *Picea*, *Tsuga*, and *Larix* are parasitized to some degree. In addition, about 80 percent of the *Pinus* and 50 percent of the *Pseudotsuga* species are dwarf mistletoe hosts. The few species that are not known to be parasitized are mostly local endemics.

4. *Arceuthobium* has a base chromosome number of $x = 14$. No hybridization or polyploidy is known in the genus. The absence of hybridization and polyploidy has apparently led to a dendritic pattern of evolution that resulted in clearly demarcated taxa.

5. Although taxa are clearly demarcated, the differences may be cryptic and apparent for only portions of the life cycle. The genus has undergone extreme morphological reduction due to the parasitic habit. Species and subspecies differ only in the number of discontinuous variables. With the possible exception of *A. vaginatum* subsp. *vaginatum* and *cryptopodum*, even subspecies do not intergrade.

6. Most taxa are sympatric with other members of the genus somewhere in their geographic range. In addition, the flowering periods of sympatric species often overlap. If the taxa are compatible, gene exchange should occur, but does not. Even though the differences among taxa are less pronounced than in some autotrophic groups, each should be regarded as a separate species. All dwarf mistletoe taxa are relatively true breeding, so cannot be considered as ecotypes or geographic races.

SUGGESTIONS FOR FURTHER RESEARCH

Research into the host-parasite relationships of the dwarf mistletoes should include investigation of the genetic and physiological basis for host specificity. Studies such as Greenham and Leonard's (1965) on the amino acid components of dwarf mistletoes and their hosts should be continued. Research similar to the study of the ultrastructure of *Arceuthobium pusillum* in compatible and noncompatible hosts (Tainter and French 1969b) should be expanded because it could provide much-needed basic information on the host-parasite relationship.

Attempts to grow dwarf mistletoes *in vitro* (Blakely 1959, Bonga and Chakraborty 1968) should be continued. Studies should be conducted on the comparative evolution of the dwarf mistletoes and their hosts, and crossing experiments between various taxa attempted.

Dwarf mistletoe pollination, pollinators, and effective distances of pollen transport should be experimentally investigated.

Local dispersal of dwarf mistletoes by their explosive fruits has been studied in some detail (Hinds and Hawksworth 1965), but little is known of the long-range dispersal of these plants. Presumably birds are involved, but experimental data are lacking.

Specific areas suggested for study are:

1. Complete chromosome counts for New World species not yet studied (*A. globosum*, *A. guatemalense*, *A. rubrum*), two subspecies of *A. vaginatum*, and all the Old World species. Make comparative karyotype studies of all members of the genus.

2. Study all the Old World species to determine whether they can be ranked into the three stages of evolutionary divergence we propose for the New World species.

3. Conduct detailed field and experimental studies on *Arceuthobium oxycedri* populations throughout its vast range (from the Azores to India to Kenya) to determine whether geographic segregates are discernible.

4. Study the hosts, biology, morphology, and life history of the very poorly known *A. chinense* and *A. pini* in southeastern Asia.

5. Determine by field and morphological studies whether the central Mexican (Durango) and southern Mexican populations (Hidalgo, Veracruz, Oaxaca) of *A. gillii* subsp. *nigrum* are, in fact, the same taxon.

6. Determine whether the marked differences we found between the Guatemalan and central Mexican populations of *A. globosum* are continuous or discontinuous by making field studies in southern Mexico.

7. Determine with certainty the taxonomic status of the dwarf mistletoe on *Pinus herrerai* in Durango, Mexico, which we tentatively classed as *A. vaginatum* subsp. *durangense*.

8. Determine more fully in the field the host and geographical distributions of the Mexican and central American dwarf mistletoes.

9. Determine, particularly in Ontario and Quebec, the northern limits of *Arceuthobium pusillum*.

10. Conduct field and experimental studies to determine the consistency of differences observed in populations of *A. occidentale* on its

three principal hosts: *Pinus sabiniana, P. radiata,* and *P. muricata.*

11. Clarify the status of the dwarf mistletoes on *Pinus monticola* in northern California and southern Oregon, where *Arceuthobium cyano-* *carpum, A. californicum,* and *A. tsugense* all parasitize this tree. We consider some of our identifications to be tentative, until field studies are completed on the parasites on *P. monticola.*

LITERATURE CITED

ANONYMOUS.
1939. Plantae Chinenses Forresterianae. Edinburgh Roy. Bot. Gard. Notes 17: 1–405.

ADAM, DAVID P.
1967. Late-Pleistocene and recent palynology in the central Sierra Nevada, California. *In* Quaternary Paleoecology, E. J. Cushing and H. E. Wright, Eds. p. 275–301. New Haven, Conn.: Yale Univ. Press.

ALSTON, R. E., RÖSLER, H., NAIFEH, K., and MABRY, T. J.
1965. Hybrid components in natural interspecific hybrids. Nat. Acad. Sci. Proc. 54: 1458–1465.

ANDERSON, EDGAR.
1948. Hybridization of the habitat. Evolution 2: 1–9.

——
1951. Concordant versus discordant evolution in relation to introgression. Evolution 5: 133–144.

ANDERSON, RALPH L., and KAUFERT, F. H.
1959. Brooming response of black spruce to dwarfmistletoe infection. Forest Sci. 5: 356–364, illus.

ANDRESEN, J. W.
1966. A. multivariate analysis of the *Pinus chiapensis-monticola-strobus* phylad. Rhodora 68: 1–24, illus.

ANDREWS, STUART R., and DANIELS, JOHN P.
1960. A survey of dwarfmistletoes in Arizona and New Mexico. U.S. Dep. Agr. Forest Serv., Rocky Mt. Forest and Range Exp. Sta., Sta. Pap. 49, 17 p., illus. Ft. Collins, Colo.

AXELROD, DANIEL I.
1966. The Pleistocene Soboba flora of Southern California. Univ. Calif. Pub. Geol. Sci. 60: 1–79, illus.

BAGCHEE, K.
1952. A review of work on Indian tree diseases and decay of timber and methods of control. Indian Forest. 78(11): 540–546.

BAKER, RICHARD G.
1969. Late Quaternary pollen and plant microfossils from abandoned-lagoon sediments near Yellowstone Lake, Wyoming. Ph.D. thesis, Univ. Colo., 114 p., illus.

BARANYAY, J. A.
1962. Phenological observations on western hemlock dwarf mistletoe (*Arceuthobium campylopodum* Gill forma *tsugensis*). Can. Dep. Forest. Entomol. and Pathol. Br., Bimon. Progr. Rep. 18(4): 3–4.

——
1970. Lodgepole pine dwarf mistletoe in Alberta. Can. Dep. Fish. and Forest. Pub. 1286, 22 p., illus.

BARLOW, B. A.
1964. Classification of the Loranthaceae and Viscaceae. Linn. Soc. N. S. W. Proc. 89: 268–272.

—— and WIENS, D.
1971. The cytogeography of the Loranthaceous mistletoes. Taxon 20: 291–312.

BATE-SMITH, E. C.
1962. The phenolic constituents of plants and their taxonomic significance. J. Linn. Soc. (Bot.) 58: 95–173.

BECKMAN, KENT M., and ROTH, LEWIS F.
1968. The influence of temperature on longevity and germination of seed of western dwarf mistletoe. Phytopathology 58: 147–150.

BECKWITH, L. C., and ANDERSON, R. L.
1956. The forest insect and disease situation. Lake States, 1956. U.S. Dep. Agr. Forest Serv., Lake States Forest Exp. Sta., Sta. Pap. 42, 26 p., illus. St. Paul, Minn.

BEER, A.
1951. Die Zwerg-oder Wacholder Mistel (*Arceuthobium*) under ihre künstliche Aufzucht. Garten-Z.: Illus. Flora 74(2): 13–15.

BERNARD, F. J. P.
1957. Notes sur la distribution du faux-gui. Natur. Can. 84 (6/7): 153–155.

BHANDARI, N. N., and NANDA, KANAN.
1968. Studies in the Viscaceae. I. Morphology and embryology of the Indian dwarfmistletoe, *Arceuthobium minutissimum* Hook. f. Phytomorphology 18: 435–450.

BLAKELY, L. M.
1959. Studies on the *in vitro* culture of *Pseudotsuga menziesii* and *Arceuthobium douglasii.* Mont. Acad. Sci. Proc. (1958) 18: 21–25.

BONGA, J. M.
1964. An unusual witches' broom on black spruce caused by eastern dwarf mistletoe. Forest Sci. 10: 77–78, illus.

1969a. Growth potential of seeds and site requirements of eastern dwarfmistletoe. Can. Dep. Fish. and Forest., Bimon. Res. Notes 25: 10–11.

1969b. The morphology and anatomy of holdfasts and branching radicles of *Arceuthobium pusillum* cultured in vitro. Can. J. Bot. 47: 1935–1938, illus.

—— and CHAKRABORTY, C.
1968. In vitro culture of a dwarf mistletoe, *Arceuthobium pusillum*. Can. J. Bot. 46: 161–164, illus.

BOYCE, J. S.
1961. Forest pathology. Ed. 3, 572 p., illus. N. Y.: McGraw-Hill Book Co.

BRANDIS, DIETRICH.
1907. Indian trees. 767 p., illus. London: Constable and Co.

BROWER, A. E.
1960. Dwarf mistletoe in Maine. Maine Field Natur. 16: 35–38, illus.

BROWN, DONALD H.
1970. Recent discoveries extend distribution range of two destructive diseases of limber pine in southeastern Montana. Plant Dis. Rep. 54: 441.

CALIFORNIA FOREST PEST CONTROL ACTION COUNCIL.
1968. Forest pest conditions in California—1967. Calif. Div. Forest., Sacramento, Calif. 24 p., illus.

CASPARY, R.
1872. Schriften der Physicalisch-Oeconomischen Gesellschaft zu Königsberg XIII. (Original not seen, cited from Conwentz, 1886).

CHANEY, R. W., and MASON, H. L.
1930. A Pleistocene flora from Santa Cruz Island, California. Carnegie Inst. Wash., Pub. 415: 1–24, illus.

—— and Mason, H. L.
1933. A Pleistocene flora from the asphalt deposits at Carpinteria, California. Carnegie Inst. Wash., Pub. 415: 45–79, illus.

CHIOVENDA, EMILIO.
1911. Plantae novae vel minus notae e regionae Aethiopica. Ann. di Bot. IX (Fasc. 2): 125–152.

COHEN, LEON I.
1954. The anatomy of the endophytic system of the dwarf mistletoe, *Arceuthobium campylopodum*. Amer. J. Bot. 41: 840–847, illus.

1963. Studies on the ontogeny of the dwarf mistletoes, *Arceuthobium*. II. Homology of the endophytic system. Amer. J. Bot. 50: 409–417, illus.

1968. Development of the staminate flower in the dwarf mistletoe, *Arceuthobium*. Amer. J. Bot. 55: 187–193, illus.

1970. Development of the pistillate flower in the dwarf mistletoes, *Arceuthobium*. Amer. J. Bot. 57: 477–485, illus.

CONWENTZ, H.
1886. Die Angiospermen des Bernsteins. *In* Die Flora des Bernsteins by H. R. Goeppert and A. Menge. v. II, 140 p., illus. Danzig.

COOKE, WM. BRIDGE.
1955. Fungi of Mount Shasta (1936–1951). Sydowia Ann. Mycol. 9: 94–215.

COULTER, JOHN M., and NELSON, AVEN.
1909. New manual of botany of the central Rocky Mountains (vascular plants). 646 p., illus. N. Y.: Amer. Book Co.

CRITCHFIELD, WILLIAM B.
1957. Geographic variation in *Pinus contorta*. Harvard Univ. Maria Moors Cabot Found. Pub. 3, 118 p., illus.

—— and LITTLE, E. L.
1966. Geographic distribution of the pines of the world. U.S. Dep. Agr. Misc. Pub. 991, 97 p.

DANSER, B. H.
1931. The Loranthaceae of the Netherland Indies. Buitenzorg Jard. Bot. Bull. Ser. III, 11(3–4): 233–519.

1936. Miscellaneous notes on Loranthaceae: 9–15. Blumea 2: 34–73, illus.

1937. A revision of the genus *Korthalsella*. Buitenzorg Jard. Bot. Bull. Ser. III, 14: 115–159, illus.

1950. A theory of systematics. Bibl. Biotheor. 4: 113–180.

DARLINGTON, C. D.
1958. The evolution of genetic systems. Ed. 2, 265 p. N. Y.: Basic Books.

DATTA, R. M.
1951. Occurrence of a hermaphrodite flower in *Arceuthobium minutissimum* Hook. f., the smallest known dicotyledonous plant. Nature 167: 203–204, illus.

1956. Flowering time of *Arceuthobium minutissimum* Hook. f. Sci. and Cult. 22: 233.

DAUBENMIRE, R.
  1961. Vegetative indicators of rate of height growth in ponderosa pine. Forest Sci. 7: 24–34.
——— and DAUBENMIRE, JEAN B.
  1968. Forest vegetation of eastern Washington and northern Idaho. Wash. Agr. Exp. Sta. Tech. Bull. 60, 104 p., illus.
DAVIS, P. H., and HEYWOOD, V. H.
  1963. Principles of angiosperm taxonomy. 556 p., illus. Princeton, N.J.: Oliver and Boyd.
DILLON, LAWRENCE S.
  1956. Wisconsin climate and life zones in North America. Science 123: 167–176, illus.
DIXIT, S. N.
  1962. Rank of the subfamilies Loranthoideae and Viscoideae. Bot. Surv. India Bull. 4(1/4): 49–55.
DOBZHANSKY, THEODOSIUS.
  1951. Genetics and the origin of species. 364 p., illus. N.Y.: Columbia Univ. Press.
DOUGLAS, DAVID.
  1914. Journal kept by David Douglas during his travels in North America, 1823–1827. 364 p. N.Y.: Antiq. Press Ltd. (Reprinted 1959).
DOWDING, E. SILVER.
  1931. Floral morphology of *Arceuthobium americanum*. Bot. Gaz. 91: 42–54, illus.
EATON, R. J.
  1931. Peculiar aspects of the New England distribution of *Arceuthobium pusillum*. Rhodora 33: 92–101, illus.
——— and DOW, R.
  1940. New England mistletoe. New Engl. Natur. 9: 1–5, illus.
ELLIOTT, K. R., LAUT, J. G., and BRANDT, N. R.
  1967. Manitoba—Saskatchewan region. Can. Dep. Forest. Annu. Rep. Forest Insect and Dis. Surv. 1966: 75–94.
ENGLER, A., and KRAUSE, K.
  1935. Loranthaceae. *In* A. Engler, Die Natürlichen Pflanzenfamilien. 16b: 98–203, illus. Berlin: Duncker and Humbolt.
ERDTMAN, G.
  1952. Pollen morphology and plant taxonomy. Angiosperms. 539 p., illus. Waltham, Mass.: Chron. Bot.
ESTABROOK, G. F.
  1967. An information theory model for character analysis. Taxon 16: 86–97.
——— and ROGERS, DAVID J.
  1966. A general method of taxonomic description for a computed similarity measure. BioScience 16: 789–793, illus.

ETHERIDGE, D. E.
  1968. Preliminary observations on the pathology of *Pinus caribaea* Morelet in British Honduras. Commw. Forest. Rev. 47: 72–80, illus.
FERNALD, M. L.
  1950. Gray's manual of botany. Ed. 8, 1632 p., illus. N.Y.: Amer. Book Co.
FORBES, R. S., UNDERWOOD, G. R., and VAN SICKLE, G. A.
  1968. Maritimes region. Can. Dep. Forest. and Rural Develop. Annu. Rep. Forest Insect and Dis. Surv. 1967: 17–33.
FOWELLS, H. A.
  1965. Silvics of forest trees of the United States. U.S. Dep. Agr., Agr. Handb. 271, 762 p., illus.
GILL, L. S.
  1935. *Arceuthobium* in the United States. Conn. Acad. Arts and Sci. Trans. 32: 111–245, illus.
——— and HAWKSWORTH, FRANK G.
  1961. The mistletoes. A literature review. U.S. Dep. Agr. Tech. Bull. 1242, 87 p.
GORDON, ALAN G.
  1968. Ecology of *Picea chihuahuana* Martínez. Ecology 49: 880–896, illus.
GORRIE, R. MACLAGAN.
  1929. A destructive parasite of the Himalayan blue pine. Indian Forest. 35: 613–617, illus.
GRAHAM, DONALD P.
  1959a. A new host for the larch dwarfmistletoe. Plant Dis. Rep. 43: 594.
———
  1959b. Dwarfmistletoe survey in Coeur d' Alene National Forest. U.S. Dep. Agr. Forest Serv., Intermt. Forest and Range Exp. Sta., Res. Note 68, 5 p., illus. Ogden, Utah.
———
  1959c. Dwarfmistletoe survey in Kootenai National Forest. U.S. Dep. Agr. Forest Serv., Intermt. Forest and Range Exp. Sta., Res. Note 67, 5 p., illus. Ogden, Utah.
——— and FRAZIER, WILLIAM E.
  1962. Dwarfmistletoe survey in northeastern Washington. U.S. Dep. Agr. Forest Serv., Intermt. Forest and Range Exp. Sta., Res. Note 103, 8 p., illus. Ogden, Utah.
——— and LEAPHART, CHARLES D.
  1961. Larch and lodgepole pine dwarfmistletoes attack Scotch pine. J. Forest. 59: 375–376, illus.

GRAY, A.
  1850. Plantae Lindheimerianae, Part II. Boston J. Natur. Hist. 6: 141–240.

GRAZIANO, M. N., WIDMER, G. A., JULIANI, R., and COUSSIO, J. D.
  1967. Flavonoids from the Argentine mistletoe *Psittacanthus cuneifolius*. Phytochemistry 6: 1709–1711.

GREENHAM, C. G., and LEONARD, O. A.
  1965. The amino acids of some mistletoes and their hosts. Amer. J. Bot. 52: 41–47.

HANDEL-MAZETTI, H.
  1929. Symbolae Sinicacae. Botanische Ergebnisse der Expedition der Akademie der Wissenschaften in Wien nach Südwest—China 1914/18. Vol. II. Anthophyta. Vienna: Julius Springer.

HAWKSWORTH, FRANK G.
  1954. Observations on the age of lodgepole pine tissues susceptible to infection by *Arceuthobium americanum*. Phytopathology 44: 552, illus.

———
  1956a. Notes on the host relationships of *Arceuthobium americanum* and *A. vaginatum* f. *cryptopodum*. Plant Dis. Rep. 40: 252.

———
  1956b. Upper altitudinal limits of dwarfmistletoe on lodgepole pine in the central Rocky Mountains. Phytopathology 46: 561–562.

———
  1958. Rate of spread and intensification of dwarfmistletoe in young lodgepole pine stands. J. Forest. 56: 404–407, illus.

———
  1961a. Dwarfmistletoe of ponderosa pine in the Southwest. U.S. Dep. Agr. Tech. Bull. 1246, 112 p., illus.

———
  1961b. Abnormal fruits and seeds in *Arceuthobium*. Madroño 16: 96–101, illus.

———
  1965a. Notes on *Arceuthobium* on bristlecone pine. Leafl. West. Bot. 10: 163–164.

———
  1965b. Life tables for two species of dwarfmistletoe. I. Seed dispersal, interception, and movement. Forest Sci. 11: 142–151, illus.

———
  1967. Distribution of ponderosa pine dwarf mistletoe on the South Rim of Grand Canyon, Arizona. Plant Dis. Rep. 51: 1049–1051, illus.

———
  1968. Lodgepole pine dwarf mistletoe on ponderosa pine. Plant Dis. Rep. 52: 125–127, illus.

———, ESTABROOK, G. F., and ROGERS, D. J.
  1968. Application of an information theory model for character analysis in the genus *Arceuthobium* (Viscaceae). Taxon 17: 605–619, illus.

——— and GRAHAM, D. P.
  1963. Dwarfmistletoes on spruce in the Western United States. Northwest Sci. 37: 31–38, illus.

———, LIGHTLE, PAUL C., and SCHARPF, ROBERT F.
  1968. *Arceuthobium* in Baja California, Mexico. Southwest. Natur. 13: 101–102.

——— and PETERSON, R. S.
  1959. Notes on the hosts of three pine dwarf-mistletoes in northern Colorado. Plant Dis. Rep. 43: 109–110, illus.

——— and WIENS, DELBERT.
  1964. A new species of *Arceuthobium* from Arizona. Brittonia 16: 54–57, illus.

——— and WIENS, DELBERT.
  1965. *Arceuthobium* in Mexico. Brittonia 17: 213–238, illus.

———, WIENS, DELBERT, and GRAHAM, DONALD P.
  1967. Dwarfmistletoe on Brewer spruce in Oregon. Northwest Sci. 41: 42–44, illus.

——— and WIENS, D.
  1970a. Biology and taxonomy of the dwarf mistletoes. Annu. Rev. Phytopathol. 8: 187–208.

——— and WIENS, D.
  1970b. New taxa and nomenclatural changes in *Arceuthobium* (Viscaceae). Brittonia 22: 265–268.

HEDGCOCK, GEORGE G.
  1915. Notes on some diseases of trees in our National Forests. V. Phytopathology 5: 175–181.

——— and HUNT, N. REX.
  1917. Notes on *Razoumofskya campylopoda*. Phytopathology 7: 315–316.

HEIL, H.
  1923. Die Bedeutung des Haustoriums von *Arceuthobium*. Centralbl. f. Bakt., Abt. II. 59: 26–55, illus.

HEINRICHER, E.
  1915a. Uber Bau und Biologie der Bluten von *Arceuthobium oxycedri* (DC.) M.B. Akad. Wiss. Wien, Math.-natur. Kl. Sitzungsber. Abt. I. 124: 481–504, illus.

1915b. Beiträge zur Biologie der Zwergmistel, *Arceuthobium oxycedri*, besonders zur Kenntnis des anatomischen Baues under der Mechanik ihrer explosiven Beeren. Akad. Wiss. Wien, Math.-natur. Kl. Sitzungsber. Abt. I. 124: 1–50, illus.

1920. *Arceuthobium oxycedri* (DC.) M. Bieb. auf *Cupressus*. Ber. Deut. Bot. Ges. 38: 220–223.

1924. Das Absorptionssystem der Wacholdermistel (*Arceuthobium oxycedri* [DC.] M.B.) mit besonderer Berücksichtigung seiner Entwicklung under Leistung. Akad. Wiss. Wien, Math.-natur. Kl. Sitzungsber. Abt. I. 132: 143–194.

1930. Ueber *Arceuthobium oxycedri* (DC.) M. Bieb. auf *Chamaecyparis sphaeroides* Spach. *pendula* Hort. und Einer Hexenbesen, der Durch den Einfluss des Arceuthobiums auf Dieser Cupressinee Entstand. Planta 10: 374–380.

HINDS, T. E., HAWKSWORTH, F. G., and McGINNIES, W. J.
1963. Seed discharge in *Arceuthobium*. A photographic study. Science 140: 1236–1238, illus.

―――― and HAWKSWORTH, F. G.
1965. Seed dispersal velocity in four dwarf-mistletoes. Science 148: 517–519, illus.

HITCHCOCK, C. L., and CRONQUIST, A.
1964. Vascular plants of the Pacific Northwest. Part 2, 597 p., illus. Seattle: Univ. Wash. Press.

HOFFMAN, G. F.
1808. Enumeratio plantarum et seminum hort botanici mosquensis. 8 p. Moscow.

HOOKER, J. D.
1886. The flora of British India. v. 5, 203–228. London: L. Reeve and Company.

HOOKER, W. J.
1840. Flora Boreali-Americana. v. 1, 277–278, illus. London.

HORD, H. H. V., and QUIRKE, D. A.
1956. Province of Ontario, forest disease survey. Can. Div. Forest Biol., Forest Insect and Dis. Surv., Annu. Rep. 1955: 56–69.

HOUSE, H. D.
1935. Dwarf mistletoe on white pine. Rhodora 37: 268.

HOWELL, J. T.
1966. *Viscum album* in California. Leafl. West. Bot. 10: 244.

HULTÉN, ERIC.
1968. Flora of Alaska and neighboring territories. 1008 p., illus. Stanford, Calif.: Stanford Univ. Press.

HUNT, D. R.
1962. Some notes on the pines of British Honduras. Empire Forest. Rev. 41: 134–145, illus.

IRWIN, H. S., and ROGERS, D. J.
1967. Monographic studies in *Cassia* (Leguminosae-Caesalpinoideae). II. A taximetric study of section *Apoucouita*. N.Y. Bot. Gard. Mem. 16: 71–118, illus.

JANSSEN, C. R.
1968. Myrtle Lake: A late- and post-glacial pollen diagram from northern Minnesota. Can. J. Bot. 46: 1397–1408, illus.

JEPSON, W. L.
1925. A manual of the flowering plants of California. 1238 p., illus. Berkeley: Univ. Calif.

JONES, B. L., and GORDON, C. C.
1965. Embryology and development of the endosperm haustorium of *Arceuthobium douglasii*. Amer. J. Bot. 52: 127–132, illus.

KHANNA, S. K., VISWANATHAN, P. N., TEWARI, C. P., and OTHERS
1968. Biochemical aspects of parasitism by the angiosperm parasities: Phenolics in parasites and hosts. Physiol. Plant. 21: 949–959.

KLIEJUNAS, JOHN T.
1969. *Arceuthobium pusillum* on eastern larch in Wisconsin. Plant Dis. Rep. 53: 76.

KOMAROV, V. L.
1936. Flora of the U.S.S.R. v. 4: 108–111 Moscow and Leningrad.

KORSTIAN, C. F., and LONG, W. H.
1922. The western yellow pine mistletoe: Effect on growth and suggestions for control. U.S. Dep. Agr. Bull. 1112, 35 p., illus.

KROTKOV, P. V.
1940. Botanical explorations in the Bruce Peninsula. Roy. Can. Inst. Trans. 23 (Pt. 1): 3–65.

KRUTZSCH, W. VON.
1962. Stratigraphisch bzw. botanisch wichtige neue Sporen und Pollenformen aus dem deutschen Tertiär. Geologie 11: 265–319, illus.

KUANG-FANG, TS'ENG, and CHUNG-LIANG, CH'EN.
1957. The flavonoids in Chinese drugs. IV. Chinese mistletoe. The isolation of a flavone arabinoside from Kwang-Chi-Sheng (*Loranthus parasiticus*). Yao Hsüeh Pao 5: 317–325. (Chem. Abstr. 55, 24734, 1961).

———— and SHIH-CHUEH, LI.
    1957. Chinese mistletoe. I. The chemical constituents of *Viscum album* subspecies *coloratum.* Yao Hsüeh Pao 5: 169–177. (Chem. Abstr. 56, 10587, 1962).

KUIJT, JOB.
    1953. Dwarf mistletoe on ponderosa pine in British Columbia. Can. Dep. Agr. Div. Forest Biol., Bimon. Progr. Rep. 9(5): 4.

————
    1954. Some notes on the larch mistletoe in British Columbia. Can. Dep. Agr. Div. Forest Biol., Bimon. Progr. Rep. 10(6): 2.

————
    1955. Dwarf mistletoes. Bot. Rev. 21: 569–627, illus.

————
    1956. A new record of dwarf mistletoe on lodgepole and western white pine. Madroño 13: 170–172, illus.

————
    1960a. The distribution of dwarf mistletoes, *Arceuthobium,* in California. Madroño 15: 129–139, illus.

————
    1960b. Morphological aspects of parasitism in the dwarf mistletoes (*Arceuthobium*). Univ. Calif. Pub. Bot. 30: 337–436, illus.

————
    1963. Distribution of dwarf mistletoes and their fungus hyperparasites in western Canada. Nat. Mus. Can. Bull. 186: 134–148, illus.

————
    1964. A peculiar case of hemlock mistletoe parasitic on larch. Madroño 17: 254–256.

————
    1969. The biology of parasitic flowering plants. 246 p., illus. Berkeley: Univ. Calif. Press.

————
    1970. A systematic study of branching patterns in dwarf mistletoe (*Arceuthobium*). Torrey Bot. Club Mem. 22(4): 1–38, illus.

LANJOU, J., and STAFLEU, F. A.
    1964. Index herbariorum. I. The herbaria of the World. Regnum Veg. 31: 1–251.

LARSEN, M. J., and GROSS, H. L.
    1970. *Arceuthobium americanum* in Ontario. Can. Dep. Fish. and Forest. Bimon. Res. Notes 26: 40–41, illus.

LAURENT, T. H.
    1966. Dwarfmistletoe on Sitka spruce—a new host record. Plant Dis. Rep. 50: 921.

LAUT, JOHN G.
    1967. Eastern dwarf mistletoe on jack pine in Manitoba. Plant Dis. Rep. 51: 899–900.

LECOMTE, H.
    1915. Loranthacées d' Chine et d' Indo-Chine. Notulae Syst. 3: 165–176.

LEONARD, O. A., and HULL, R. J.
    1965. Translocation relationships in and between mistletoes and their hosts. Hilgardia 37: 115–153, illus.

LEOPOLD, ESTELLA B.
    1967. Late-Cenozoic patterns of plant extinction. *In* Pleistocene extinctions, the search for a cause. P. S. Martin and H. E. Wright, Eds. p. 203–246, illus. New Haven, Conn.: Yale Univ. Press.

LEVEILLÉ, H.
    1904. Dispersion de l' *Arceuthobium* en France. Acad. Int. Geogr. Bot. Bull. 13: 88.

LINSDALE, MARY ANN, HOWELL, J. T., and LINSDALE, JEAN M.
    1952. Plants of the Toiyabe Mountains area, Nevada. Wasmann J. Biol. 10: 129–200, illus.

LITTLE, ELBERT L., JR.
    1953. Check list of native and naturalized trees of the United States (including Alaska). U.S. Dep. Agr., Agr. Handb. 41, 472 p.

————
    1966. A new pinyon variety from Texas. Wrightia 3: 181–187.

McANDREWS, J. H.
    1966. Postglacial history of prairie, savanna, and forest in northwestern Minnesota. Torrey Bot. Club. Mem. 22(2): 1–72, illus.

MADRIGAL SÁNCHEZ, XAVIER.
    1967. Contribución al conocimiento de la ecologia de los bosques de oyamel (*Abies religiosa* (H.B.K.) Schl. et Cham.) en el Valle de Mexico. Inst. Nac. de Invest. Forest. Mex. Tech. Bol. 18, 94 p., illus.

MARIE-VICTORIN, FRERE.
    1943. Les hautes pinèdes d' Haiti. Natur. Can. 70: 245–258, illus.

MARSCHALL VON BIEBERSTEIN, F. A.
    1819. Flora taurico-caucasica exhibens stirpes phaerogamas, in Chersoneso taurica et regionibus caucasicis sponte crescentes. v. 3: 654 p.

MARTIN, G. H.
    1926. Diseases of forest and shade trees, ornamental and miscellaneous plants in the United States in 1925. Plant Dis. Rep. Suppl. 50: 413–478.

MARTÍNEZ, MAXIMINO.
    1948. Los pinos Mexicanos. Ed. 2., 361 p., illus. Mexico City: Univ. Nac. Autónoma de Mex.

———— 1963. Las Pináceas Mexicanas. Ed. 3, 401 p., illus. Mexico City: Univ. Nac. Autónoma de Mex.

MASON, H. L.
1934. Contributions to Paleontology. IV. Pleistocene flora of the Tomales formation. Carnegie Inst. Wash., Pub. 415: 81–179, illus.

MILLER, DOUGLAS R., and BYNUM, H. H.
1965. Dwarfmistletoe found on foxtail pine in California. Plant Dis. Rep. 49: 647–648, illus.

MIROV, N. T.
1967. The genus *Pinus*. 602 p., illus. N.Y.: Ronald Press.

MOLNAR, A. C., HARRIS, J. W. E., ROSS, D. A., and GINNS, J. H.
1968. British Columbia region. Can. Dep. Forest. and Rural Develop. Annu. Rep. Forest Insect and Dis. Surv. 1967: 108–124.

MUIR, JOHN A.
1968. Biology of dwarf mistletoe (*Arceuthobium americanum*) in Alberta. Can. Dep. Fish. and Forest., Calgary, Alberta. Inter. Rep. A-15, 29 p., illus.

MUNZ, P. A.
1935. A manual of Southern California botany. 642 p., illus. Claremont, Calif.: Claremont Coll.

———— and KECK, D. D.
1959. A California flora. 1681 p. Berkeley: Univ. Calif. Press.

NASH, R. W.
1955. Dwarf or false mistletoe (*Arceuthobium pusillum* Peck.) Maine Forest. Comm. Bien. Rep. 30(1953–1954): 126–127.

NELSON, A.
1913. Contributions from the Rocky Mountain herbarium XIII. Bot. Gaz. 56: 63–71.

OFFORD, HAROLD R.
1964a. Diseases of Monterey pine in native stands of California and in plantations in western North America. U.S. Forest Serv. Res. Pap. PSW-14, 37 p., illus. Pacific Southwest Forest and Range Exp. Sta., Berkeley, Calif.

———— 1964b. A new record of dwarfmistletoe on planted Monterey pine in California. Plant Dis. Rep. 48: 912.

PALHINHA, R. T.
1942. Algumas consideracões sobre a distribuicão geografica e a ecologia do *Arceuthobium oxycedri* (DC.) Marsh.-Bieb. Soc. Broteriana Bol. 16: 2A Ser.: 137–143.

PARMETER, J. R., Jr., and COBB, F. W., Jr.
1967. Inoculation of Monterey pine with dwarf mistletoe from bishop pine. Plant Dis. Rep. 51: 856.

———— and SCHARPF, R. F.
1963. Dwarfmistletoe on red fir and white fir in California. J. Forest. 61: 371–374, illus.

PECK, C. H.
1872. Report of the second class, in the second department. (Botany). Albany Inst. Transl. 7: 186–204.

PEIRCE, GEORGE J.
1905. The dissemination and germination of *Arceuthobium occidentale* Eng. Ann. Bot. 19: 99–113, illus.

PIPER, C. V.
1906. Flora of the State of Washington. U.S. Nat. Herb. Contrib. 11: 222–223, illus.

PISEK, A.
1924. Antherenentwichlung und meiotische Teilung bei der Wacholdermistel (*Arceuthobium oxycedri* (DC.) M.B.); Antherenbau und Chromosomenzahlen von *Loranthus europaeus* Jacq. Akad. Wiss. Wien, Math.-natur. Kl. Sitzungsber. Abt. I. 133: 1–15, illus.

POMERLEAU, RENÉ.
1942. Le gui de l' epinette noire dans le Quebec. Natur. Can. 69: 11–31, illus.

POTTER, LOREN D., and ROWLEY, JOANNE.
1960. Pollen rain and vegetation, San Augustin Plains, New Mexico. Bot. Gaz. 122: 1–25, illus.

POWELL, J. M.
1968. Natural infection of Scots pine by lodgepole pine dwarf mistletoe in Canada. Plant Dis. Rep. 52: 409–410.

RAJAGOPALIENGAR, A. S.
1955. On a new species of land shells of the genus *Kaliella* Branford from the Simla Hills (Mollusca, Gastropoda; family Zonitidae). Rec. Indian Mus. 51(1): 19–22.

ROGERS, D. J., and APPAN, S. G.
1969. Taximetric methods for delimiting biological species. Taxon 18: 609–624.

———— and FLEMING, H. S.
1964. A computer program for classifying plants. II. A numerical handling of nonnumerical data. BioScience 14: 15–28.

————, FLEMING, HENRY S., and ESTABROOK, GEORGE
1967. Use of computers in studies of taxonomy and evolution. *In* Evolutionary Biology, T. Dobzhansky, M. K. Hecht, and W. C. Steere, Eds. 169–196. N.Y.: Meridith Pub. Co.

Roth, Lewis F.
  1959. Natural emplacement of dwarfmistletoe seed on ponderosa pine. Forest Sci. 5: 365–369, illus.

———

  1966. Foliar habit of ponderosa pine as a heritable basis for resistance to dwarf mistletoe. *In* Breeding Pest-Resistant Trees, H. D. Gerhold and others, Eds. 221–228, illus. Oxford: Pergamon Press.

———

  1967. Resistance of ponderosa pine to dwarf mistletoe. Phytopathology 57: 1008 (Abstr.).

Scharpf, Robert F.
  1965. Flowering and seed dispersal of dwarfmistletoe (*Arceuthobium campylopodum*) in California. U.S. Forest Serv. Res. Note PSW-68, 6 p., illus. Pacific Southwest Forest and Range Exp. Sta., Berkeley, Calif.

———

  1969a. Temperature affects penetration and infection of pines by dwarf mistletoe. Forest Sci. 15: 149–151.

———

  1969b. Dwarf mistletoe on red fir—infection and control in understory stands. USDA Forest Serv. Res. Pap. PSW-50, 8 p., illus. Pacific Southwest Forest and Range Exp. Sta., Berkeley, Calif.

———

  1969c. *Cytospora abietis* associated with dwarf mistletoe on true firs in California. Phytopathology 59: 1657–1658.

——— and Hawksworth, F. G.
  1968. Dwarf mistletoe on sugar pine. U.S. Dep. Agr. Forest Pest Leafl. 113, 4 p., illus.

——— and Parmeter, J. R., Jr.
  1962. The collection, storage, and germination of seeds of a dwarfmistletoe. J. Forest. 60: 551–552, illus.

——— and Parmeter, J. R., Jr.
  1967. The biology and pathology of dwarfmistletoe, *Arceuthobium campylopodum* f. *abietinum*, parasitizing true firs (*Abies* spp.) in California. U.S. Dep. Agr. Tech. Bull. 1362, 42 p., illus.

Scheffer, T. C., and Hedgcock, G. G.
  1955. Injury to northwestern forest trees by sulfur dioxide from smelters. U.S. Dep. Agr. Tech. Bull. 1117, 49 p., illus.

Schrenk, H. von.
  1900. Notes on *Arceuthobium pusillum*. Rhodora 2: 2–5, illus.

Shea, K. R., and Howard, Benton.
  1969. Dwarf mistletoe control: A program for research and development in the West. West. Forest Pest Conditions [San Francisco, Calif., 1968] Proc. p. 25–32. West. Forest. and Conserv. Ass., Portland, Oreg.

Sippell, W. L., Rose, A. H., and Larsen, M. J.
  1968. Ontario region. Can. Dep. Forest. and Rural Develop. Annu. Rep. Forest Insect and Dis. Surv. 1967: 51–75.

Smith, R. B.
  1965. Some results of artificial inoculation with western hemlock dwarf mistletoe seed. Can. Dep. Forest., Bimon. Progr. Rep. 21(6): 3–4.

———

  1966a. Hemlock and larch dwarf mistletoe seed dispersal. Forest. Chron. 42: 395–401, illus.

———

  1966b. Time of germination of hemlock dwarf mistletoe seeds. Can. Dep. Forest., Bimon. Progr. Rep. 22(5): 5–6.

———

  1969. Assessing dwarf mistletoe on western hemlock. Forest Sci. 15: 277–285, illus.

———

  1970a. Infection of western larch by hemlock dwarf mistletoe. Can. Dep. Fish. and Forest. Bimon. Res. Notes 26: 16–17.

———

  1970b. Infection of Engelmann spruce by hemlock dwarf mistletoe. Can. Dep. Fish. and Forest. Bimon. Res. Notes 26: 14.

——— and Craig. H. M.
  1968. Infection of Scots, Monterey and ponderosa pines by western hemlock dwarf mistletoe. Can. Dep. Forest. and Rural Develop., Bimon. Res. Notes 24: 10–11.

Sokal, Robert R., and Sneath, Peter H. A.
  1963. Principles of numerical taxonomy. 359 p., illus. San Francisco: W. H. Freeman Co.

Strivastava, L. M., and Esau, K.
  1961. Relation of dwarfmistletoe (*Arceuthobium*) to the xylem tissue of conifers. I. Anatomy of parasite sinkers and their connection with host xylem. Amer. J. Bot. 48: 159–167, illus.

Standley, Paul C., and Steyermark, Julian A.
  1946. A flora of Guatemala. Chicago Natur. Hist. Mus. Fieldiana: Bot. 24, part IV, 433 p., illus.

Stebbins, G. L.
  1950. Variation and evolution in plants. 643 p. N.Y.: Columbia Univ. Press.

STEVENS, ROBERT E., and HAWKSWORTH, FRANK G.
1970. Insects and mites associated with dwarf mistletoes. USDA Forest Serv. Res. Pap. RM–59, 12 p., illus. Rocky Mt. Forest and Range Exp. Sta., Ft. Collins, Colo.

STUCHLIK, LEON.
1964. Pollen analysis of the Miocene deposits at Rypin (N.W. of Warsaw). Acta Palaeobot. 5(2): 1–111, illus.

TAINTER, F. H.
1968. The embryology of *Arceuthobium pusillum*. Can. J. Bot. 46: 1473–1476, illus.

——— and FRENCH, D. W.
1967. Dwarfmistletoe on eastern larch in Minnesota. Plant Dis. Rep. 51: 481, illus.

——— and FRENCH, D. W.
1968. Further observations of dwarf mistletoe on eastern larch in Minnesota. Phytopathology 58: 880–881.

——— and FRENCH, D. W.
1969a. Dwarf mistletoe parasite in spruce. Minn. Acad. Sci. J. 35: 122-123, illus.

——— and FRENCH, D. W.
1969b. The ultrastructure of *Arceuthobium pusillum* in a compatible and noncompatible host. Phytopathology 59: 1052 (Abstr.).

THODAY, D., and JOHNSON, EMMA TREVOR.
1930. On *Arceuthobium pusillum* Peck. I. The endophytic system. Ann. Bot. 44: 393–413, illus.

THOMAS, R. W.
1954. Dwarf mistletoe on spruce. Can Dep. Agr. Div. Forest Biol., Bimon. Progr. Rep. 10(1): 3.

THORNE, ROBERT F.
1968. Synopsis of a putatively phylogenetic classification of the flowering plants. Aliso 6: 57–66.

TIEGHEM, P. VAN.
1895. Sur le genre *Arceuthobium* considéré comme type dúne tribu distinct dans la famille de Loranthacées. Soc. Bot. France Bull. 42: 625–631.

TUBEUF, C. VON.
1919. Uberblick über die Arten der Gattung *Arceuthobium* (*Razoumowskia*) mit besonderer Berücksichtigung ihrer Biologie und praktischen Bedeutung. Naturwiss. Z. Forst-u. Landwirt. (Stuttgart) 17: 167–273, illus.

TURRILL, W. B.
1920. *Arceuthobium oxycedri* and its distribution. Kew Bull. Misc. Inform. 8: 264–268.

———
1926. The Loranthaceae of the Balkan Peninsula. Kew Bull. 1926: 376–379.

TUTIN, T. G., HEYWOOD, V. H., BURGES, N. A., and OTHERS.
1964. Flora Europaea, vol. I. 464 p., illus. Cambridge, England: Cambridge Univ. Press.

U.S. DEPARTMENT OF AGRICULTURE.
1960. Index of plant diseases in the United States. U.S. Dep. Agr., Agr. Handb. 165, 531 p.

———
1962. 1961 Annual Report. U.S. Dep. Agr. Forest Serv., Intermt. Forest and Range Exp. Sta., 46 p., illus. Ogden, Utah.

———
1963. 1962 Annual Report. U.S. Dep. Agr. Forest Serv., Intermt. Forest and Range Exp. Sta., 55 p., illus. Ogden, Utah.

VALDIVIA SÁNCHEZ, JOSÉ DE JESUS.
1964. Patología Forestal. I. El muérdago enano (*Arceuthobium* sp.) en los bosques de la zona noreste de Michoacán. Com. Forest. Michoacán Bol. 15, 67 p., illus.

VASEK, F. C.
1966. The distribution and taxonomy of three western junipers. Brittonia 18: 350–372.

WAGENER, WILLIS W.
1962. Dwarfmistletoe incubation period on ponderosa and Jeffrey pines in California. Forest Sci. 8: 16–20, illus.

———
1965. Dwarfmistletoe removal and reinvasion in Jeffrey and ponderosa pine, northeastern California. U.S. Forest Serv. Res. Note PSW-73, 8 p. Pacific Southwest Forest and Range Exp. Sta., Berkeley, Calif.

WAHRHAFTIG, C., WOLFE, J. A., LEOPOLD, ESTELLA B., and LANDPHERE, M. A.
1969. The coal-bearing group in the Nenana coal field, Alaska. U.S. Geol. Surv. Bull. 1274–D, 30 p.

WALLDEN, BERTIL.
1961. Misteln vid dess nordgräns [The mistletoe at its northern limit]. Svensk Bot. Tidskr. 55(3): 427–549.

WATSON, SERENO.
1880. Botany of California. II. *Apetalae, Gymnospermae* Monocotyledonous or endogenous plants, Cryptogamous plants. 105–107. Cambridge, Mass.: Welch, Bigelow and Co.

WATTS, W. A.
1970. The full-glacial vegetation of northwestern Georgia. Ecology 51: 17–33, illus.

WEBER, WILLIAM A.
1965. Plant geography in the southern Rocky Mountains. *In* The Quaternary of the United States, H. E. Wright and D. G. Frey, Eds. 453–468. Princeton, N.J., Princeton Univ. Press.

WEIR, J. R.
1915a. A new host for a species of *Razoumofskya*. Phytopathology 5:73.

———
1915b. *Razoumofskya tsugensis* in Alaska. Phytopathology 5:229.

———
1916a. Larch mistletoe: some economic considerations of its injurious effects. U.S. Dep. Agr. Bull. 317, 25 p., illus.

———
1916b. Mistletoe injury to conifers in the Northwest. U.S. Dep. Agr. Bull. 360: 1–39, illus.

———
1916c. *Pinus ponderosa* and *P. jeffreyi*, hosts for *Razoumofskya americana*. Phytopathology 6:414.

———
1917. New hosts for *Razoumofskya americana* and *R. occidentalis abietina*. Phytopathology 7:140.

———
1918a. Experimental investigations on the genus *Razoumofskya*. Bot. Gaz. 56: 1–31, illus.

———
1918b. New hosts for *Razoumofskya laricis*. Phytopathology 8:62–63.

WESTER, D. H.
1921. Sur les constituants chimiques de quelques Loranthacées. Rec. des Trav. Chim. des Pays-Bas. 40:707–723, illus.

WHITEHEAD, DONALD R.
1963. "Northern" elements in the Pleistocene flora of the Southeast. Ecology 44: 403–406.

———
1964. Fossil pine pollen and full-glacial vegetation in southeastern North Carolina. Ecology 45:767–777, illus.

———
1969. Wind pollination in the angiosperms: Evolutionary and environmental considerations. Evolution 23:28–35.

——— and BARGHOORN, ELSO S.
1962. Pollen analytical investigations of Pleistocene deposits from western North Carolina and South Carolina. Ecol. Monogr. 32:347–369.

——— and DOYLE, MICHAEL V.
1969. Late-Pleistocene peats from Long Beach, North Carolina. Southeast. Geol. 10: 1–16, illus.

WICKER, ED F.
1965. Biology and control of dwarf mistletoes on Douglas-fir and western larch. Ph.D. thesis, Wash. State Univ., 186 p. (Diss. Abstr. 26(6):3006).

———
1967a. Seed destiny as a klendusic factor of infection and its impact upon propagation of *Arceuthobium* spp. Phytopathology 57: 1164–1168, illus.

———
1967b. Appraisal of biological control of *Arceuthobium campylopodum* f. *campylopodum* by *Colletotrichum gloeosporioides*. Plant Dis. Rep. 51:311–313.

———
1969. Susceptibility of coastal form and central Montana Douglas-fir to *Arceuthobium douglasii*. Plant Dis. Rep. 53: 311–314

——— and SHAW, C. GARDNER.
1968. Fungal parasites of dwarf mistletoes. Mycologia 60:372–383, illus.

WIDMER, G. A., and COUSSIO, J. D.
1969. Flavonoids of *Phrygilanthus flagellaris*. Phytochemistry 8:517.

WIENS, DELBERT.
1962. A taxonomic study of the acataphyllous species of *Phoradendron*. Ph.D. thesis, Claremont Coll., Calif., 126 p. (Diss. Abstr. 22:5285).

———
1964. Chromosome numbers in North American Loranthaceae (*Arceuthobium*, *Phoradendron*, *Psittacanthus*, *Struthanthus*). Amer. J. Bot. 51:1–6, illus.

———
1968. Chromosomal and flowering characteristics in dwarf mistletoes (*Arceuthobium*). Amer. J. Bot. 55:325–334, illus.

——— and BARLOW, B. A.
1971. The cytogeography of the Viscaceous and Eremolepidaceous mistletoes. Taxon 20: 313–332.

WILLDENOW, C. L.
1806. Caroli Linnaei Species Plantarum. v. 4(2):737–741.

WILSON, CHARLES L.
1969. Use of plant pathogens in weed control. Annu. Rev. Phytopathol. 7: 411–434.

WIRTH, MICHAEL, ESTABROOK, GEORGE F., and

ROGERS, DAVID J.
    1966. A graph theory model for systematic biology with an example for the Oncidiinae (Orchidaceae). Syst. Zool. 15: 59–69, illus.

WOOD, A.
    1871. American botanist and florist. 832 p., N.Y.: Barnes and Burr.

WRIGHT, JONATHAN W.
    1955. Species crossability in spruce in relation to distribution and taxonomy. Forest Sci. 1: 319–349, illus.

YEATMAN, C. W.
    1967. Biogeography of jack pine. Can. J. Bot. 45: 2201–2211, illus.

ZALASKY, H.
    1956. Provinces of Manitoba and Saskatchewan, forest disease survey. Div. Forest Biol., Forest Insect and Dis. Surv., Annu. Rep. 1955: 82.

ZAVARIN, E., CRITCHFIELD, W. B., and SNAJBERK, K.
    1969. Turpentine composition of *Pinus contorta* × *Pinus banksiana* hybrids and hybrid derivatives. Can. J. Bot. 47: 1443–1453.

ZEFIROV, B. M.
    1955. De *Arceuthobio oxycedri* (DC.) M.B. in Cupresso parasitico. Akad. Nauk. SSSR. Bot. 17: 110–111, illus.

APPENDIX

Glossary

ADAPTIVE RADIATION. The evolution of species into a diversity of previously unoccupied ecological niches.

ADVANCED TAXA. Plants that have derived characters not present in their ancestors (see p. 38).

ALLOPLOID. An individual of hybrid origin whose sets of chromosomes are derived from different parental species.

ANISOPHASIC WITCHES' BROOM. See non-systemic witches' broom.

ANTHESIS. The period of flowering.

ARCHESPORIUM. A cell or group of cells from which spores (including pollen) are derived.

AUTOPLOID. An individual which has one or more exact duplications of the diploid set of chromosomes.

BIVALENT. An homologus pair of chromosomes in the synapsed, or paired, state during prophase of the first meiotic division.

CHIASMA. The microscopically visible, apparent exchange of chromatid parts between homologous chromosomes during prophase of the first meiotic division.

CHROMATOGRAPHY. Separation of chemical compounds by allowing a solution of them to seep through an adsorbent material (paper in our studies) so that the different compounds become adsorbed in separate colored layers.

CONNATE. A uniting of parts, particularly similar structures united to form a single organ.

CONVERGENCE. An evolutionary phenomenon whereby similar forms or functions occur in groups which are not closely related.

CROSS-OVER. Parasitism by a dwarf mistletoe on a tree other than its principal host.

DECUSSATE. An arrangement of shoots in that the parts alternate in pairs at right angles (see fig. 1).

DENDRITIC EVOLUTION. A pattern of evolution in which distinct lineages are evident.

DICHASIUM. A type of inflorescence, which in its basic form consists of an older apical flower subtended laterally by two younger flowers of axillary origin.

DIMORPHISM. The occurrence of two forms, often associated with morphological differences relating to sex.

DIOECIOUS. The situation in which each individual of a species possesses only a single sex.

DIPLOID. An individual which has twice the number of chromosomes which characterizes a gamete; i.e. the presence of both members of homologous pairs of chromosomes.

DIPLOXYLON. The hard or yellow pines, one of the two major groups of the genus *Pinus*.

DIRECT FLOWERING. A plant with uninterrupted development of the floral buds from initiation to anthesis.

DISTAL. Part of a structure farthest from the point of attachment (cf. proximal).

DIVARICATE. Parts spreading widely away from one another.

ENDOPHYTIC SYSTEM. The "root-like" parts of dwarf mistletoe within the host tissues. The endophytic system consists of "strands" within the cortex and "sinkers" which are embedded in successive layers of xylem.

EPIGYNOUS. Originating from above the ovary; generally used to describe situations where the ovary is situated below the perianth.

EPIPHYTE. A plant growing on another plant from which it derives no benefit other than support, such as various orchids or bromeliads.

EXTRA-LIMITAL HOSTS. Infection of trees that do not occur within the natural range of a particular dwarf mistletoe. Susceptibility of such trees may be established either by inoculations or by introducing trees into areas where the dwarf mistletoe occurs.

FLABELLATE. Fan shaped, a branching pattern produced by the continued development of superposed axillary buds.

GENOME. The haploid (n) set of chromosomes.

GIRDLE. The point on a vegetative branch or main stem of a conifer between two annual growth segments. This is frequently, but incorrectly, referred to as a "node."

GLABROUS. Bald, without hairs or trichomes.

GLAUCOUS. A usually delicate whitish waxy coating which is easily rubbed away.

HAPLOID. A situation where each nucleus contains only one member of each homologous pair of chromosomes; the n number of chromosomes.

HAPLOXYLON. The white or pinyon pines; one of the two major groups of the genus *Pinus*.

HOLDFAST. A disc-like swelling at the distal end of the radicle through which infection of the host takes place.

HOLOTYPE. The single specimen designated by an author of a taxonomic name to which that name is permanently attached.

INDIRECT FLOWERING. The intervention of a rest period between the initiation of a floral bud and anthesis.

INFLORESCENCE. A flower cluster or mode of bearing fllowers.

ISOPHASIC WITCHES' BROOMS. See systemic witches' broom.

ISOTYPE. A specimen collected at the same place and time and by the same collector as the holotype.

KARYOTYPE. The morphological and quantitative characterization of chromosome set, including such features as size, centromere position, arm length, satellites and chromosome member.

LECTOTYPE. A specimen selected from the original material on which a taxon is based, when no holotype was designated originally, or when the holotype is missing or destroyed.

LENTICULAR. Shaped like a double-convex lens; not spherical.

MEDELIAN. A type of inheritance which is allelomorphic, i.e. exhibits alternate forms, usually with respect to dominance and recessiveness.

MEGASPOROGENESIS. A meiotic nuclear division in plants which produces megaspores, which in turn give rise to mega- or female gametophytes. The megagametophyte in flowering plants (embryo sac) eventually produces the egg and associated cells at maturity.

MEIOSIS. A type of cell division which produces gametes (in animals) or spores (in plants) which are characterized by having the reduced or haploid (n) chromosome number, i.e. one member of each homologous chromosome pair.

MICROSPOROGENESIS. A meiotic nuclear division in plants which produces microspores (pollen grains) which in turn produce a micro- or male gametophyte. The microgametophyte in flowering plants (pollen tube) eventually produces the sperm nuclei.

NEOTYPE. A specimen designated as the type when the original type and all specimens on which the name was based has been either destroyed or are missing.

NONSYSTEMIC WITCHES' BROOM. Witches' broom in which the dwarf mistletoe shoots remain concentrated near the original point of infection (compare with systemic broom. p. 26).

PALEOBOTANY. The study of fossil plants.

PALYNOLOGY. The study of pollen.

PARASITE. An organism, such as mistletoe, that obtains sustenance from another organism.

PEDICELLATE JOINT. The point of attachment of the flower or fruit to the pedicel.

PERIANTH. A collective term for the sepals and petals.

PHENOLOGY. The relationship between seasonal and periodic biological phenomena, e.g. flowering and fruiting times.

PHOTOPERIOD. A light period, usually the daylight portion of a 24-hour period at a particular time of the year.

PHYLAD. A natural group of any rank, usually considered with respect to its evolutionary origin or history; any evolutionary line of development.

PHYLETIC. The evolutionary history of a group of organisms.

POLYMORPHISM. The occurrence of two or more forms within a population.

POLYPLOIDY. The exact duplication of entire cromosome sets.

PRIMARY BRANCHING. The basic, decussate type of branching exhibited by all species of *Arceuthobium*.

PRIMITIVE TAXA. Plants that have characters also possessed by their ancestors (see p. 38).

PRINCIPAL HOSTS. The main, or most susceptible hosts, for a particular dwarf mistletoe (see p. 16).

PROXIMAL. Part of a structure closest to the point of attachment (cf. distal).

RADICLE. The growing tip of the hypocotyl in a germinating seed.

RECOMBINATION INDEX. The haploid number of chromosomes plus the chiasma frequency.

RECOMBINATION POTENTIAL. The possibility for expressing genetic variability which is determined by the genetic system (cf. recombination index).

RELICTUAL. A population or species occurring in only a small geographical portion or portions of its previous distribution.

RETICULATE EVOLUTION. A netlike structure of relationships, normally resulting from hybridization and alloploidy.

SECONDARY BRANCHING. Branching that develops in addition to primary branching. It may be either flabellate or verticillate.

SEGMENT. The single years' growth in length of a vegetative branch or main stem of a conifer. This is often, but incorrectly, referred to as an "internode."

SYMPATRY. Occurring together; used specifically in this study to denote situations where temporal and spatial consideration should permit hybridization between taxa unless they are reproductively isolated.

SYSTEMIC WITCHES' BROOMS. Witches' brooms in which the endophytic system keeps pace with the growth of the infected host branch. Dwarf mistletoe shoots are scattered along the branch (see p. 26).

TAXIMETRICS. Analyses associated with numerical taxonomy.

TAXON (plural Taxa). A taxonomic unit of any rank (species, subspecies, form, etc.).

TETRAPLOIDY. A polyploid condition characterized by four sets of chromosomes.

TRICOME. An epidermal appendage or hair.

TYPE. A specimen which is the basis of a taxonomic name, usually a holotype, but sometimes also lectotypes or neotypes.

VERTICILLATE (whorled). The occurrence of more than two leaves or branches at a single node.

VISCOUS. Sticky, generally used in this study to indicate the material around the seed of dwarf mistletoes.

WHORLED. See verticillate.

Scientific and Common Tree Names

Most names are from Little (1953) or Critchfield and Little (1966)

Abies amabilis (Dougl.) Forbes—Pacific silver fir
Abies balsamea (L.) Mill.—balsam fir
Abies bracteata D. Don—bristlecone fir
Abies concolor (Gord. & Glend.) Lindl.—white fir
Abies durangensis Martínez
Abies grandis (Dougl.) Lindl.—grand fir
Abies guatemalensis Rehd.
Abies hickeli Flous & Gaussen
Abies lasiocarpa (Hook.) Nutt.
    var. *lasiocarpa*—subalpine fir
    var. *arizonica* (Merriam) Lemm.—corkbark fir
Abies magnifica A. Murr.
    var. *magnifica*—California red fir
    var. *shastensis* Lemm.—Shasta red fir
Abies mexicana Martínez
Abies oaxacana Martínez
Abies pindrow Royale—Pindrow fir
Abies procera Rehd.—noble fir
Abies religiosae (H.B.K.) Schlecht. & Cham.
Abies vejarii Martínez

Chamaecyparis thyoides (L.) B.S.P.—Atlantic white-cedar
Cupressus macrocarpa Hartw.—Monterey cypress
Juniperus brevifolia Ant.
Juniperus communis L.
Juniperus drupacea Labill.
Juniperus excelsa Bieb.
Juniperus macropoda Boiss.
Juniperus oxycedrus L.
Juniperus phoenicia L.
Juniperus procera Hochst.
Juniperus rufescens Link
Juniperus sabina L.
Juniperus semiglobosa Regel
Juniperus seravschanica Komarov
Juniperus turcomanica B. Fedtsch
Larix europae DC.—European larch
Larix laricina (Du Roi) K. Koch—eastern larch
Larix leptolepis (Sieb. & Zucc.) Gord.—Japanese larch
Larix lyallii Parl.—subalpine larch
Larix occidentalis Nutt.—western larch

Picea abies (L.) Karst.—Norway spruce
Picea breweriana S. Wats.—Brewer spruce
Picea chihuahuana Martínez
Picea engelmannii Parry—Engelmann spruce
Picea glauca (Moench) Voss—white spruce
Picea mariana (Mill.) B.S.P.—black spruce
Picea mexicana Martínez
Picea pungens Engelm.—blue spruce
Picea rubens Sarg.—red spruce
Picea sitchensis (Bong.) Carr.—Sitka spruce
Pinus albicaulis Engelm.—whitebark pine
Pinus aristata Engelm.—bristlecone pine
Pinus attenuata Lemm.—knobcone pine
Pinus ayacahuite Ehrenb.—Mexican white pine
Pinus balfouriana Grev. & Balf.—foxtail pine
Pinus banksiana Lamb.—jack pine
Pinus bungeana Zucc.—lacebark pine
Pinus caribaea Morelet—Caribbean pine
Pinus cembroides Zucc.—Mexican pinyon
Pinus chiapensis (Martínez) Andresen
Pinus contorta Dougl. ex Loud.—lodgepole pine
    subsp. contorta—shore pine
    subsp. bolanderi (Parl.) Critchf.
    subsp. murrayana (Balf.) Critchf.
    subsp. latifolia (Engelm. ex Wats.) Critchf.
Pinus cooperi C. E. Blanco—Cooper pine
Pinus coulteri D. Don—Coulter pine
Pinus culminicola Andresen & Beaman—Potosí pine
Pinus douglasiana Martínez—Douglas pine
Pinus durangensis Martínez—Durango pine
Pinus edulis Engelm.—pinyon
Pinus engelmannii Carr.—Apache pine
Pinus flexilis James—limber pine
Pinus greggii Engelm.—Gregg pine
Pinus griffithii McClelland—blue pine
Pinus hartwegii Lindl.—Hartweg pine
Pinus herrerai Martínez
Pinus jeffreyi Grev. & Balf.—Jeffrey pine
Pinus lambertiana Dougl.—sugar pine
Pinus lawsonii Roezl—Lawson pine
Pinus leiophylla Schiede &Deppe
    var. leiophylla
    var. chihuahuana (Engelm.) Shaw—Chihuahua pine
Pinus lumholtzii Robins. & Fern.—Lumholtz pine

Pinus maximartinezii Rzedowski—Martínez pine
Pinus michoacana Martínez—Michoacán pine
Pinus monophylla Torr. & Frém.—singleleaf pinyon
Pinus montezumae Lamb.—Montezuma pine
Pinus monticola Dougl.—western white pine
Pinus mugo Turra—Swiss mountain pine
Pinus muricata D. Don—bishop pine
Pinus nelsonii Shaw—Nelson pinyon
Pinus occidentalis Sw.—West Indian pine
Pinus oocarpa Schiede
Pinus palustris Mill.—longleaf pine
Pinus patula Schiede & Deppe—Mexican weeping pine
Pinus pinaster Ait.—maritime pine
Pinus pinceana Gord.—Pince pinyon
Pinus pinea L.—Italian stone pine
Pinus ponderosa Laws.—ponderosa pine
    var. ponderosa
    var. scopulorum Engelm.
    var. arizonica (Engelm.) Shaw—Arizona pine
Pinus pringlei Shaw—Pringle pine
Pinus pseudostrobus Lindl.
Pinus quadrifolia Parl.—Parry pinyon
Pinus radiata D. Don—Monterey pine
Pinus resinosa Ait.—red pine
Pinus rudis Endl.
Pinus rzedowskii Madrigal and Caballero
Pinus sabiniana Dougl.—Digger pine
Pinus strobiformis Engelm.—southwestern white pine
Pinus strobus L.—eastern white pine
Pinus sylvestris L.—Scotch pine
Pinus tabulaeformis Carr.—Chinese pine
Pinus tenuifolia Benth.
Pinus teocote Schiede & Deppe
Pinus torreyana Parry—Torrey pine
Pinus virginiana Mill.—Virginia pine
Pinus washoensis Mason & Stockwell—Washoe pine
Pseudotsuga macrocarpa (Vasey) Mayr—bigcone Douglas-fir
Pseudotsuga menziesii (Mirb.) Franco—Douglas-fir
    var. menziesii
    var. glauca (Beissn.) Franco
Thuja orientalis L.—Oriental arborvitae
Tsuga canadensis (L.) Carr.—eastern hemlock
Tsuga heterophylla (Raf.) Sarg.—western hemlock
Tsuga mertensiana (Bong.) Carr.—mountain hemlock

Specimens Examined

Herbaria

The dwarf mistletoe specimens that were examined for these studies are tabulated in the following lists: the host, location, collector, year of collection, and herbarium where the collection is housed is given for each specimen. The herbaria in which specimens were examined and their abbreviations are listed below. An asterisk indicates an abbreviation not in the 1964 edition of Index Herbariorum (Lanjou and Stafleu 1964).

ARIZ—University of Arizona, Tucson

BLH—Cranbrook Institute of Science, Bloomfield Hills, Michigan

BM—British Museum, London, England

CAS—California Academy of Sciences, San Francisco

COLO—University of Colorado, Boulder

CFB—Canadian Dep. Forestry, Calgary, Alberta

CS—Colorado State University, Fort Collins

DAVFP—Canadian Dep. Forestry, Victoria, British Columbia

DS—Dudley Herbarium, Stanford University

EAP—Escuela Agrícola Panamericana, Tegucigalpa, Honduras

F—Field Museum of Natural History, Chicago

FPB*—U.S. Forest Service, Forest Pathology Herbarium, Berkeley, California

FPF*—U.S. Forest Service, Forest Pathology Herbarium, Fort Collins, Colorado

FPT*—Canadian Dep. Forestry, Forest Pathology, Toronto, Ontario

GH—Gray Herbarium, Harvard University

ILL—University of Illinois, Urbana

INIF*—Instituto Nacional de Investigaciones Forestales, Mexico D. F.

JEPS—Jepson Herbarium, University of California, Berkeley

K—Royal Botanic Garden, Kew, England

MEXU—Institute de Biología, Mexico D. F.

MICH—University of Michigan, Ann Arbor

MIN—University of Minnesota, Minneapolis

MNA*—Museum of Northern Arizona, Flagstaff

MO—Missouri Botanical Garden, St. Louis

MSC—Michigan State University, East Lansing

NY—New York Botanical Garden, New York

OSC—Oregon State University, Corvallis

PH—Academy of Natural Sciences, Philadelphia, Pennsylvania

POM—Pomona College, Claremont, California

RM—Rocky Mountain Herbarium, University of Wyoming, Laramie

RSA—Rancho Santa Ana, Claremont, California

SRSC—Sul Ross State College, Alpine, Texas

UC—University of California, Berkeley

US—U.S. National Museum, Washington, D.C.

UT—University of Utah, Salt Lake City

UTC—Utah State University, Logan

WINF—Canadian Department of Forestry, Winnipeg, Manitoba

WIS—University of Wisconsin, Madison

WSP—Washington State University, Mycological Herbarium, Pullman

WTU—University of Washington, Seattle

Z—Universität Zurich, Switzerland

Three collector abbreviations are used in the specimens cited list: (Hawksworth = H, Lightle = L, and Wiens = W). An asterisk (*) after the collection denotes a specimen used in the taximetric analyses. The following abbreviations are used in the collection citations:

boundary = bdy.	mountain = mtn.
canyon = can.	National = Nat.
creek = cr.	not dated = n.d.
collector unknown = col.?	range = R.
county = co.	Reservation = Res.
Experimental = Exp.	route = Rte.
Forest = For.	road = rd.
junction = Jct.	section = Sec.
miles = mi.	Station = Sta.
mount = mt.	township = T.
Monument = Mon.	

New World Taxa

1a. ARCEUTHOBIUM ABIETINUM f. sp. CONCOLORIS

Specimens Examined: on *Abies concolor* except as noted.

UNITED STATES

ARIZONA

COCONINO CO.: Kaibab Plateau, *Richards* in 1938 (UC) and on *A. lasiocarpa*, *Richards* in 1938 (WTU). Grand Can. Nat. Park, North Rim: Cape Royal rd., *Gill FP 68297** in 1934 (FPF); Fairview Point, *Peterson 37–61* in 1961 (FPF) and *H 252* in 1962 (FPF) and on *A. lasiocarpa, Peterson 39–61* in 1961 (FPF); Bright Angel Point, *H 254* in 1962 (FPF); Inspiration Point, *W. 3180* in 1962 (COLO). Grand Can. Nat. Park, South Rim: 1 mi. E of Grandview Point, *H & L 184* in 1962 (FPF) and *H & Scharpf 702* in 1964 (FPF).

CALIFORNIA

ALPINE CO.: 8 mi. SW of Silver Cr. on Rte. 4, *H & Scharpf 667* in 1964 (FPF). BUTTE CO.: Jonesville, *Copeland 414* in 1930 (ARIZ, CAS, MO, POM, RM, RSA, UC, US, Z) and *Copeland* in 1929 (UC). CALAVERAS CO.: 12 mi. SW of Tamarack on Rte. 4, *H & Scharpf 662* in 1964 (FPF). DEL NORTE CO.: 0.25 mi. S of Oregon bdy. on O'Brien-Happy Camp rd., *H & Hinds 999** in 1966 (FPF) and on *A. grandis*, *H & Hinds 998* in 1966 (FPF). ELDORADO CO.: US 50 near Camino, *Kuijt 1272* in 1957 (UC); Tahoma, *Kuijt 1340* in 1957 (UC) and on *Pinus contorta*, rare, *Kuijt 1341* in 1957 (UC). FRESNO CO.: 2 mi. S of summit on Shaver Lake—Dinkey Cr. rd., *Quick 53-27* in 1953 (CAS); Huntington Lake, *Wall* in 1919 (CAS); Bubbs Cr. and Charlotte Cr., *Howell 15674* in 1940 (CAS). GLENN CO.: Bear Wallow rd. near Alder Springs, *Boyce 1906* in 1930 (FPF); Plaskett Ranger Sta. *Boyce 1905** in 1930 (FPF). HUMBOLDT Co.: Lasseck's Peak, *Kildare 2634* in 1926 (DS, UC); Humboldt Mill, vicinity of Eureka, on *Abies grandis*, *Tracy 1060* in 1901 (UC). KERN CO.: Portuguese Pass, 7 mi. N of Summit Guard Sta., *W. 3610* in 1964 (FPF). LASSEN CO.: Crater Mtn., 15 mi. W of Eagle Lake, *Meinecke* in 1914 (FPF) and *Whitney 1703* in 1934 (UC). MADERA CO.: 1 mi. E of Fish Camp, *H 30* in 1954 (FPF); Bass Lake, *Gill & Wright FP 68161* in 1932 (FPF); Mile High Point, 27 mi. from North Fork on Mammoth Pool rd., *H 937** in 1966 (FPF); Ellis (now Benedict) Meadows, *Zieman* in 1917 (FPF). MODOC CO.: Warner Mtns.: Cedar Pass, *Alava* in 1957 (UC); 2.5 mi. W of Patterson Guard Sta., *H & Hinds 1002** in 1966 (FPF). MARIPOSA CO.: Yosemite, *Hedgcock & Meinecke FP 4823* in 1910 (FPF); Fish Camp, *Hedgcock & Meinecke FP 4834* in 1910 (FPF); 1 mi. E of Fish Camp, *H** in 1963 (FPF). MENDOCINO CO.: Van Damme State Park, on *Abies grandis*, *Kuijt 1216* in 1957 (UC) and *H & Scharpf 855* in 1966 (FPF). NEVADA CO.: 2 mi. N of Truckee, *W 3228* in 1962 (COLO, FPF); Hobart Mills, *Boyce FP 15981* in 1914 (FPF); Bear Valley [6 mi. SE of Sierra City], *Jepson* in 1898 (JEPS); Gaston Ridge, 5 mi. N of Washington, *Howell 2459* n.d. (CAS). PLACER CO.: Trail to Mt. Ellis, above Homewood, *Schreiber 891* in 1933 (UC); Carnelian Bay, Lake Tahoe, *Blakely 3793* in 1960 (CAS). PLUMAS CO.: Chester, *Meinecke FP 10754* in 1914 (FPF); Bucks Lake, *Scharpf* in 1963 (FPF); 4 mi. SE of Almanor Jct. on US 89, *W 3232* in 1962 (COLO, FPF); 3 mi. SE of Almanor Jct. on US 89, *W 3233** in 1962 (COLO, FPF); Lassen Buttes, *Brown 675* in 1897 (MO, US); Taylorsville, *Clemens* in 1919 (CAS). SAN BERNARDINO CO.: San Bernardino Mtns.: 10 mi. N of Big Bear Lake, *Gill & Wright FP 68225* in 1931 (FPF); Barton Flat, 3 mi. above Camp Angelus, *W. 3210* in 1962 (COLO, FPF); Lost Creek, *Munz & Johnston 8576* in 1924 (POM); Barton Flats, *Ross 1917* in 1937 (POM); Inspiration Point, *Perkins* in 1917 (ILL). SHASTA CO.: 22 mi. N of Lassen Nat. Park entrance on Rte. 89, *Kuijt 1365* in 1957 (UC); 4 mi. N of Lassen Nat. Park entrance on Rte. 89, *H & W 648* in 1964 (FPF); Rte. 89 at Pondosa Jct., on *Pinus lambertiana*, *Kuijt 1369* in 1957 (UC). SIERRA CO.: Sierraville, *Meinecke & Boyce FP 17193* and *FP 17194* in 1915 (FPF). SISKIYOU CO.: Mt. Shasta, Sisson South Trail, *Cooke 16132* in 1941 (COLO, MO, PH); Can. Cr., *Hedgcock FP 1858* in 1917 (FPF); N side Cascade Gulch, Mt. Shasta, *Cooke 17722* in 1947 (WTU); Bartle-Whitehorse rd., *Newcomb 156* in 1957 (UC); Sisson South Trail, *Cooke 13574* in? (DS); Shackelford Cr. [8 mi. W of Greenview], *Butler 270* in 1908 (UC); Joe Cr., 10 mi. S of Copper, Oregon, *H & W 635* in 1964 (FPF); 5 mi. E of US 99 on Mt. Shasta rd., *H & W 641* in 1964 (FPF); Along trail on N side of Black Butte, *H & W 643* in 1964 (FPF); Base of Mt. Shasta, *Engelmann* in 1880 (MO); Trestle rd. to Hilts, N of Oak Knoll Ranger Sta., *Quick 60-21* in 1960 (CAS). TEHAMA CO.: 2 mi. N of Hole-in-Ground Campground, S of Mineral, *Kuijt 1503* in 1958 (UC). TULARE CO.: Hollow Log Camp, [near General Grant], *Dudley* in 1900 (DS); Sequoia Nat. Park, 1 mi. N of Lodgepole, *W. 3613* in 1961 (FPF). TUOLUMNE CO.: Cow Cr., *Gill FP 68060* in 1932 (FPF), *Quick* in 1966 (FPF) and on *Pinus lambertiana*, *Quick* in 1966 (FPF); Strawberry, *Wright FP 68052* in 1931 (FPF); Long Barn, *Wright FP 68115* and *FP 68116* in 1932 (FPF); Pinecrest, *Gill FP 68224* in 1932 (FPF) and on *Pinus lambertiana*, *Gill FP 68224* in 1932 (FPF); Tuolumne Grove, *Peterson 63-139* in 1963 (FPF); 7 mi. E of Long Barn, *W 3223* in 1962 (COLO, FPF); 5 mi. E of Long Barn, *Kuijt 1431* in 1957 (UC); 5.1 mi. E of Nat. For. bdy. on Rte. 120, *Kuijt 1393* in 1957 (UC); Yosemite Nat. Park, Tuolumne Can., *Clemens* in 1919 (CAS).

NEVADA

CLARK CO.: Charleston Mtns.: Little Falls, *Clokey 5433* in 1935 (CAS, DS, FPF, RM, UC, US, WTU) and *5434* in 1935 (CAS, DS, FPF, RM, US, WTU); Charleston Park, *W 3204* and *3033* in 1962 (COLO, FPF); Deer Cr. Grade, 3 mi. E of Lee Can., *Train 2154* in 1918 (ARIZ, UC); Lee Can., *Heller 11060* in 1913 (DS, MO, PH, UC); Deer Cr. Campground, *Breedlove 1109* in 1961 (DS); without locality, *Jaeger* in 1926 (POM); Lee Can., 5 mi. W of Deer Cr. Jct., *H & Scharpf 674* in 1964 (FPF); Kyle Can., 2.5 mi. W of Ranger Sta., *H & Scharpf 676** in 1964 (FPF). WASHOE CO.: Vicinity of Reno, *Hitchcock 559* in 1913 (US).

CURRY CO.: S of Humbug Mtn., on *Abies grandis*, *Ferris 7828* in 1929 (DS); Grizzly Mtn., 0.5 mi. E of Gold Beach, on *Abies grandis*, *Theisen* in 1965 (FPF), DESCHUTES CO.: McKenzie Pass, on *A. grandis*, *Gill FP 68186** in 1932 (FPF); 9 mi. W of Sisters, on *A. grandis*, *W 3244* in 1962 (COLO, FPF); 7.5 mi. W of Sisters on Rte 242, on *A. grandis*, *H & W 613* in 1964 (FPF) and *H & Hinds 990* in 1966 (FPF); 14 mi. NW of Sisters on US 126, on *A. grandis*, *H & W 615* in 1964 (FPF). JACKSON CO.: 10 mi. E of Butte Falls, *Graham* in 1964 (FPF): Long John Cr. [SSW of Ashland], *Wheeler 3005* in 1934 (CAS, POM, WTU); 11 mi. SW of Ashland on Copper rd., *H & W 637* in 1964 (FPF); Summit of Siskiyou Mtns., near Siskiyou Sta., on *A. grandis*, *Abrams 12130* in 1927 (DS); W Fork of Evans Cr., 18 mi. NE of Grants Pass, *Graham* in 1966 (FPF); 8 air mi. S of Ashland, *Graham* in 1965 (FPF); 18 air mi. E of Ashland, *Howard* in 1964 (FPF); Fish Lake rd., 12 mi. SE of Butte Falls, *Graham* in 1965 (FPF). JEFFERSON CO.: 3 mi. E of Santiam Pass on US 20, on *A. grandis*, *H & Scharpf 1257* in 1969 (FPF). JOSE-PHINE CO.: Flat Top Mtn., 24 air mi. W of Grants Pass, *Graham* in 1963 (FPF), *H & W 632* in 1964 (FPF), and *Bynum* in 1967 (FPF) and on *Picea breweriana*, *Graham* in 1963 (FPF), *H & W 631* in 1965 (FPF), and *Bynum* in 1967 (FPF). KLAMATH CO.: Hamner Butte, [S of Davis Lake] on *A. grandis*, *Childs 28* in 1939 (OSC) and *Englerth FP 91031* in 1939 (OSC); 9 mi. N of Fort Klamath on Rte. 62, *H & W 626* in 1964 (FPF); 31 mi. W of Klamath Falls on Rte. 66, *H & W 629* in 1964 (FPF); vicinity of Crater Lake, *Weir 2429* in 1916 (FPF, ILL) and on *A. amabilis*, *Weir 2423* in 1916 (FPF, ILL). LAKE CO.: Silver Lake, *Jaenicke FP 21285* in 1916 (FPF); W Fork of Silver Cr., 12 mi. SW of Silver Lake, *Stewart* in 1968 (FPF); 1 mi. N of Bly Summit, 8 mi. SW of Beatty on Rte. 140, *H & W 874* in 1966 (FPF).

UTAH

KANE CO.: 8 mi. S of Navajo Lake on Zion Park rd., *W 4122* in 1966 (FPF, UT).

WASHINGTON

KLICKITAT CO.: Falcon Valley, on *A. grandis*, *Suksdorf 2246* in 1893 (FPF, MO, UC, US); Snowden, ca. 12 mi. NE of White Salmon, on *A. grandis*, *Graham** in 1964 (FPF) and *H & W 592* in 1964 (FPF).

1b. *ARCEUTHOBIUM ABIETINUM* f. sp. *MAGNIFICAE*

Specimens Examined: on *Abies magnifica* (including var. *shastensis*) except as noted.

CALIFORNIA

AMADOR CO.: E of Lower Bear Res., *Quick 54–87* in 1954 (CAS). BUTTE CO.: Summit of Humboldt rd. near Jonesville, *Copeland* in 1928 (UC); "Big Summit," Jonesville, *Copeland* in 1931 (UC). CALAVERAS CO.: 10 mi. above Dorrington, *Wright FP 68050* in 1931 (FPF) and *FP 68123* in 1932 (FPF); 8 mi. SW of Tamarack on Rte. 4, *H & Scharpf 663* in 1964 (FPF). EL DORADO CO.: S end of Echo Lake, *Howell 22902* in 1946 (CAS). HUMBOLDT CO.: Trinity Summit, E of Corral Prairie, *Tracy 10571* in 1932 (UC); South Fork Mtn., near Blake Lookout, *Tracy 8950* in 1930 (JEPS, WTU). FRESNO CO.: Huntington Lake, *Miller FP 98112* in 1965 (FPB). MADERA CO.: Haskell Meadow, *Miller FP 97956* in 1910 (FPB). KERN CO.: Greenhorn Mtns., N side Sundry Peak, *Howell 38844* in 1962 (CAS). MARIPOSA CO.: 5 mi. E of Fish Camp, *H* in 1963 (FPF). NEVADA CO.: Hobart Mills, *Boyce FP 15982* in 1914 (FPF, ILL); 5 mi. E of Hobart Mills, *Gill FP 68223* in 1931 (FPF). PLUMAS CO.: Grizzly Summit, SW of Bucks Lake, *Scharpf FP 98107* in 1964 (FPB); Claremont Peak near Quincy, *Weatherby 1674* in 1955 (CAS, RM, RSA). SHASTA CO.: Lassen Nat. Park on main rd., 10 mi. E of N entrance, *H & W 650** in 1964 (FPF). SISKIYOU CO.: near head of E Fork of Indian Cr., *Evans* in 1912 (FPB); 0.5 mi. E of Siskiyou Nat. For. bdy. on Happy Camp-O'Brien rd., 14 air mi. NNW of Happy Camp, *H & Hinds 1000** in 1966 (FPF); Kidder Cr. [ca. 11 mi. WSW of Greenview], *Gill & Sargent FP 68181** in 1932 (FPF). TRINITY CO.: South Fork Mtn., near Hyampom, *Boyce 30* in 1914 (FPF); South Fork Mtn., *Parks & Tracy 11532* in 1941 (RM, RSA, UC, US, WTU). TULARE CO.: Bald Mtn., Kaweah River Valley, *Dudley 1395* in 1896 (DS); Roaring River, *Meinecke* in 1910 (FPB); Mosquito Cr. near Mineralking, *Hopping* in 1913 (FPB); 17 mi. NW of Lodgepole, *W 3615** in 1964 (FPF). TUOLUMNE CO.: Pinecrest, *Scharpf** in 1963 (FPF); Yosemite Nat. Park, 7 mi. E of Crane Flat Jct. on Tioga Pass rd., *H 938** in 1966 (FPF). COUNTY UNCERTAIN: Lassen Nat. Park, *Boldenbeck* in 1910 (DS).

OREGON

JOSEPHINE CO.: Flat Top Mtn., ca. 24 air mi. W of Grants Pass, on *A. procera; Bynum* in 1967 (FPF): Oregon Caves Nat. Mon., Sike Mtn. Trail, *Root & Gooding FP 68274** in 1932 (FPF); near Bolen Mtn., S of Oregon Caves, *Theisen* in 1966 (FPF). KLAMATH CO.: Bay on W side of Upper Klamath Lake, on *A. procera*, *Peck 9525* in 1920 (WTU); near Crater Lake, on *A. procera*, *Weir 2427* in 1916

(FPF, ILL). COUNTY UNCERTAIN: Ashland-Klamath Falls wagon rd., *Weir 2426* in 1916 (ILL).

2. *ARCEUTHOBIUM ABIETIS-RELIGIOSAE*

Specimens Examined:

MEXICO

JALISCO: NW Slopes of Nevado de Colima, on *Abies* sp., *McVaugh & Wilber 10130* in 1949 (MICH). MEXICO: Ixtaccihuatl, on *Abies religiosa, Purpus 6491* in 1912 (MO, UC, US); Popocatepetl, on *Abies religiosa*, Balls B4228 *in* 1938 (BM, K, UC, US); 17 km E of Amecameca, on *Abies religiosa, H & W 373** in 1963 and *1229* in 1969 (FPF); District Temascaltepec, vicinity of Mesón Viejo, on *Abies religiosa, Hinton 3278* in 1933 (K, US); Sultepec rd. 10 mi. S of Nevado de Toluca Jct., on *Abies religiosa, Peterson 68–91** in 1968 (FPF). NUEVO LEÓN: Cerro Potosí, on *Abies vejarii, H & W 394*, 396*, 3359* in 1963 (COLO, FPF); Municipio de Derrumbadero, in moister canyons above Santa Elena, San Juanito to San Miguel and E as far as Los Toros, on *Abies* sp., *Mueller* in 1935 (MO).

3. *ARCEUTHOBIUM AMERICANUM*

Specimens Examined: Host is *Pinus contorta* except as noted. For these records the varieties *murrayana* and *latifolia* are not distinguished because these can be determined by the geographic area involved (Critchfield 1957).

CANADA
ALBERTA

N fork of N branch of Saskatchewan River, *Brown 795* in 1908 (PH); Kananaskis For. Exp. Sta., *Muir 64–327* in 1964 (FPF) and on *Pinus sylvestris, Powell* in 1968 (CFB, FPF); Banff Nat. Park: Bankhead, *Brown 794* in 1906 (MO,PH, US). 2 mi. E of Lake Louise, *H & Baranyay 90* in 1961 (FPF); 4 mi. W of Lake Louise, *Petty 64–568* in 1964 (FPF); Eisenhower Jct.; on *Picea glauca, H & Baranyay 92* in 1961 (FPF); 1.5 mi. E of Eisenhower Jct., *H & Baranyay 91* in 1961 (FPF); Cypress Hills, W of Spring Cr. Ranger Sta., *Breitung 5586* in 1947 (MO); Cypress Hills, Elkwater, *Lawrence* in 1967 (FPF, WINF); Jasper Nat. Park, Snaring River, on *Picea glauca, Bourchier* in 1954 (CFB, FPF); 7 mi. W of Cold Lake, on *Pinus banksiana, Wilkinson* in 1960 (CFB, FPF); 38 mi. SE of Conklin, on *Pinus banksiana, Wilkinson* in 1961 (CFB, FPF); 20 mi. NW of Slave Lake Town, on *Pinus banksiana, Smith* in 1962 (CFB, FPF); 2 mi. W of Fort Assiniboine, on *Pinus banksiana, Emond & Layton* in 1966 (CFB, FPF); 23 mi. SW of Clearwater Ranger Sta., *Smith* in 1966 (CFB, FPF); 3 mi. SW of Clearwater Ranger Sta., *Smith* in 1965 (CFB, FPF); 2 mi. N and 2 mi. E of St. Vincent, on *Pinus*

banksiana, Layton in 1966 (CFB, FPF); 4 mi. NW of Rocky, *Smith* in 1966 (CFB, FPF).

BRITISH COLUMBIA

Guichon Cr., 13 mi. S of Savona, *Hitchcock & Martin 7425* in 1941 (COLO, DS, MO, POM, RM, RSA, UC, WTU); 10 mi. N of Clinton, *Calder, Parmalee & Taylor 16644* in 1956 (COLO, US); Prince George, *Calder, Savile & Ferguson 14363* in 1954 (WTU); Kleena Kleen P. O., 50° 57'N, 124° 52' W, *Calder, Parmalee & Taylor 19159* in 1956 (DS, WTU); 3 mi. S of Ta Ta Cr., N of Cranbrook, *Calder & Savile 11374* in 1953 (UC, US); near Allenby, *McCallum* in 1940 (UC); Settlers rd., Kootenny Nat. Park, *Morf 64–86* in 1964 (FPF); 20 mi. NW of Kelowna, *Stewart* in 1965 (FPF); 2.5 mi. SW of Telkwa, *Calder, Savile & Ferguson 15273* in 1954 (US); Bonaparte River, *Macoum* in 1889 (US); Salmon Arm, *Weir 8444* in 1913 (ILL); 25 mi. SE of Kelowna, *Kuijt* in 1954 (DAVFP, FPF); Perry Cr., *Kuijt 598* in 1954 (DAVFP, FPF); Moyie River, *Kuijt* in 1954 (DAVFP, FPF); between Yahk and Moyie Lake, *Kuijt* in 1954 (DAVFP, FPF); 33 mi. N of Rock Cr., *Kuijt* in 1954 (DAVFP, FPF); 1 mi. S of Beaverdell, *Kuijt* in 1954 (DAVFP, FPF); Carmi, *Kuijt 591* and *592* in 1954 (DAVFP, FPF); McCulloch, *Kuijt 589* in 1954 (DAVFP, FPF); Thompson River, *Kuijt* in 1954 (DAVFP, FPF); 8 mi. N of Kimberly, *Kuijt 528* in 1954 (DAVFP, FPF); 45 mi. S of Radium, *Kuijt* in 1953 (DAVFP, FPF); Windermere, *Kuijt 535* in 1953 (DAVFP, FPF); Kootenay Park, *Kuijt* in 1954 (DAVFP, FPF); 12 mi. N. of Clinton, *Kuijt* in 1954 (DAVFP, FPF); Jesmond, *Kuijt* in 1954 (DAVFP, FPF); Pavilion Mtn., *Kuijt* in 1954 (DAVFP, FPF); Eholt, *Kuijt* in 1954 (DAVFP, FPF); Balfour, *Kuijt* in 1954 (DAVFP, FPF); Manning Park, 10 mi. E of Allison Summit, *Kuijt* in 1954 (DAVFP, FPF); Manning Park, Sunday Summit, *Kuijt** in 1954 (DAVFP, FPF); Moyie Lake, *Kuijt* in 1954 (DAVFP, FPF); Mt. Robson Park, Fraser River, *Kuijt* in 1954 (DAVFP, FPF); Mt. Robson Park, Yellowhead, *Kuijt 536* in 1953 (DAVFP, FPF); 100-Mile House, *Simms* in 1955 (DAVFP, FPF); Manning Park, near E bdy, *Sugden* in 1960 (DAVFP, FPF); Alexis Cr., *Simms* in 1955 (DAVFP, FPF).

MANITOBA

Near Cowan, on *P. banksiana, Riley 47–208* in 1947 (MO, RM); Victoria Beach, on *P. banksiana, Jackson* in 1924 (ILL) and *Löve & Löve 5740* in 1953 (US); Belaire Provincial For., on *P. banksiana, Lawrence* in 1967 (FPF, WINF); Iskwasum Lake, on *Pinus banksiana, Laut* in 1968 (FPF, WINF); Black Island, Lake Winnipeg, on *Pinus banksiana, Lawrence* in 1968 (FPF, WINF).

SASKATCHEWAN

Prince Albert, on planted *P. contorta*, *Beveridge* in 1968 (FPF, WINF); MacDowall, on *P. banksiana*, *Blumer 5177* in 1913 (FPF); Lac la Ronge, on *P. banksiana*, *McLeod* in 1965 (FPF, WINF); Cumberland House on *P. banksiana*, *Crawford* in 1967 (FPF, WINF); S shore of Lake Athabaska, on *P. banksiana*, *McLeod* in 1966 (FPF, WINF); Lac la Loche, on *P. banksiana*, *Rentz* in 1967 (FPF, WINF); Mile 10.7 on Cumberland rd., on *P. banksiana*, *Crawford* in 1968 (FPF, WINF); Mile 15 on Turner Lake rd., on *P. banksiana*, *Laut* in 1968 (FPF, WINF); Ile a' la Crosse, on *P. banksiana*, *Laut* in 1968 (FPF, WINF).

UNITED STATES

CALIFORNIA

ALPINE CO.: Sandy Flat, N Stanislaus River [4 mi. NE of Alpine], *Stanford 629* in 1927 (RM); 5 mi. W of Alpine Co. bdy. on Rte. 4, on *P. ponderosa*, *Kuijt 1411* in 1957 (UC); 0.5 mi. W of grade summit on Rte. 4, on *P. ponderosa*, *Kuijt 1412* in 1957 (UC). CALAVERAS CO. Rte. 4 near Alpine Co. bdy., *Peterson 63–134** in 1963 (FPF); 3 mi. SW of Tamarack on Rte. 4, *H & Scharpf 664* in 1964 (FPF). EL DORADO CO.: US 50 at Pyramid Cr., *Kuijt 1513* in 1958 (UC); Lily Lake, Glen Alpine Can., *Abrams 12753* in 1903 (DS, MO, POM, UC); 16 mi. S of Tahoe City, on *P. ponderosa*, *Kuijt 1335* in 1957 (UC); 1.1 mi. N of Meyers on US 50, *H & W 838* in 1966 (FPF); 9 mi. E of Kyburz on US 50, *H & W 839* in 1966 (FPF). FRESNO CO.: Huntington Lake, *Solbrig 2420* in 1957 (UC) and *Perkins* in 1920 (ILL); House Meadows, N fork of Kings River [5 mi. W of Wishon Dam], *Hall & Chandler 426* in 1900 (UC); Vermillion Valley, *Quibell & Quibell 2641* in 1953 (RSA). KERN CO.:Havileah [7 mi. S of Bodfish], *Coville & Funston 1596* in 1891 (FPF; US). LASSEN CO.: Bridge Cr., 7–8 mi. SW of Eagle Lake, *Whitney 1717* in 1934 (UC). MADERA CO.: Red's Meadow to Rainbow Falls, *Raven 3678* in 1951 (RSA); Devils Post Pile Nat. Mon., *H & Scharpf 670* in 1964 (FPF). MARIPOSA CO.: Tenaya Lake, *Root* in 1919 (FPF, ILL) and *H 939* in 1966 (FPF); Little Yosemite Valley, *Bolander 5095* in 1866 (MO, UC, US), *Rodin 877* in 1946 (UC); Merced Lake Trail, Yosemite, *Schreiber 1948* in 1935 (UC); Upper Yosemite Valley, *Lemmon* in 1878 (MO). MONO CO.: 4.3 mi. W of Jct. of Rtes. 120 and 395, *Kuijt 1390* in 1957 (UC); 2 mi. W of Lee Vining, on *P. jeffreyi*, *Peterson 63–129* in 1963 (FPF);

W of Lee Vining on Tioga Pass rd., *Krebill & Nelson 468* in 1967 (FPF). NEVADA CO.: 4 mi. from Truckee, *Wright FP 68107* in 1932 (FPF); Hobart Mills, *Gill FP 68063* in 1931 (FPF); Donner State Park, *H* in 1963 (FPF); Donner Lake, *Dudley* in 1893 (DS) and *Sonne* in 1898 (US); near Truckee, *Sonne* in 1898 (UC), *Wright FP 68048* in 1931 (FPF), *Gill FP 68227* in 1931 (FPF). PLACER CO.: Near Cisco, *Boyce 40* in 1919 (FPF); 7 mi. W of Soda Springs, *W 3226* in 1962 (COLO, FPF); N Tahoe Meadow, Lake Tahoe, *Schreiber 776* in 1932 (UC); 3.5 mi. N of Tahoe City on Rte. 89, *Kuijt 1332* in 1957 (UC); 8.5 mi. W of Soda Springs, on *P. ponderosa*, *Kuijt 1330* in 1957 (UC); 10 mi. N of Tahoe City on Rte. 89, on *P. ponderosa*, *Kuijt 1331* in 1957 (UC); 9.2 mi. N of Tahoe City on Rte. 89, on *P. jeffreyi*, *Kuijt 1343* in 1957 (UC). PLUMAS CO.: Chester, *Meinecke FP 17053* in 1914 (FPF); 18 mi. N of Greenville, *Kuijt 1350* in 1957 (UC); Graegle Cr. near Lake Center Camp, *Mason 1079* in 1924 (JEPS, UC); 8 mi. W of Rte. 89 on Webber Lake rd., *H & W 657* in 1964 (FPF); Buck's Ranch, *Meinecke* in 1920 (FPF); Little Grizzly Valley, on *P. jeffreyi*, *Boyce* in 1915 (FPF). SHASTA CO.: Thousand Lake Basin, *Peirson 10136* in 1932 (RSA); Lassen Nat. Park on main rd. 10 mi. E of north entrance, *H & W 651* in 1964 (FPF); headwaters of Hat Cr., *Eggleston 7459* in 1911 (MO, US). SIERRA CO.: Gold Lake, *Gill FP 68046* in 1931 (FPF); 9.5 mi. N of Truckee, *Kuijt 1344* in 1957 (UC); Webber Lake, "*Loran*", n.d., (UC). SISKIYOU CO.: Military Pass, NE side Mt. Shasta, *Cooke 16034* in 1941 (DS, UC); Mt. Shasta, Sisson, *Pendleton* in 1919 (FPF, ILL); 3 mi. S of Tennant, *Boyce* in 1914 (FPF); N fork of Sacramento River, *Raven 10456* in 1959 (CAS). TEHAMA CO.: Mineral, *Meinecke FP 97934* in 1911 (FPB); Mineral Campground, near Ranger Sta., *Kuijt 1358* in 1957 (UC); Deer Cr., 1.5 mi. S of Jct. of Rtes. 32 and 36, *Kuijt 1501* in 1958 (UC); Deer Cr., 1 mi. E of Rtes. 89 and 36 on Rte. 32, *Waters 242* in 1958 (JEPS); 13 mi. W of Rtes. 36 and 89 at Lake Almanor, on *P. ponderosa*, *Kuijt 1354 & 1355* in 1957 (UC); 7 mi. W of Rtes. 36 and 89 at Lake Almanor, on *P. ponderosa*, *Kuijt 1352* in 1957 (UC). TULARE CO.: Long Meadow, *Peterson 63–149** in 1963 (FPF); Bakeoven Meadows, S fork Kern River, *Howell 27038* in 1950 (DS, UC, US); Jct. Meadows, Kern River, *Raven 8349* in 1955 (UC); Sequoia Nat. Park; 13 mi. NW of Lodgepole, *W 3614* in 1964 (FPF); Funston Camp [11 mi. SE of Mineral King], *Peirson 1720* in 1919 (RSA); ridge between Monache and Bakeoven Meadows, *Munz 15220* in 1950 (RSA). TUOLUMNE CO.: Pinecrest, *Wright FP 68114* in 1932 (FPF) and *Gill FP 68229* in 1931 (FPF). COUNTY UNCERTAIN: N California border, Salmon Nat. For., *Galbreath FP 1691* in 1909 (FPF).

COLORADO

BOULDER CO.: 3 mi. S of Ward on Rte. 160, *H & Gill* in 1958 (FPF); 1.5 mi. W of Rte. 160 on Brainard Lake rd., *H 418* in 1963 (FPF); Allenspark, *Johnston & Thompson FP 24881* in 1917 (FPF); Niwot Hill, near Ward, *Schmoll 498* in 1922 (COLO); Pine Glade School, *Ramaley 3754* in 1907 (COLO); Ward, *Newman* in 1922 (COLO); near Nederland, *W 2966* in 1961 (COLO); Allenspark, on *P. ponderosa*, *H 828* in 1965 (FPF). CHAFFEE CO.: Alpine, *Brandegee* in 1880 (FPF); 8 mi. W of Buena Vista, *H 445* in 1963 (FPF); Forest City, *Brandegee 12201* in 1880 (MO). CLEAR CREEK CO.: Silver Plume, *Bethel FP 27111* in 1918 (FPF); 0.5 mi. SE of Alice, *H & W 283* in 1963 (FPF); 4.4 mi. E of Berthoud Pass, *Greene & Richter 112* in 1962 (COLO, FPF); Clear Cr. Valley, *Engelmann* in 1874 (MO, UC); Empire, *Patterson 297* in 1892 (MO, UC, US); 3 mi. W of Bergen Park, *H 566* in 1964 (FPF); above Empire, *Engelmann* in 1874 (MO); Bergen Park, *Greene* in 1873 (MO); Empire, *Torrey* in 1872 (MO); Georgetown, *Wootson 23* in 1873 (US). DOUGLAS CO.: Rampart Range rd., 5 mi. S of Long Hollow Jct., *H 205* in 1962 (FPF). EAGLE CO.: Mt. of the Holy Cross, *Coulter 7655* in 1873 (MO, PH, US) and *Hedgcock FP 624* in 1909 (FPF); Red Cliff, *Gayman FP 26295* in 1917 (FPF); 5 mi. E of Vail on US 6, *H 947* in 1966 (FPF). GILPIN CO.: Rollinsville, *Wheeler 830* in 1901 (COLO, RM); Rollinsville, on *P. ponderosa*, *Hedgcock FP 22598* in 1916 (FPF); Tolland, *Bethel 317* in 1921 (CS), *Gayman & Hinson* in 1917 (FPF), *Hedgcock FP 22592* in 1916 (FPF, UC); Lake Eldora, *Hedgcock FP 22549* in 1916 (FPF). GRAND CO.: Granby, *Bethel* in 1906 (CS), *Benson 4907* in 1933 (POM); Fraser, *Hedgcock & Johnston FP 26068* in 1917 (FPF); Idlewild, *Hedgcock FP 1649* in 1909 (FPF); 6 mi. W of Fraser, *H 81* in 1961 (FPF); 18 mi. S of Parshall on Leal rd., *Hinds & H* in 1960 (FPF); 8.3 mi. N of Fraser on US 40, *Greene & Richter 113* in 1962 (COLO, FPF); 11.3 mi. N of Granby on US 34, *Greene & Richter 114* in 1962 (COLO, FPF); Grand Lake, col.? in 1881 (MO) and *Shear & Bessey 5317* in 1898 (US). GUNNISON CO.: 5 mi. E of Taylor Park on Cottonwood Pass rd., *H 945* in 1966 (FPF); 2.5 mi. W of Monarch Pass on US 50, *Hinds 63–13* in 1963 (FPF). JACKSON CO.: North Park, *Barber* in 1874 (US); E side of Buffalo Pass, *H 414* in 1963 (FPF); Silver Cr., 4 mi. S of Gould, *H 415** in 1963 (FPF); Silver Cr., 4 mi. SE of Gould, on *Picea engelmannii*, *H 934* in 1966 (FPF); 1 mi. N of Willow Cr. Pass, *H 416* in 1963 (FPF); Big Cr. Lake, *H 830* in 1965 (FPF); near Wyoming line on Rte. 127, *Davidson & Gill FP 89991* in 1952 (FPF). JEFFERSON CO.: Redskin Cr., *Hill FP 68279* in 1932 (FPF). LAKE CO.: Leadville, *Clokey 2684* in 1916 (DS, FPF, ILL, RM, UC, US) and *Schedin &*

Schedin, n.d. (RM). LARIMER CO.: Longs Peak Inn, *Cooper 23* in 1908 (RM); 9.8 mi. W of Pingree Park rd. on Crown Point rd., *H 411* in 1963 (FPF); Rocky Mountain Nat. Park, Glacier Basin, *Smith* in 1937 (CS); 5 mi. W of Redfeather Lakes, *H 190* in 1960 (FPF); 4 mi. W of Redfeather Lakes, *H 407** in 1963 (FPF); Longs Peak Valley, *Kiener 5686* in 1937 (COLO); Buckhorn Mtn., Stove Prairie Summit, *H 553* in 1964 (FPF); 2 mi. W of Buckhorn Ranger Sta., *H 560* in 1964 (FPF); Bear Gulch, 6 mi. W of Masonville, *H 711* in 1964 (FPF); Stove Prairie Summit, on *P. ponderosa*, *H 192* in 1961 (FPF); 3 mi. E of Creedmore Lakes rd., on *P. ponderosa*, *H 261* in 1962 (FPF); Boulder Ridge, on *P. ponderosa*, *H 263* in 1962 (FPF), Tie Siding-Cherokee Park rd., on *P. ponderosa*, *H 286* in 1962 (FPF); 1 mi. W of Redfeather lakes, on *P. ponderosa*, *H 408* in 1963 (FPF); Devils Cr. on Sand Cr. Pass rd., on *P. ponderosa*, *Schacht* in 1962 (FPF); 0.5 mi. E of Buckhorn Ranger Sta., on *P. ponderosa*, *H 555* in 1963 (FPF); Pennock Cr., 2 mi. S of Pinge Park rd., on *P. ponderosa*, *H 563* in 1964 (FPF); Bear Gulch rd., 6 air mi. W of Masonville, on *P. ponderosa*, *H 712* in 1964 (FPF); 4 mi. W of Redfeather Lakes, on *P. flexilis*, *H 258* in 1962 (FPF); 3 mi. W of Redfeather Lakes, on *P. flexilis*, *H 409* in 1963 (FPF); 4.8 mi. W of Pingree rd. on Crown Point rd., on *P. flexilis*, *H 412* in 1963 (FPF); Pennock Cr. 2 mi. S of Pingree Park rd., on *P. flexilis*, *H 561* in 1964 (FPF); 5 mi. W of Redfeather Lakes, on *Picea engelmannii*, *H 189* in 1961 (FPF); 4 mi. W of Redfeather Lakes on *Picea engelmannii*, *H 406* in 1963 (FPF); SE of Chambers Lake, on *Picea engelmannii*, *Schacht* in 1962 (FPF); N Fork Poudre River, ca. 7 mi. W of Redfeather Lakes on *Picea engelmannii*, *H 559* in 1964 (FPF); 1 mi. E of Buckhorn Ranger Sta., on *Picea pungens*, *H 554* in 1964 (FPF). MOFFAT CO.: Cold Spring Mtn., 0.25 mi. E of Utah and 1.5 mi. S of Wyoming, *Brown* in 1965 (FPF). PARK CO.: Fairplay, *Gill FP 68140* in 1932 (FPF); 3 mi. NW of Fairplay, *H 447* in 1963 (FPF); Summit of Kenosha Pass on US 285, *H 448* in 1963 (FPF); 4.4 mi. N of Grant on Geneva Basin rd., *H 450* in 1964 (FPF) and on *P. aristata*, *H 449* in 1963 (FPF); 0.3 mi. E of Santa Maria, *H 451* in 1963 (FPF) and on *P. ponderosa*, *H 452* in 1963 (FPF); Payne Gulch [near Bailey], on *P. flexilis*, *Hill FP 68236* in 1932 (FPF). ROUTT CO.: Walton Cr. Campground, *Hinds 63–21* in 1963 (FPF); Steamboat Springs, *Galpin* in 1908 (FPF); Hahn's Peak, *Edmonston FP 188* in 1908 (FPF) and on *Picea engelmannii*, *Edmonston FP 199* in 1908 (ILL); 0.25 mi. S of Trout Cr. Campround (T. 3 N., R. 86 W., Sec. 18), *H, Andrews & Buchanan* in 1961 (FPF); 9 mi. E of Clark, *H 191* in 1961 (FPF); 4 mi. SE of Clark, *H 413* in 1963 (FPF); Seedhouse, E of Clark, *Weber 6725* in 1951 (COLO, WTU); 8 mi. E of

Clark, *Weber 6093* in 1951 (COLO); near Steamboat Springs, *Greene & Richter 115* in 1962 (COLO). SUMMIT CO.: Breckenridge, *Seay FP 33403* in 1917 (FPF), *Mackenzie 78* in 1901 (MO, PH, RM, US); Dillion, *Shear 3764* in 1896 (RM); near Dillon, *W 3260* in 1962 (COLO); Mt. Baldy near Breckenridge, *Henderson* in 1897–1909 (MO). COUNTY UNCERTAIN: Sawatch Range, *Brandegee* in 1880 (PH, UC); South Park, *Wolf & Rothrock 70* in 1873 (PH) and *Hall & Harbour 574* in 1862 (MO); Middle Park, *Patterson* in 1875 (PH) and *Torrey* in 1872 (MO); Latitude 39–41°, *Parry 574* in 1862 (US).

IDAHO

ADAMS CO.: Evergreen, *Hedgcock FP 1908* in 1909 (FPF). BEAR LAKE CO.: 7 mi. NW of Liberty on Rte. 36, *H & Hinds 1007* in 1966 (FPF). BENEWAH CO.: 1 mi. S of Emida, *Owenbey & Owenbey 2023* in 1940 (ARIZ, DS, MO, POM, UC, US, WTU); S end of Coeur d' Alene Lake, col.? in 1891 (UC). BLAINE CO.: Near source of Wood River, *Henderson 3581* in 1895 (US). BOISE CO.: Idaho City, *Weir 8456* in 1917 (ILL). BONNER CO.: Priest Lake, *Hedgcock & Weir 8456* in 1917 (ILL). BONNER CO.: Priest Lake, *Hedgcock & Weir FP 9489* in 1911 (FPF) and *Piper 3701* in 1901 (US). BONNEVILLE CO.: SW of Victor, *Peterson 62–14* in 1962 (FPF); 11 mi. NE of Swan Valley on Rte. 31, *H & Hinds 1120* in 1968 (FPF). CAMAS CO.: Boise River, 10 mi. NE of Elmore Co. bdy., *Peterson 62–51* in 1962 (FPF). CASSIA CO.: 14 mi. W of Oakley on Rogerson rd., *H & Hinds 1005* in 1966 (FPF). CARIBOU CO.: Diamond Cr., 18 mi. NE of Soda Springs, *Mentz* in 1914 (ILL); 4 mi. W of Freedom, Wyoming on Rte. 34, *H & Hinds 1119* in 1968 (FPF). CUSTER CO.: Redfish Lake, *Macbride & Payson 3654* in 1916 (MO, RM); Marsh Cr., 25 mi. NW of Stanley, *Cronquist 2829* in 1941 (MO). FRANKLIN CO.: Franklin Basin, *Peterson 63–361* in 1963 (FPF). FREMONT CO.: Eccles [near Pineview], *Hedgcock FP 879* in 1909 (FPF); Big Springs, *Hedgcock FP 888* in 1909 (FPF); Buffalo For. Camp on Buffalo River, *Cronquist 1613* in 1929 (MO). IDAHO CO.: Warren Divide, 4 mi. from Warren, *Stillinger & Root* in 1920 (ILL); 14 mi. S of Salmon River on US 95, *Peterson 62–47* in 1962 (FPF); 7 mi. N of Burgdorf on Salmon River rd., *H 972* in 1966 (FPF). KOOTENAI CO.: Coeur d' Alene, *Weir 8442** in 1917 (FPF, RM, US) and *Weir 9829* in 1918 (FPF, ILL), and on *P. ponderosa*, *Weir 2387*, n.d. (FPF, ILL); Fishhook Cr., *Gill FP 68200** in 1932 (FPF); Rathdrum, *Sandberg, MacDougal & Heller 892* in 1892 (DS, US); Hayden Lake, *Weir 8440* in 1917 (FPF, ILL); without locality, *Sandberg 9358* in 1892 (MO, RM, WTU) and *Lieberg* in 1892 (PH). LEMHI CO.: Gibbonsville, *Wolpert* in 1917 (ILL); 4 mi. N of Gibbonsville on US 93, *H & Hinds 1124* in 1968 (FPF); 20–25 mi.

mi. N of Salmon on US 93, *Gill & Hinds FP 89981* in 1951 (FPF); Parker Mtn., ca. 18 mi. WNW of Challis, [listed as Custer Co.], *Macbride & Payson 3270* in 1916 (MO, RM, US); SW of Salmon, between Williams Cr. and Moccasin Cr., *Krebill 127* in 1964 (FPF); 4 mi. E of Gibbonsville, on *P. ponderosa*, *Peterson 63–295* in 1963 (FPF). MADISON CO.: Hawley Ranger Sta., *Peterson 62–17* in 1962 (FPF). TETON CO.: Packsaddle Can., W of Driggs, *Peterson 62–10* in 1962 (FPF). TWIN FALLS CO.: 15 mi. E of Rogerson on Oakley rd., *H & Hinds 1004* in 1966 (FPF); 30 mi. W of Oakley, *Benlow* in 1917 (FPF, ILL). VALLEY CO.: Deadwood Basin, *Korstian* in 1918 (FPF, ILL); 3 mi. NW of McCall on shore of Payette Lake, *H 976* in 1966 (FPF); Smith Ferry, *Benlow* in 1917 (ILL); 13 mi. E of Cascade, on *P. ponderosa*, *Jones 5076* in 1934 (UC, WTU). COUNTY UNCERTAIN: Middle Fork of Salmon River, *Trey* in 1941 (US); Ross, *Weir 8389* in 1915 (ILL); Lemhi Nat. For., on *P. flexilis*, *Weir* in 1917 (ILL).

MONTANA

BEAVERHEAD CO.: Pioneer Mtns., 11 mi. S of Dewey on Can. Cr. rd., *H & Wicker 949* in 1966 (FPF); 2.5 mi. E of Lemhi Pass, *H & Hinds 1121* in 1968 (FPF). CARBON CO.: Woohoe Cr., near Red Lodge, *Langnor* in 1917 (ILL). CASCADE CO.: Neilhart, *Langnor* n.d. (ILL). DEERLODGE CO.: 3 mi. N of US 10A on Warm Springs rd., *H & Wicker 951* in 1966 (FPF); Warm Springs Ranger Sta., *Peterson 62–18* in 1962 (FPF). FLATHEAD CO.: Glacier Nat. Park: Bowman Lake, *Jones* in 1910 (POM) and McDowell Lake, *Standley 16335* in 1919 (US). GALLATIN CO.: West Yellowstone, *Payson & Payson 1937* in 1920 (MO, RM) and *Hopkins 426* in 1922 (US); Hyalite Can., *Weber 1957* in 1941 (COLO); Shoefelt Ranger Sta. [9 mi. SE of Bozeman], *Hedgcock FP 4338* in 1910 (FPF). GLACIER CO.: 7.8 mi. S of St. Mary on US 89, *H 89* in 1961 (FPF); 0.7 mi. S of Going-to-Sun Chalets, *Gill FP 68205* in 1932 (FPF). GRANITE CO.: Emerine Lookout rd., on *Pinus albicaulis*, *H & Wicker 952* in 1966 (FPF); Skalkaho Pass, *Peterson 62–60** in 1962 (FPF); Garnet, *Scheuber* in 1902 (UC, US); Stumptown Cr. near Phillipsburg, *Hughes* in 1917 (FPF, ILL); Georgetown, *Wolpert* in 1917 (FPF, ILL). LINCOLN CO.: Libby, *Smith* in 1915 (ILL). MEAGHER CO.: Little Belt Mtns.; Sheep Cr., *Langnor* in 1918 (ILL); Adams Cr., 16 mi. N of White Sulfur Springs, *Gill FP 89984* in 1948 (FPF). MINERAL CO.: St. Regis, *Weir 7473* in 1918 (ILL); 6 mi. W of St. Regis on US 10, *H & Wicker 954* in 1966 (FPF); east of Savenac Nursery [near Haugan], *Hubert* in 1915 (ILL); De Borgia, *Hughes* in 1917 (FPF, ILL). MISSOULA CO.: Lolo Hot Springs, *Barkley & Barkley 3505* in 1938 (MO, UC,

US); Seeley Lake, *Weir 9780* in 1918 (ILL). PARK CO.: Specimen Cr., *Swingle* in 1933 (CS, RM, WTU). PHILLIPS CO.: Little Rocky Mtns., Midvale, *Umbach 594* in 1903 (ARIZ, DS, RM, US). RAVALLI CO.: Darby, on *P. ponderosa, Weir 2382* in 1916 (ILL) and on *P. albicaulis, Weir 2379* in 1916 (ILL); Alta, *Jones* in 1909 (US). SANDERS CO.: Thompson Falls, *Hedgcock & Weir FP 9443* in 1911 (FPF). SILVER BOW CO.: Highland Mtns., 5 mi. SE of US 91 on Highland lookout rd., *H & Wicker 950* in 1966 (FPF). COUNTY UNCERTAIN: Big Adrian Gulch near Helena, *Starz* in 1893 (DS).

NEVADA

COUNTY UNCERTAIN: Without locality, *Wheeler* in 1872 (US).

OREGON

BAKER CO.: Jim Cr. fork of Eagle Cr., 30 mi. NE of Baker, *Graham* in 1965 (FPF); Horse Cr., 20 mi. W of Baker, *Graham* in 1965 (FPF). CLACKAMAS CO.: Lemiti Butte, SE corner of co., *Thompson* in 1968 (FPF). CROOK CO.: N Big Meadow, *Nelson 845* in 1905 (RM); Laidlow area, *Whited 3171* in 1906 (US). DESCHUTES CO.: 18 mi. W of Bend, *Ferris & Duthie 467* in 1919 (DS, RM); Head of Fall River [9 mi. NW of La Pine], *Peck 14322* in 1925 (DS, PH); near Pistol Butte, ca. 9 mi. N of La Pine, on *P. ponderosa, H & Scharpf 1261* in 1969 (FPF); 10 mi. NW of Sisters on US 126, *H & W 614* in 1964 (FPF); 21 mi. S of Bend on US 97, *H & W 618* in 1964 (FPF); Pringle Butte, *H 988* in 1966 (FPF); 4 mi. E of McKenzie Pass on Rte. 242, *H & Hinds 993* in 1966 (FPF). DOUGLAS CO.: Diamond Lake, *Henderson 11501* in 1929 (PH); 20 mi. NE of Union Cr. on Rte. 230, *H 1143* in 1968 (FPF). GRANT CO.: Whitman Nat. For., Bates, *Boyce FP 40120* in 1920 (OSC) and *Boyce 703* in 1920 (FPF); Dixie Butte rd., 5 mi. N of US 26, *H 979* in 1966 (FPF); 10 mi. N of John Day, *Graham** in 1964 (FPF); 15 mi. N of John Day, *Graham* in 1964 (FPF); John Day Exp. For. [9 mi. E of Bates], *Childs 245* in 1955 (OSC); Dixie Pass on Rte. 26, *H & W 581* in 1964 (FPF); Dry Meadow, ca. 24 air mi. E of Seneca, *H & Scharpf 1269* in 1969 (FPF). HARNEY CO.: [was Crook Co.], Black Butte [27 mi. NW of Burns], *Cusick 2691* in 1901 (MO, POM, RM, UC, US). JACKSON CO.: 22 mi. E of Ashland on Lake of the Woods rd., *H & W 871* in 1966 (FPF). JEFFERSON CO.: Metolius area, *Gill FP 68190* in 1932 (FPF). JOSEPHINE CO.: Waldo [7 mi. S of Cave Jct.], on *P. jeffreyi, Weir 2384* in 1916 (FPF, ILL); Oregon Mtn. [14 mi. SW of Cave Jct.], on *P. attenuata,*

Weir 2376 in 1916 (FPF, ILL) and *2374* (ILL). KLAMATH CO.: Crater Lake Nat. Park, *Gill FP 68185* in 1932 (FPF); T. 23 S., R. 7 E. [NE of Crescent], *Overbay FP 68282* in 1932 (FPF); 15 mi. SW of Crescent Lake, *Childs 67* in 1937 (OSC); Crescent, *Peck 9594* in 1928 (DS, MO, PH); Crescent, *Boyce FP 40198* in 1921 (OSC); 7 mi. S of Crescent, *Peck 21639* in 1943 (UC); 6 mi. S of Rte. 58 on Windigo Pass rd., *H & W 620* in 1964 (FPF); 5 mi. W of US 97 on Rte. 230, *H & W 623* in 1964 (FPF); S of Sand Cr. [5 mi. N of Yamsey Ranger Sta.], *Childs 14* in 1947 (OSC); Fort Klamath, *Walpole 234 & 323* in 1899 (US) and *Meinecke* in 1915 (FPF); Buck Lake, *Applegate 2478* in 1898 (US); 7 mi. N of Fort Klamath, *Meinecke* in 1913 (FPF); Crater Lake, on *P. ponderosa, Dachnowski-Stokes* in 1913 (US). LAKE CO.: Dairy Cr. Guard Sta. [13 mi. NE of Quartz Pass], *Steward & Steward 7471* in 1958 (DS, US). LINN CO.: 0.5 mi. W of Rte. 22 near Rte. 20, *Steward 6605* in 1953 (RSA, WTU). UMATILLA CO.: Langdon Lake, 20 mi. E of Weston on Rte. 204, *H & W 591* in 1964 (FPF). UNION CO.: 3 mi. SE of Kamela, *H & W 586* in 1964 (FPF). WALLOWA CO.: 6 mi. SE of Wallowa, *Sampson & Pearson 21* in 1907 (US); Billy Meadows [30 mi. NNE of Enterprise,] *Coville 2487, 2488, 2489, 2490,* and *2491* in 1907 (US). WASCO CO.: Bear Springs, *Hansbrough FP 68270* in 1931 (FPF); 20 mi. NW of Warm Springs on US 26, *H & W 612* in 1964 (FPF). COUNTY UNCERTAIN: Big Meadows, Deschutes River, *Leiberg 520* in 1894 (DS, MO, POM, RM, US); Blue Mtns., *Nuttall* n.d. (MO, PH).

UTAH

CACHE CO.: Jct. of Rte. 89 and Beaver Mtn. rd., *Mielke* in 1952 (UC). DAGGETT CO.: 45.5 mi. S of Manila on Rte. 44, *Greene & Richter 116* in 1962 (COLO, FPF); 19 mi. S of Manila on Rte. 44, *H 568* in 1964 (FPF) and on *P. ponderosa, H 569* in 1964 (FPF). SUMMIT CO.: Kamas, *Hedgcock FP 9339* in 1911 (FPF) and *FP 22718* in 1916 (FPF); 8 mi. E of Kamas, on *P. ponderosa, Hedgcock FP 22719* in 1916 (FPF, UC); 20 mi. E of Kamas on Rte. 150, *Peterson 62–4* in 1962 (FPF) and on *P. ponderosa, Peterson 62–5* in 1962 (FPF); Kamas Canyon at Shingle Cr., *Peterson 65–90* in 1965 (FPF), on *Pseudotsuga menziesii, Peterson 65–88* in 1965 (FPF) and on *Picea pungens, Peterson 65–89* in 1965 (FPF); Uinta Mtns., 6 mi. S of Wyo. bdy. on Rte. 150, *H 1188* in 1969 (FPF). COUNTY UNCERTAIN: Uinta Mtns., *Greeman & Greeman 4650* in 1931 (MO); Little Bush Cr. Knob, Ashley Nat. For., [Uintah Co.?], *Harrison & Larson 7859* in 1936 (COLO).

WASHINGTON

CHELAN CO.: Washington For. Reserve, head of Twenty-five-mile Cr. [W side of Chelan Lake near Stormy Mtn.], *Gorman 576* in 1897 (US). FERRY CO.: Sherman Cr. near Growden, *Wicker* in 1961 (WSP); Boulder Cr., *Eggleston 10599* in 1914 (US); 1.5 mi. W of Sherman Pass on Rte. 30, *H, Stewart & Thompson 1131* in 1968 (FPF). KITTITAS CO.: Ellensburg, *Brandegee 1069* in 1883 (US). KLICKITAT CO.: Near Swauk Pass, on US 97, 18 mi. N of US 10, *Wicker* in 1966 (FPF); Falcon Valley, *Suksdorf* in 1883 (PH, US). OKANOGAN CO.: 8 mi. E of Methow, *Graham* in 1964 (FPF). PEND OREILLE CO.: 3 mi. SW of Newport on US 2, *H & Wicker 1126* in 1968 (FPF). SKAMANIA CO.: SW of Mt. Adams, col.? in 1915 (ILL). SPOKANE CO.: 21 mi. SW of Newport on US 2, *H & Wicker 1127* in 1968 (FPF); Little Spokane River, *Hedgcock FP 67206* in 1934 (FPF); 5 mi. SW of Deer Park on US 395, *H, Stewart & Thompson 1128* in 1968 (FPF). STEVENS CO.: Northport, *Hedgcock FP 47157* and *FP 47756* in 1928 (FPF); 13 mi. E of Northport, *Hedgcock FP 49544* in 1929 (FPF); 12 mi. E of Northport, *Hedgcock FP 47529* in 1928 (FPF); Alladin, [15 mi. NE of Colville], *Hedgcock FP 54116* in 1931 (FPF); Colville, *Hedgcock FP 54116* in 1931 (FPF); Colville, *Hedgcock FP 59245* in 1933 (FPF). YAKIMA CO.: Big Klickitat River, N of Mt. Adams, *Henderson 2539* in 1892 (WTU); 7 mi. E [as "W"] of Chinook Pass, *Thompson 15105* in 1940 (DS, MO, PH, RSA, UC, US, WTU); Tieton Cr., 2 mi. SW of Tieton Lake, *H & W 599* in 1964 (FPF); 1 mi. W of Rimrock, N of Tieton Lake, *Stewart* in 1968 (FPF). COUNTY UNCERTAIN: Cascade Mtns., *Tweedy* in 1882 (MO).

WYOMING

ALBANY CO.: Medicine Bow Mtns.: Centennial, *Hedgcock FP 15834* in 1914 (FPF, UC); Lake Cr., *Hedgcock FP 15849* in 1914 (FPF); Fox Park, *Hedgcock FP 15965* in 1914 (FPF, RSA, UC), *Hedgcock FP 15848* in 1914 (FPF, UC), *Evans FP 17832* in 1915 (FPF), *Hedgcock & Johnston FP 26425* in 1917 (FPF), *Evans FP 17843* in 1915 (FPF); Libby Lodge, *Owenby 875* in 1935 (RM); Mtn. Home, *Osterhout 2523* in 1897 (RM); 6 mi. W of Centennial on Rte. 130, *Greene & Richter 126* in 1962 (COLO, FPF); Libby Cr., *Williams 2402* in 1935 (MO, US). Laramie Mtns.: East of Laramie, *Weir 9874* in 1918 (FPF, ILL); head of Pole Cr., *Nelson & Nelson 6833* in 1899 (RM); Sherman, *Letterman* in 1884 (PH); Boulder Ridge, 7 mi. SW of Tie Siding, *H. 285* in 1962 (FPF); east of Laramie, on *P. ponderosa*, *Weir 9875* in 1918

(FPF, ILL). Laramie Mtns., 5 mi. E of Interstate 80 on Happy Jack rd., *H & Bailey 1009* in 1966 (FPF) and, on *P. ponderosa*, *H & Bailey 1010* in 1966 (FPF). Pole Mtn.: on *P. ponderosa*, *Simmons* in 1917 (ILL); near Happy Jack, on *P. ponderosa*, *H 193* in 1960 (FPF) and *Porter 8756* in 1961 (RM). BIGHORN CO.: Bighorn Mtns., Meadowlark Lake, *H 265** in 1962 (FPF). CARBON CO.: Encampment, *Edmonston FP 51* in 1908 (FPF); 2 mi. E of Medicine Bow Lodge, *Greene & Richter 125* in 1962 (COLO, FPF). CONVERSE CO.: Laramie Mtns., Cold Springs, *Simmons* in 1917 (ILL). FREMONT CO.: Popo Agie Campground, ca. 17 air mi. SSW of Lander, *Stewart* in 1967 (FPF); Fossil Hill, ca. 12 air mi. SW of Lander, *Stewart* in 1967 (FPF): 6 mi. E of Togwotee Pass on US 287, *H 272* in 1962 (FPF); Horse Cr., 14 miles NW of Dubois, *H 273* in 1962 (FPF); Wiggins Fork, 16 mi. N of Dubois, *H 275* in 1962 (FPF); Long Cr., 21 mi. WNW of Dubois, *H 276* in in 1962 (FPF); 1 mi. SE of Sheridan Guard Sta., *278* in 1962 (FPF); T Cross Ranch, Dubois, *Cox FP 68228* in 1931 (FPF); Wiggins Fork, Shoshone Nat. For., on *P. flexilis*, *H 274* in 1962 (FPF); 23 mi. WNW of Dubois, on *P. flexilis*, *Stewart* in 1964 (FPF). JOHNSON CO.: Bighorn Mtns.: Duck Cr. Burn, ca. 20 mi. W of Buffalo on US 16, *H 264* in 1962 (FPF); 2 mi. E of Elgin Park, on *P. ponderosa*, *Stewart* in 1965 (FPF). LINCOLN CO.: 28 mi. W of La Barge on La Barge Can. rd., *H & Hinds 1118* in 1968 (FPF). NATRONA CO.: N Entrance Casper Mtn. Park, *Peterson 125–61* on 1961 (FPF). PARK CO.: Cody Can. at Mormon Cr., *H 266* in 1962 (FPF); Cody Can., Pahaska Teepee, on *P. flexilis*, *Gill & Davidson* in 1954 (FPF). SHERIDAN CO.: Bighorn Mtns.: Burgess Ranger Sta., 27 air mi. W of Sheridan, *Stewart* in 1966 (FPF); E fork of South Tongue River, 20 air mi. W of Big Horn, *Stewart in* 1966 (FPF). SUBLETTE CO.: 8.8 mi. N of Pinedale on Faler Cr. rd., *H 545* in 1963 (FPF); Pine Cr., near inlet to Fremont Lake, *Krebill 538* in 1967 (FPF); The Rim, 13.4 mi. SE of Bondurant on US 187, *H 546* in 1963 (FPF) and on *P. flexilis*, *H 547* in 1963 (FPF). 12.3 mi. E of US 89 on US 187, *H 548* in 1963 (FPF). TETON CO.: Jackson Hole, *Reed 1831* in 1948 (RM); Jackson Hole, Coulter Bay Jct., *H 271* in 1962 (FPF); 10.7 mi. NE of Jackson, *H 549* in 1963 (FPF); 4.9 mi. N of Moose, *H 550* in 1963 (FPF); 11.2 mi. W of Togowotee Pass on US 287, *H 551* in 1963 (FPF); 3 mi. S of Jenny Lake, *Greene & Richter 118* in 1962 (COLO, FPF); 1 mi. N of Teton Nat. Park on US 287, *Greene & Richter 119* in 1962 (COLO, FPF); Double Diamond Ranch near Moose, *Williams* in 1963 (RM). UINTA CO.: Black Fork Camp, SE of Evanston, *Haugl* in 1916 (ILL). YELLOWSTONE NAT. PARK: Fire Hole Basin, (Hayden Expedition) in 1872 (PH); Fountain Geyser, *Oleson 328* in 1904 (RM); Upper Basin, *Cooper 106y* in 1906 (RM); Sylvan Pass, *H 267* in

1962 (FPF) and on *P. flexilis, H 268* in 1962 (FPF); Yellowstone Lake Lodge, *H 269* in 1962 (FPF); Lewis River, 7 mi. N of S entrance on US 287, *H 270* in 1962 (FPF): Upper Madison, *Rydberg & Bessey 3938* in 1897 (PH, RM, US); Madison River, *Nelson & Nelson 5515* in 1899 (RM, MO, UC, US); Mammoth Hot Springs, *Greene & Richter 121* in 1962 (COLO, FPF); 8 mi. W of Can., *Greene & Richter 122* in 1962 (COLO, FPF); 1 mi. E of Fishing Bridge, *Greene & Richter 124* in 1962 (COLO, FPF); Geyser Basin, Firehole River, *Jones 5372* in 1934 (WTU); Upper Geyser Basin, *Setchell* in 1905 (UC); Yellowstone Lake, *Hayden* in 1871 (PH); Cache Cr., *Tweedy 449* in 1885 (UC); Lake Fork, *Hayden* in 1860 (MO); (without locality) *Forwood* in 1882 (MO) and *Mearns 4513* in 1902 (US). COUNTY UNCERTAIN: Hebron, *Hedgcock & Johnston FP 26433* in 1917 (FPF); near E entrance, Yellowstone Nat. Park, *Greene & Richter 123* in 1962 (COLO); Cooperton, *Garrett* in 1918 (ILL); Copper City, *Garrett* n.d. (UT).

4. *ARCEUTHOBIUM APACHECUM*

Specimens Examined: All on *Pinus strobiformis*.

UNITED STATES

ARIZONA

APACHE CO.: 4 mi. S of Eagar on Big Lake rd., *H & L 210* in 1962 (FPF); Escudilla Mtn., *Andresen & Simpson 1787** in 1962 (FPF). COCHISE CO.: Chiricahua Mtns.: Rustler Park, *Andresen & Miles 631* in 1960 (FPF); Onion Saddle, *Gilbertson* in 1968 (FPF) and *H & L 156* in 1962 and *1107* in 1968 (FPF). GRAHAM CO.: Graham Mtns.: *Ellis FP 89431* in 1939 (FPF); Treasure Park, *Stouffer & Gill FP 68292* and *FP 68293* in 1934 (FPF) and *Gill FP 89313* in 1936 (FPF); 0.5 mi. E of Hospital Flat, *H & L 228* in 1962 (FPF) and *1105* in 1968 (FPF). GREENLEE CO.: Blue Summit, *Gill FP 68306* in 1934 (FPF); 1 mi. S of Mogollon Rim on US 666, *L 64–21* in 1964 (FPF). PIMA CO.: Santa Catalina Mtns.: (without locality), *Hedgcock FP 9782* in 1911 (FPF, ILL) and *Shreeve* in 1908 (ARIZ); Mt. Lemmon, *Peterson 62–145** in 1962 (FPF); Soldiers Camp, *Goodding* in 1934 (RM) and *Gill FP 68128* in 1932 (FPF); head of Marshall Gulch, *Gill FP 68130* in 1932 (FPF); Bear Wallow, *H & L 167* in 1962 (FPF). Rincon Mtns., Mica Mtn., *Ela* in 1968 (FPF).

NEW MEXICO

CATRON CO.: 6 mi. S of Luna on US 260, *H & L 212* in 1962 (FPF); 7 mi. E of Mogollon on Rte. 78, *H & L 220* in 1962 (FPF); Mangas Mtn., *H & Scharpf 696** in 1964 (FPF); 1 mi. E of Fox Mtn., ca. 20 mi. N of Apache Cr., *H & L 929* in 1966 (FPF).

GRANT CO.: Hillsboro Peak, *Metcalfe 1173* in 1904 (CAS, FPF, MO, POM, UC, US); Emory Pass, *H & L 121* in 1962 (FPF) and *1102* in 1968 (FPF); 24 mi. N of Mimbres on Rte. 61, *L 65–40* in 1965 (FPF); Mimbres Valley and its east can. tributary, *Holzinger* in 1911 (US); 4 mi. E of Rte. 25 on Signal Peak rd., ca. 13 mi. N of Silver City, *H & L 891* in 1966 (FPF). LINCOLN CO.: Capitan Mtns.: E side Capitan Peak, *Martin 902* in 1945 (WTU); Seven Cabins Can., *Gill, Ellis & Hackleman** FP 89490* and *Ellis FP 89492* in 1938 (FPF); 1–2 mi. E of Capitan Gap, *H & L 105,. 107, 109* in 1962 (FPF) and *1098* in 1968 (FPF). SOCORRO CO.: San Mateo Mtns.: Hughes Sawmill, (4 mi. SW of Mt. Withington), *Long FP 21128** in 1915 (FPF); on Rte. 52, 12 mi. S of US 60, *L 65–36* in 1965 (FPF) and 13 mi. S, *H & L 1117* in 1968 (FPF). Magdalena Mtns.: North Baldy Mtn., *L 66–19* in 1966 (FPF).

MEXICO

COAHUILA: Sierra del Carmen, Ocampo, *H, L & Muñoz 1032* in 1967 (FPF).

5. *ARCEUTHOBIUM BICARINATUM*

Specimens Examined: All on *Pinus occidentalis*.

DOMINICAN REPUBLIC

AZUA PROV.: Las Cañitas, *Fuertes 1033* in 1912 (ILL, US, Z) and *Gasbarro** in 1963 (FPF); San Jose de Ocoa, Bejucal, *Ekman 12024* in 1929 (US). BARAHONA PROV.: Between Pedernales and Aceital, *Howard & Howard 8129* in 1946 (BM, US). LA VEGA PROV.: Constanza, *Allard 17432* in 1947 (US) and *H & W 1193* in 1969 (FPF); 26 km. S of Constanza on Valle Nueva rd., *H & W 1199* in 1969 (FPF). SAN JUAN PROV.: Sabana Nueva, *Howard & Howard 9125* in 1946 (US); 10 km. N of Hato Nueva, *Gasbarro** in 1963 (FPF). SANTIAGO PROV.: Pico des Rubio, *Jiminez 1069* in 1946 (US).

HAITI

DEPT. DE L' OUEST: Vicinity of Furcy, *Leonard 4690* in 1920 (US); Massif de la Selle, *Ekman 1313* in 1924 (US) and *Proctor 10771** and *10772* in 1955 (US); Mormes des Commissiares, *Holdrige 1328* in 1942 (BM, F, MO, UC, US).

6. *ARCEUTHOBIUM BLUMERI*

Specimens Examined: All on *Pinus strobiformis*.

UNITED STATES

ARIZONA

COCHISE CO.: Huachuca Mtns., Carr Can., *Goodding 309* in 1909 (ARIZ); 1.2 mi. W of Reef, *H & L 235** in 1962 (FPF) and *1109** in 1968 (FPF).

SANTA CRUZ CO.: Santa Rita Mtns.: Upper Florida Can., *Graham* in 1939 (DS); Mt. Wrightson Trail, 4 mi. from end of rd. in Madera Can., *H 796* in 1965 (FPF).

MEXICO

CHIHUAHUA: 36 mi. SW of La Junta, *H & W 296* in 1963 (FPF); 13 mi. W of El Vergel, *H & W 314* in 1963 (FPF); 13 mi. SE of Mesa Huacán on Chico rd., *H & W 475* in 1963 (FPF); 65 mi. SW of Matachic on Ocampo rd., *H & W 493** in 1963 (FPF); "Sierra Madre," *Giguieliat* in 1912 (ILL). DURANGO: 15 mi. W of El Salto on Rte. 40, *H & W 350* and *530** in 1963 (FPF); 48 mi. S of Durango on La Flor rd., *H & W 516* in 1963 (FPF); 19 mi W of Santiago Papasquiaro, *H & W 536** in 1963 (FPF). NUEVO LEÓN: Cerro Potosí, *Andresen & Steinhoff A2047* in 1962 (FPF) and *H & W 392* in 1963 (FPF).

7. ARCEUTHOBIUM CALIFORNICUM

Specimens Examined: All on *Pinus lambertiana* except as noted.

UNITED STATES

CALIFORNIA

BUTTE CO.: Big Bar Mt. Ridge, E of Pulga, *Quick 53–32* in 1953 (CAS). DEL NORTE CO.: 0.5 mi. E of Sourdough Jct., ca. 10 air mi. N of Gasquet, on *P. monticola*, *Miller* in 1969 (FPF). KERN CO.: Greenhorn Mtns.: 4 mi. N of Summit Guard Sta., *W 3609** in 1964 (FPF); near Tiger Flat, *Howell 38805* in 1962 (CAS). LAKE CO.: 23.5 mi. N of Upper Lake on Pillsbury Lake rd., *H & W 862* in 1966 (FPF). LOS ANGELES CO.: Between Wrightwood and Kratka Ridge, *Embree* in 1956 (UC); 0.5 mi. E of Vincent Gulch Divide, *Krebill 247* in 1956 (FPF); Little Rock-Bear Cr. Divide, *Ewan 10110* in 1936 (MO). MADERA CO.: Ellis (now Benedict) Meadow, *Meinecke FP 17062* in 1914 (FPF); Fish Cr. on Rock Cr. rd., *H 9* in 1953 (FPF); Soquel-Bass Lake rd., *Gill & Wright FP 68160** in 1932 (FPF) 5 mi. N of Bass Lake on Soquel rd., *H & H 1146* in 1968 (FPF). MARIPOSA CO.: Mariposa Grove, *Hedgcock & Meinecke FP 4822* in 1910 (FPF); Fish Cr. Camp, *Hedgcock & Meinecke FP 4833* in 1910 (FPF, ILL); Willow Cr., *Hedgcock & Meinecke FP 4838* in 1910 (FPF); Fish Camp, *Hedgcock & Meinecke FP 4827* in 1910 (FPF); 1 mi. E of Fish Camp, *H** in 1963 (FPF); 0.5 mi. SW of Fish Camp, *H 660* in 1964 (FPF). NEVADA CO.: Graniteville, *Boyce 32* in 1917 (FPF). PLUMAS CO.: Massack, *Gill & Wagener FP 68041* in 1931 (FPF); Silver Lake, near Quincy, *Scharpf** in 1963 (FPF); Slate Cr., 5.5 mi. W of Quincy, *W 3230** in 1962 (COLO, FPF) and *H & W 654* in 1964 (FPF); Meadow Valley, *Weatherby 1667* in 1955 (CAS, RM,

RSA, UC); Feather River Exp. For. near Quincy, *Meinecke* n.d. (FPF). RIVERSIDE CO.: San Jacinto Mtns., Idyllwild, *Meinecke FP 20151* in 1915 (FPF, ILL), *Cooper & Silva 923* in 1943 (ARIZ, RSA); 8 mi. N of Idyllwild, *H 740* in 1965 (FPF). SAN BERNARDINO CO.: San Antonio Mtns., Coldwater Fork of Lytle Cr., *Johnston 1688* in 1917 (DS, UC). San Bernardino Mtns.: Inspiration Point, *Perkins* in 1917 (ILL); Baldy Notch-Stockmans Flat, *W 2808* in 1961 (COLO, FPF); W slope Job Peak, *Ewan 3564* in 1929 (POM, UC); ridge E of Foxesee Cr., *Peirson 2818* in 1920 (RSA); 1 mi. E of Lake Gregory, *H 730* in 1965 (FPF). SAN DIEGO CO.: Cuyamaca Mtns., Cuyamaca Peak, *Cox* in 1967 (FPF, UT). SHASTA CO.: 0.5 mi. S of Siskiyou Co. bdy. on Rte. 89, *W 3238** in 1962 (COLO, FPF); head of Tom Neal Cr. (ca. 3 mi. SE of Castella), *Wyckoff & Randall* in 1920 (ILL). SIERRA CO.: Between Downieville and Forest, *Boyce 31* in 1916 (FPF). SISKIYOU CO.: SE of Bartle on Rte. 89, *H & W 644* in 1964 (FPF); Dillon Mt. rd., T. 13 N, R. 6 E, Sec. 5, 12 mi. N of Somes Bar, *Miller FP 98034* in 1962 (FPB). TEHAMA CO.: 2 mi. N of Hole-in-Ground Campground, S of Mineral, *Kuijt 1502* in 1958 (UC). TULARE CO.: Sequoia Nat. Park, Crystal Cave Jct., *W 3611* in 1964 (FPF). TUOLUMNE CO.: 5.1 mi. E of Nat. For. bdy. on Rte. 120, *Kuijt 1394* in 1957 (UC).

OREGON

CURRY CO.: Saddle Mtn., T. 37 S., R. 12 W., Sec. 20, ca. 15 air mi. ESE of Gold Beach, on *P. monticola*, *Bynum* in 1967 and 1968 (FPF) and on *Picea breweriana*, *Bynum* in 1967 and 1968 (FPF). JOSEPHINE CO.: Oregon Mt. (14 mi. SW of Cave Jct.), *Weir 3191* in 1916 (FPF, ILL) and *Theisen* in 1964 (FPF) and on *P. monticola*, *Weir 3240* in 1916 (FPF, ILL); 6.5 mi. SSW of O'Brien on Oregon Mtn. rd., on *P. monticola*, *H & Hinds 994* in 1966 (FPF). COUNTY UNCERTAIN: Ashland-Klamath Falls wagon rd., *Weir 3288* in 1916 (FPF, ILL) and on *P. monticola*, *Weir 3239* in 1916 (FPF, ILL).

8. ARCEUTHOBIUM CAMPYLOPODUM

Specimens Examined: on *Pinus ponderosa* var. *ponderosa* except as noted.

MEXICO

BAJA CALIFORNIA: Sierra de San Pedro Mártir: Low hills NW of La Encantada, on *P. jeffreyi*, *Wiggins & Demaree 5018* in 1930 (DS, F, POM, RSA, US); without locality, as *Pinus* sp., probably *P. jeffreyi*, *Brandegee* in 1893 (UC); 0.25 mi. N of La Encantada, on *P. jeffreyi*, *H & Scharpf 765* in 1965 (FPF); La Grulla, on *P. jeffreyi*, *H & Scharpf 767* in 1965 (FPF). Sierra Juárez: 30 mi. S of La Rumorosa on Laguna Hanson rd., on *P. jeffreyi*, *L & Gill 64–35* in 1964 (FPF); 8 mi. W of Laguna Hanson, on *P. jeffreyi*, *H & Scharpf 783* in 1965 (FPF).

UNITED STATES

CALIFORNIA

ALPINE CO.: Silver Cr. Campground, E side Ebbetts Pass, on *P. jeffreyi*, *Munz 21347* in 1955 (RSA); 5 mi. SW of Silver Cr. on Rte. 4, on *P. jeffreyi*, *H & Scharpf 668* in 1964 (FPF). BUTTE CO.: Jonesville, on *P. jeffreyi*, *Copeland* in 1931 (UC). CALAVERAS CO.: 15 mi. SW of Tamarack on Rte. 4, *H & Scharpf 661** in 1964 (FPF); Angels Camp, *Eggelston 9718* in 1913 (US). DEL NORTE CO.: Near Gasquet, on *P. attenuata*, *Tracy 16464* in 1939 (DS, JEPS, UC, US, WTU); Smith River, between bridges 1 and 2, on *P. attenuata*, *Kildare 10484* in 1931 (DS: Gordon Mtn., on rd. from Gasquet to Big Bar, on *P. attenuata*, *Newcomb 165* in 1957 (UC); Grassy Flat Guard Sta. [5 mi. E of Gasquet], on *P. attenuata*, *Wright FP 91563* in 1947 (OSC); Bear Wallows, 2 mi. N of Sanger Peak, on *P. attenuata*, *Kildare 8785* in 1929 (DS); Gasquet Mtn., on *P. attenuata*, *Eastwood 12138* in 1923 (CAS); 0.5 mi. N of Gasquet, *H & W 863* in 1966 (FPF); 4 mi. NE of Gasquet on old toll rd., on *P. attenuata*, *H & W 865* in 1966 (FPF); 6 mi. NE of Gasquet on old toll rd., *H & W 867* in 1966 (FPF) and on *P. contorta* subsp. *contorta*, *H & W 866* in 1966 (FPF); Ship Mtn. trail, on *P. jeffreyi*, *Weir 3189* in 1916 (ILL); 18 Mile Cr. Can., Elk Camp Ridge, on *P. contorta* subsp. *contorta*, *Parks & Parks 24063* in 1930 (UC). ELDORADO CO.: 3 mi. S of Meyers on U.S. 50, on *P. jeffreyi*, *Peterson 63–315** in 1963 (FPF); Kyburz, *Rossbach 237* in 1955 (UC); Lake Tahoe, Emerald Bay, *Boyce FP 97944* in 1913 (FPB); 8 mi. E of Kyburz on US 50, *H & W 840* in 1966 (FPF); 3 mi. NW of Placerville on Rte. 49, *H & W 842* in 1966 (FPF); Fallen Leaf Lake, on *Pinus contorta* subsp. *murrayana*, *Copeland 1425* in 1931 (POM); Lily Lake, Glen Alpine Can., on *P. jeffreyi*, *Abrams 12752* in 1930 (UC); 9 mi. S of Camp Richardson on Fallen Leaf Lake rd., on *P. jeffreyi*, *Pickle 57–15* in 1957 (UC); 0.5 mi. S of Camp Richardson on Fallen Leaf rd., on *P. jeffreyi*, *Kuijt 1337* in 1957 (UC). FRESNO CO.: 1.3 mi. N of Mono Hot Springs, on *P. jeffreyi*, *H* in 1963 (FPF); between Brown Cone and Dualton rd. [near Kaiser Diggings], on *P. jeffreyi*, *Quibell 280* in 1951 (DS, RSA); Camp 6, Big Creek, *Meinecke FP 97948* in 1917 (FPB). Kings Can. Nat. Park: Cedar Grove, on *P. jeffreyi*, *W 3616* in 1964 (FPF); Copper Cr. Can. Trail, on *P. jeffreyi*, *Howell 34204* in 1958 (CAS); Simpson Meadow, middle fork Kings River, *Howell 34093* in 1958 (CAS). KERN CO.: 6 mi. W of Summit Guard Sta., Glenville-Sierra Alta rd., *W 3606* in 1964 (FPF); 3

mi. N of Summit Guard Sta., on rd. to Tiger Flat, *W 3607* in 1964 (FPF); N of Tiger Flat, *Howell 38824* in 1962 (CAS); Indian Cr., on *P. jeffreyi*, *Root* in 1919 (ILL); rim of Kern Can., SW of Pine Flat, on *P. jeffreyi*, *Twisselmann 8681* in 1963 (CAS); Mt. Pinos region, on *P. jeffreyi*, *Wheeler* in 1931 (CAS). LAKE CO.: Elk Mtn. [8 mi. N of Upper Lake], *Tracy 2355* in 1905 (UC, US, WTU); Boggs Mtn. State For., *Scharpf* in 1965 (FPF); 16 mi. N of Upper Lake on Pillsbury Lake rd., *H & W 860* in 1966 (FPF); 20 mi. N of Upper Lake on Pillsbury Lake rd., on *P. attenuata*, *H & W 861* in 1966 (FPF); Upper Lake to Elk Mtn., on *P. attenuata*, *Mason 2590* in 1926 (UC); near Lucerne, on *P. attenuata*, *Sutliffe* in 1939 (CAS). LOS ANGELES CO.: San Gabriel Mtns.: Chilao, *Peirson 2322* in 1921 (JEPS); Prairie Fork, San Gabriel River, *Johnston 1720* in 1917 (POM, US, WTU); Pine Flat, *Wheeler 1115* in 1932 (UC) and on *P. coulteri*, *Sloan FP 97943* in 1914 (FPB); Crystal Lake, *Martindale in 1937* (POM); Cedar Can. off Mescal Cr., *Ewan 9924* in 1936 (MO); Little Rock-Bear Cr. Divide, on *P. coulteri*, *Ewan 10111* in 1936 (MO); Barley Flat, on *P. coulteri*, *Perkins* in 1919 (ILL); 0.5 mi. W of Big Pines, on *P. jeffreyi*, *H 728* in 1965 (FPF) and on *P. jeffreyi*, *Krebill 244* in 1965 (FPF). MADERA CO.: Bass Lake, *Gill & Wright FP 68162* in 1932 (FPF); 2 mi. NW of North Fork, *H 659* in 1964 (FPF) and *H** in 1964 (FPF); 10 mi. SE of North Fork on Mammoth Pool rd., *H 848* in 1966 (FPF). MARIPOSA CO.: Yosemite, *Hedgcock & Meinecke FP 4788* and *FP 4789* in 1910 (FPF) and *Bolander 6380* in 1866 (US); Fish Camp, *Hedgcock FP 4835* in 1910 (FPF) and on *P. jeffreyi*, *Hedgcock & Meinecke FP 4836* in 1910 (FPF); Wawona, *Posey* in 1919 (ILL); Crane Flat, on *P. jeffreyi*, *Kuijt 1407* in 1957 (UC) and *Rose 60113* in 1960 (RSA); Snow Cr., on *P. jeffreyi*, *Hall* in 1911 (UC). MENDOCINO CO.: Without locality, on *P. jeffreyi*, *Brown 941* in 1898 (FPF, MO, US). MODOC CO.: 3 mi. N of Crowder Flat Guard Sta., *Peterson 64–100* in 1964 (FPF). MONO CO.: 3 mi. E of Sonora Pass, on *P. jeffreyi*, *Kuijt 1432* in 1957 (UC). NAPA CO.: Conn Valley, *Jepson* in 1893 (JEPS); near Pacific Union College, Angwin, *Boyce 1908* in 1930 (FPF); 2 mi. N of Angwin on Pope Valley rd., *H & W 858* in 1966 (FPF). NEVADA CO.: Between Truckee and Lake Tahoe, *Gill FP 68243* in 1931 (FPF) and on *P. jeffreyi*, *Gill FP 68237** in 1931 (FPF); 1 mi. N of Lake Tahoe, *W 3227* in 1962 (COLO, FPF); 5 mi. W of Truckee, on *P. jeffreyi*, *Wright FP 68109* in 1932 (FPF). PLACER CO.: 1.5 mi. E of Tahoe State Park on Rte 28, on *P. jeffreyi*, *Kuijt 1339* in 1957 (UC); 1 mi. N of Tahoe City on Rte 89, on *P. jeffreyi*, *Kuijt 1333* in 1957 (UC). PLUMAS CO.: Chester, on *P. jeffreyi*, *Boyce FP 15983* in 1914 (FPF); 1 mi. E of Rte. 89 on Rte. 40A, on *P. jeffreyi*, *H & W 656* in 1964 (FPF); Quincy Jct., *Gill & Wagener FP*

68040 in 1931 (FPF); Quincy, Feather River Exp. For., *Boyce* in 1913 (FPF) and *Hunt FP 25071* in 1919 (FPF); Chester, *Meinecke FP 17100* in 1914 (FPF); Slate Cr., 5.5 mi. W of Quincy, *W 3231* in 1962 (COLO, FPF); 2 mi. SE of Cromberg, *W 3229* in 1962 (COLO, FPF); near Clio, *Meinecke* in 1915 (FPF); Quincy, *Boyce FP 97955* in 1913 (FPB); 21.5 mi. N of Sierraville, *Kuijt 1346* in 1957 (UC); 7.5 mi. W of Blairsden, *Kuijt 1347* in 1957 (UC); 6.5 mi. E of Jct. of Rtes. 40 & 89, near Indian Falls, *Kuijt 1348* in 1957 (UC); 5 mi. W of Quincy, *H & W 655* in 1964 (FPF); 5 mi. W of Meadow Valley, on *P. contorta* subsp. *murrayana*, *Gill & Wagener FP 68039* in 1931 (FPF). RIVERSIDE CO.: San Jacinto Mtns.: *Spenser 1018* in 1919 (POM); *Grant 1113* in 1901 (ARIZ, US); and on *P. jeffreyi*, *Munz & Johnston 8705* in 1924 (POM). Idyllwild-Banning, *Clokey & Anderson 6574* in 1935 (POM, RM, RSA, UC, WTU); Idyllwild, *Perkins* in 1916 (ILL); 8 mi. N of Idyllwild on Rte. 74, *H 739* in 1965 (FPF); 11 mi. N of Idyllwild on Rte. 74, on *P. coulteri*, *H 738* in 1965 (FPF); 2 mi. SE of Idyllwild, on *P. jeffreyi*, *H 742* in 1965 (FPF); Tahquitz Ridge, on *P. jeffreyi*, *Meyer 688* in 1929 (JEPS); Pine Cove, *Cooper 1547* in 1944 (RSA); Strawberry Valley, *Wheeler 242* in 1931 (DS, POM) and on *P. coulteri*, *Grand* n.d. (DS); 0.6 mi. SE of Keen Camp Summit on Rte. 74, on *P. coulteri*, *Kuijt 1497* in 1958 (UC); Tripp Mill, on *P. coulteri*, *Meinecke FP 20152* in 1915 (FPF). Santa Rosa Mtns.: Peak rd. 9 mi. from Rte. 74, on *P. jeffreyi*, *H 745* in 1965 (FPF). SAN BERNARDINO CO.: San Bernardino Mtns.: *Engelmann* in 1880 (MO); on *P. coulteri*, *Parish* in 1892 (JEPS) and *Parish & Parish 966* in 1884 (MO, US); Big Bear Lake, *Gill & Wright FP 68240** in 1931 (FPF) and *W 2444* in 1959 (RSA, UC, US) and *2741* in 1960 (RSA); Camp Angelus, *W 3211* in 1962 (COLO, FPF); Wrightwood, *W 3212* in 1962 (COLO, FPF); S fork of Santa Ana River, *Munz 6260* in 1922 (POM) and on *P. jeffreyi*, *Peirson 1721* in 1909 (RSA); 2 mi. E of Bluff Lake, *Munz 10566* in 1926 (POM); Bear Valley, on *P. jeffreyi*, *Abrams 2818* in 1902 (FPF, MO, POM, WTU, Z); 5 mi. W of Arrowbear, on *P. jeffreyi*, *Raven 16874* in 1961 (RM, RSA); Mill Cr. rd. near Big Bear, on *P. jeffreyi*, *Howell 386A* in 1927 (RSA); Snow Valley W of Big Bear, on *P. jeffreyi*, *H 731* in 1964 (FPF); 2 mi. W of Snow Valley, on *P. coulteri*, *H 734* in 1965 (FPF); 3 mi. SW of Running Springs on Rte. 30, on *P. coulteri*, *H 736* in 1965 (FPF) and, on *P. attenuata*, *H 735* in 1965 (FPF); City Cr. rd., on *P. attenuata*, *Johnston* in 1924 (POM). SAN DIEGO CO.: Without locality, on *P. coulteri*, *Weir* in 1913 (ILL); Julian, on *P. coulteri*, *Bethel FP 24449* in 1918 (FPF); 4 mi. W of Julian, on *P. coulteri*, *Wiggins 2106* in 1926 (DS, UC); 4.1 mi. S of Julian on Rte. 79, on *P. coulteri*, *Kuijt 1471* in 1958 (UC); 4 mi. SW of

Julian, on *P. coulteri*, *H 751* in 1965 (FPF); 5 mi. SW of Pine Valley, *H & Scharpf 789* in 1965 (FPF). Cuyamaca Mtns.: *Palmer* in 1875 (UC); Cuyamaca Lake, *Roos 1240* in 1937 (POM); Base of Stonewall Peak, on *P. coulteri*, *Wiggins 2725* in 1926 (DS, UC). Laguna Mtns.: *Huey* in 1946 (RSA); Laguna, *Schoenfeldt 3600* in 1894 (UC); 5 mi. N of Laguna Mtn. Lodge, on *P. jeffreyi*, *H 752* in 1965 (FPF); Laguna Campground, on *P. coulteri*, *Wiggins 2817* in 1927 (DS) and on *P. coulteri*, *Munz 8350* in 1924 (POM). SANTA BARBARA CO.: Los Olivos, on *P. jeffreyi*, *Hartley & Weir* in 1912 (ILL). SHASTA CO.: 3 mi. N of north entrance to Lassen Nat. Park on Rte. 89, *W 3236* in 1962 (COLO, FPF); Sisson Tavern Park, col.? *FP 97945* in 1913 (FPB); Jct. of Rtes. 89 and 299, *Kuijt 1366* in 1957 (UC); 12 mi. N of Rte. 299 on Rte. 89, *H & W 646* in (FPF); Lassen Nat. Park, 8 mi. E of N entrance, *H & W 649* in 1964 (FPF); Long Valley, SW of Burney Falls, on *P. jeffreyi*, *Scharpf FP 98114* in 1965 (FPB); between Oak Run and Whitmore, *Anderson* in 1949 (CAS). SIERRA CO.: Sierraville, *Lemmon* in 1875 (MO); Lemon Can., Sierraville, on *P. jeffreyi*, *Meinecke & Boyce FP 17196* in 1915 (FPF); 20.5 mi. N of Truckee, on *P. jeffreyi*, *Kuijt 1345* in 1957 (UC); 2 mi. W of Bassetts, on *P. contorta* subsp. *murrayana*, *Peterson 63–166* in 1963 (FPF). SISKIYOU CO.: Mt. Shasta, *Engelmann* in 1880 (FPF, MO); Yreka, *Hedgcock FP 1897* in 1909 (FPF); Scotts River, *Pond FP 193* n.d. (FPF); Mt. Shasta, *Brown 580* in 1897 (FPF, MO, US); Sisson, *Hedgcock, Meinecke & Long FP 9668* in 1911 (FPF); Big Carmen Lake, Scott Mtn. rd., [6 mi. E of Callaham], *Barbe 314* in 1955 (RSA, UC); Mt. Shasta, Sisson South Trail, *Cooke 11593* in 1938 (DS, UC); Gravely Ridge, W of Craggy Mtn., NW of Yreka, *Owenby & Brown 2428* in 1941 (UC); Can. Cr. [ca. 12 mi. SSW of Hamburg], *Hedgecock FP 1873* in 1909 (FPF); 3 mi. NW of McCloud, *Scharpf & Miller* in 1965 (FPF), and on *P. attenuata*, *Scharpf & Miller* in 1965 (FPF); Russian Cr., on *P. attenuata*, *Butler 273* in 1908 (UC); 3 mi. N of Branch Guard Sta., N of Happy Camp, on *P. attenuata*, *Kuijt 1277* in 1957 (UC); 16 mi. N of Happy Camp, on O'Brien rd., on *P. attenuata*, *H & Hinds 1001* in 1966 (FPF); Scott Mtn., on *P. jeffreyi*, *Engelmann* in 1880 (MO). TEHAMA CO.: Childs Meadow, 2 mi. W of Morgan Springs on Rte. 36, on *P. contorta* subsp. *murrayana*, *Scharpf FP 38026*, n.d. (FPB); 15 mi. W of Rte. 36 on Rte. 89, *Kuijt 1356* in 1957 (UC) and on *P. contorta* subsp. *murrayana*, *Kuijt 1357* in 1957 (UC). TRINITY CO.: Trinity, *Munns FP 9440* in 1911 (FPF); Plummer Spring, [near Peanut?], *Meinecke* in 1912 (FPF); Trail to Granite Peak, *Baker 209* in 1926 (DS); Scott Ranch, *Cantielow 1659* in 1936 (RSA). TULARE CO.: Jordan Hot Springs, *Zeile* in 1924 (JEPS); Peppermint Valley,

Dudley 758 in 1895 (DS); Whitaker For., *Benson 5705* in 1933 (POM); Mineralking, on *P. jeffreyi, Coville & Funston 1460* in 1891 (DS) and *1482* in 1891 (US); Sequoia Nat. Park, 1 mi. N of Lodgepole Campground, on *P. jeffreyi, W 3612* in 1964 (FPF); Mt. Sillman [ca. 3 mi. N of Lodgepole], on *P. jeffreyi, Hopping 391* in 1905 (UC); Little Kern River, between Lion Meadow and Trout River, on *P. jeffreyi, Dudley 1978* in 1897 (DS). TUOLUMNE CO.: Clark Fork of Tuolumne River, 1.5 mi. below Arnott Cr., on *P. jeffreyi, Wiggins 9322* in 1939 (DS, POM, UC, WTU); Crocker Sta., on *P. jeffreyi*, col.? *FP 97946* in 1915 (FPB); 2.8 mi. NE of Long Barn, on *P. jeffreyi, Thomas 10262* in 1963 (FPF, RSA); near Kennedy Meadows on Rte. 108, on *P. jeffreyi, Kuijt 1423* in 1957 (UC); Long Barn, *Gill FP 68087* and *FP 68097* in 1932 (FPF), *Wright FP 68117* in 1932 (FPF), and *Gill & Wright FP 68072* in 1932 (FPF); 6 mi. E of Long Barn, *W. 3222* in 1962 (COLO, FPF); 1 mi. E of Twain Harte, *Kuijt 1428* in 1957 (UC); Cottonwood Meadows, E of Mather, *Clausen 1777* in 1939 (DS); Pate Valley, Yosemite, *Clemens* in 1919 (CAS). VENTURA CO.: Middle Fork, Mt. Pinos, *Hall 6642* in 1905 (UC); Mt. Pinos, *Rothrock 213* in 1875 (US).

IDAHO

ADAMS CO.: Evergreen, *Hedgcock FP 1909* in 1909 (FPF); Bear, *Barr* in 1915 (ILL); 10 mi. N of Council on US 95, *H 978* in 1966 (FPF). BOISE CO.: S fork of Payette River, Garden Valley, *Miles FP 15108* in 1913 (FPF); Karney Cr., *Peterson 62–49* in 1962 (FPF). IDAHO CO.: N bank of Salmon River, 11 mi. E of Riggins, *H 970** in 1966 (FPF); MacKay Bar, on Salmon River 2 mi. E of Jct. of S fork of Salmon River, *W 4127b* in 1966 (FPF, UT). KOOTENAI CO.: Without locality, *Sandberg* in 1892 (US); Coeur d' Alene, *Weir FP 17047* in 1914 (FPF); Coeur d' Alene City Park, *Gill FP 68203** in 1932 (FPF); 5 mi. W of Coeur d' Alene, *W 3254* in 1962 (COLO, FPF); Spokane Bridge, *Heller 925* in 1892 (DS, MO); E side Coeur d' Alene Lake, 4 mi. N of inlet of Coeur d' Alene River, on *P. contorta* subsp. *latifolia, Krebill 154* in 1964 (FPF); Spirit Lake, on *P. contorta* subsp. *latifolia, Dodge* in 1916 (ILL); Fourth of July Can., on *P. contorta* subsp. *latifolia, Weir 8252* in 1914 (ILL); Fernan Lake, *H & Wicker 966** in 1966 (FPF) and on *P. contorta* subsp. *latifolia, Weir 8243* in 1916 (ILL); Hayden Lake, on *P. sylvestris, Weir* in 1920 (ILL). LEWIS CO.: Nezperce, *Anison* in 1914 (ILL).

NEVADA

CLARK CO.: Charleston Mtns: All on *P. ponderosa* var. *scopulorum; Clokey 5431* in 1935 (CAS, FPF, JEPS, WTU) and *5432* in 1935 (CS, FPF, JEPS,

WTU); Charleston Park, *W 3032* and *3205* in 1962 (COLO, FPF); Kyle Can., 2.5 mi. W of Ranger Sta., *H & Scharpf 675* in 1964 (FPF); Kyle Can., *Peterson 64–144* in 1964 (FPF). DOUGLAS CO.: Glenbrook, on *P. jeffreyi, Baker 1006* in 1902 (MO, POM, UC); E of Spooner Jct. on US 50, on *P. jeffreyi, Peterson 65–403* in 1965 (FPF); 5 mi. E of Spooner Jct. on US 50, on *P. jeffreyi, H & W 836* in 1966 (FPF). ORMSBY CO.: 2 mi. N of US 50 near Carson City, on *P. jeffreyi, Peterson* in 1960 (FPF). WASHOE CO.: Franktown, col? n.d. (PH); Hunter Cr. rd., *Kennedy* in 1907 (CAS); Incline Camp [N shore of Lake Tahoe, 3 mi. E of California bdy.], on *P. jeffreyi, Wright FP 68111* in 1932 (FPF); Bowers Mansion, 26 mi. S of Reno, on *P. jeffreyi, Archer 6396* in 1938 (MO, UC); Mtns. W of Bowers, on *P. jeffreyi, Heller 10660* in 1912 (CAS, DS, MO); N shore of Lake Tahoe, Crystal Bay, on *P. jeffreyi, Peterson 65–395* in 1965 (FPF).

OREGON

CURRY CO.: 12 mi. NW of Agness, on *P. attenuata, Graham** in 1963 (FPF). BAKER CO.: 7 mi. S of Baker, *Peterson 63–224* in 1963 (FPF); Dooley Mtn. area, 12 mi. S of Baker, *Graham* in 1965 (FPF); Sumpter, *Hedgcock FP 998* in 1909 (FPF) and on *P. contorta* subsp. *latifolia, Weir 3200* in 1913 (ILL); 23 mi. S of Baker on Rte. 7, *H & W 583* in 1964 (FPF); Buck Mtn., E Oregon [near Unity?], *Cusick 2701* in 1901 (MO, POM, RM, UC, US); Halfway, *Miller* n.d. (ILL); Squaw Cr., 28 mi. ESE of Prairie City, *Graham* in 1965 (FPF). CROOK CO.: Prineville, *Harvey FP 4159* in 1910 (FPF); Gerow Butte rd., Ochoco Nat. For., *Childs 52* in 1949 (OSC) Marks Cr. rd., Ochoco Nat. For., *Childs 61* in 1949 (OSC). DESCHUTES CO.: Deschutes River near Bend, *Nelson 866* in 1906 (RM); 10 mi. S of Sisters, *Henderson 14130* in 1931 (PH); Pringle Butte, [6 mi. NW of La Pine] *H 989* in 1966 (FPF) and *Steward & Sowder 6803* in 1954 (RSA); 9 mi. S of Bend on US 97, *H & W 617* in 1964 (FPF). DOUGLAS CO.: Big Camas Ranger Sta., *Kern* in 1915 (ILL). GRANT CO.: Strawberry Mtns., Graham Cr., Blue Mtn. Hot Springs, [8 mi. SSE of Prairie City], *Ferris & Duthie 857* in 1919 (DS); 16 mi. S of John Day on Rte. 395, *H & W 577* in 1964 (FPF); 10 mi. NE of Prairie City on Rte. 26, *H & W 580* in 1964 (FPF). HARNEY CO.: T. 24 S., R. 34 E., Sec. 34 [ca. 30 mi. ESE of Burns], *Overby FP 68281* in 1932 (FPF); Calamity Cr., [near Van], *Griffith & Morris 803* in 1901 (US); Crow Flat Ranger Sta. [ca. 18 mi. mi. N of Burns], *Porter* in 1915 (ILL); Lee Cr., 25 air mi. ESE of Seneca, *H & Scharpf 1265* in 1969 (FPF). HOOD RIVER CO.: Hood River, *W 3245* in 1962 (COLO, FPF) and *Gorman* in 1891 (WTU); without locality, *Henderson 527* in 1923 (MO).

JACKSON CO.: 18 mi. SW of Ashland, *Graham* in 1963 (FPF); Rogue Elk [near McLeod], *Stillinger* in 1919 (FPF, ILL, US); 12 mi. S of Ruch on Copper rd., *H & W 633* in 1964 (FPF). JEFFERSON CO.: Warm Springs Indian Res. *Childs FP 68272* in 1931 (FPF); Shuttle Lake, Metolius Area, *Gill FP 68191* in 1932 (FPF); Montgomery Ranch, Lower Metolius River, [13 mi. W of Metolius], *Boyce 2121* in 1931 (FPF) and *Childs 68* in 1931 (OSC). JOSEPHINE CO.: Waldo [7 mi. S of Cave Jct.], *Lewis* in 1917 (ILL); on *P. contorta* subsp. *contorta*, *Weir 3187* in 1916 (ILL); and on *P. jeffreyi*, *Lewis* in 1917 (FPF, ILL). Grants Pass, *Weir 3206* in 1916 (FPF, ILL) and on *P. attenuata*, *Weir 9868* in 1916 (FPF, ILL); 5 mi. W of Grants Pass, on *P. jeffreyi*, *Graham* in 1964 (FPF); 5 mi. N of Grants Pass, *Abrams 8677* in 1922 (DS); 6.5 mi. SSW of O'Brien on Oregon Mtn. rd., *H & Hinds 996* in 1966 (FPF) and on *P. attenuata*, *H & Hinds 995* in 1966 (FPF); Oregon Mtn. [14 mi. SW of Cave Jct.], *Weir 3194* in 1916 (ILL), on *P. contorta* subsp. *contorta*, *Theisen* in 1965 (FPF), and on *P. attenuata*, *Weir 3185* in 1916 (FPF, ILL) and *Bynum* in 1967 (FPF); 2 mi. E of Cave Jct., *Theisen* in 1965 (FPF); near Lookout Gap, 20 air mi. S of Galice, on *P. jeffreyi*, *Graham* in 1965 (FPF); Hobson Horn Lookout, 25 air mi. NW of Grants Pass, on *P. attenuata*, *Graham* in 1965 (FPF); Bain Sta., 2 mi. W of Oregon Mtn., on *P. attenuata*, *Howard* in 1964 (FPF); Oregon Mtn., on *P. jeffreyi*, *Howard* in 1964 (FPF); Wonder, on *P. jeffreyi*, *Mitchell FP 68212* in 1932 (FPF); Mt. Peavine, near Galice, on *P. attenuata*, *Childs FP 91615* in 1950 (OSC): Crescent City-Grant Pass rd., on *P. attenuata*, *Goodding & Root* in 1932 (UC); vicinity of Oregon Caves, *Weir 3193* in 1916 (ILL); 4 mi. E of Cave Jct. *H & W 869* in 1966 (FPF). KLAMATH CO.: Near Jct. of Rtes. 230 and 97, *W 3239* in 1962 (COLO); Ringo Butte, *Childs 10* in 1946 (OSC); Brookside Ranch, Swan Lake Valley, *"E.I." 3187* in 1904 (DS); Hamner Butte, *Bedwell & Childs FP 91033* and *FP 91034* in 1939 (OSC) and on *P. contorta* subsp. *murrayana*, *Childs 22* in 1939 (OSC) and *Bedwell FP 91035* in 1939 (OSC); 11 mi. NW of Rte. 97 on Rte. 58, *H & W 619* in 1964 (FPF); 14 mi. W of Klamath Falls on Rte. 66, *H & W 627* in 1964 (FPF); Applegate Ranch, Swan Lake Valley, *Walpole 417* in 1899 (US); 19 mi. NW of Klamath Falls on Rte. 140, *H & W 872* in 1966 (FPF); 14 mi. SW of Beatty on Rte. 140, *H & W 873* in 1966 (FPF). LAKE CO.: Winter Rock Mtns. near Summer Lake, *Ferris & Duthie 422* in 1919 (DS, RM); Quartz Mtn. Pass, *Detting 4255* in 1940 (UC); Warner Mtns., 1 mi. W of Warner Can. Ski Area on Rte. 140, *H & W 875* in 1966 (FPF). WALLOWA CO.: Wallowa Mtns., between Bear Cr. and Minam River, *Sheldon 8845* in 1897 (MO, US). WASCO CO: Between Friend and head of

Fifteen Mile Cr., *Milburge 1328* in 1936 (WTU); Friend, *Boyce FP 40179* in 1921 (OSC); Bear Springs, *H & W 611* in 1964 (FPF) and *Boyce 1907** in 1930 (FPF). WHEELER CO.: 1 mi. N of Nat. For. bdy. on Derr Meadows rd., ca. 12 mi. SSE of Mitchell, *H 983** in 1966 (FPF); 1 mi. N of Ochoco Divide, 11 air mi. W of Mitchell, *H 989* in 1966 (FPF); 26 mi. S of Hardman on Rte. 207, *H & Scharpf 1271* in 1969 (FPF). COUNTY UNCERTAIN: Umpqua Mtns., *Wilkes Exped. 1185* n.d. (US); Mtns. of eastern Oregon, *Cusick 2324* in 1899 (MO).

WASHINGTON

CHELAN CO.: 8 mi. NW of Chelan, *Hedgcock FP 48627* in 1929 (FPF); Rainbow Trail, 1 mi. from Stehekin River, *Ward 595* in 1946 (WTU); Peshastin, *Sandberg & Leiberg 593* in 1893 (MO, UC, US); Stehekin, Chelan Lake, *Jones* in 1911 (POM, UC) and *Graham* in 1964 (FPF); Antwine Cr. [Antoine Cr. ?, 8 mi. N of Chelan], *Harris FP 68283* in 1932 (FPF); Leavenworth, *Umback* in 1901 (US) and *Otis 1011* and *1021* in 1920 (CAS, UC). FERRY CO.: 10 mi. E of Nespelem, *Peterson 63–225* in 1963 (FPF). KITTITAS CO.: 8 mi. N of Teanaway on US 97, *Wicker* in 1966 (FPF). KLICKITAT CO.: Trout Lake, *W 3246* in 1962 (COLO, FPF); W Klickitat Co., *Suksdorf 1364* in 1892 (MO, UC, US); 1 mi. N of Satus Pass on Rte. 97, *H & W 594** in 1964 (FPF); Klickitat, *Howell 929* in 1881 (US). OKANOGAN CO.: E of Omak, *Fiker 695* in 1932 (DS, MO, US, WTU); Squaw Cr., 5 mi. SW of Methow, *Graham* in 1964 (FPF); Pateros, *Mitchell* in 1915 (ILL). PEND ORIELLE CO.: Newport, on *P. contorta* subsp. *latifolia*, *Weir 3202* in 1916 (ILL). SPOKANE CO.: 3 mi. N of Spangle, *Wicker* in 1962 (WSP); Spokane, *Weir 8475* in 1917 (FPF, RM, US) and *FP 29660* in 1918 (FPF); *Sandberg 925* in 1892 (MO, US, WTU), and *Hubert FP 91292* in 1917 (OSC). 12 mi. S of Spokane, *Hansbrough, Mielke & Joy FP 68273* in 1931 (FPF); Riverside State Park, NW of Spokane, *W 3253* in 1962 (COLO, FPF); near Spokane, *Milburge 253* in 1932 (WTU); Horseshoe Lake (NE part of co.), *Yocom* in 1947 (WTU); Tekoa Mtn. [near Latah], *St. John 3051* in 1921 (UC); Medical Lake, *Elmer 1246* in 1898 (US). STEVENS CO.: 3.5 mi. S of Gifford, *Hedgcock FP 68059* in 1931 (FPF); 4 mi. S of Kettle Falls, *Hedgcock FP 49442* in 1929 (FPF); S of Gifford, *Hedgcock FP 54990* and *FP 54991* in 1931 (FPF); N of Clark Lake, near Cedonia, *Dennis* in 1946 (WTU). YAKIMA CO.: Upper Naches River region, *Grant* in 1938 (WTU); 23 mi. E of White Pass on Rte. 14, 2 mi. W of Nat. For. bdy., *H & W 595* in 1964 (FPF). COUNTY UNCERTAIN: Colville Indian Res., Sanpoil drainage, *Childs 53* in 1948 (OSC) and *FP 91575* in 1948 (OSC); Cascade Mtns., *Tweedy* in 1882 (MO).

9. ARCEUTHOBIUM CYANOCARPUM

Specimens Examined: on *Pinus flexilis* unless as noted.

UNITED STATES

ARIZONA

COCONINO CO.: San Francisco Peaks: On *P. aristata*, *Leiberg 5884* in 1901 (US) and Fremont Pass rd., 6 mi. N of Schultz Pass rd., on *P. aristata*, *H & L 247* in 1962 (FPF).

CALIFORNIA

DEL NORTE CO.: Ship Mtn., ca. 12 air mi. SE of Gasquet, on *P. monticola*, *Reynolds* in 1916 (ILL). INYO CO.: 17 mi. W of Bishop on Sabrina Lake rd., *H & Scharpf 671** in 1964 (FPF). MONO CO.: Saddle above Convict Lake, *Kuijt 1415* in 1957 (UC): 2 mi. ESE of Lundy Lake, on *Pinus* sp., probably *flexilis*, *Hendrix 616* in 1937 (RSA, UC). RIVERSIDE CO.: San Jacinto Mtns., Tahquitz Peak, *Andresen & Cochrane 1729* in 1962 (FPF); Saddle N of Tahquitz Peak, *W 3617* in 1964 (FPF, UT). SAN BERNARDINO CO.: T. 1 N, R. 3 E, Sec. 6 (4 mi. S of Tiptop Mtn.), *Miller FP 98023* in 1962 (FPB). SIERRA CO.: 0.25 mi. N of Hawley Lake (3 mi. W of Gold Lake), on *P. monticola*, *Menzies* in 1961 (CAS). SISKIYOU CO.: Summit of Black Butte, on *P. albicaulis*, *Root & Goodding FP 68275* in 1932 (FPF), *Mielke & Zentmeyer FP 89238** in 1937 (FPF) and *H & W 642* in 1964 (FPF); N fork of Molly Cr., on *P. albicaulis*, *Butler 272* in 1908 (UC); N slope of Mt. Shastina on *P. albicaulis*, *Cooke 11576* in 1938 (DS, UC); NW side of Mt. Shastina, *Cooke 16212* in 1941 (MO, PH, UC); Scott Mtns., Toad Lake (3 mi. S of Mt. Eddy) on *P. monticola*, *Engelmann* in 1880 (ILL). TRINITY CO.: High Camp Cr., 5 mi. WNW of Mt. Eddy: On *P. monticola*, *Miller & Bynum** in 1964 (FPF), *Scharpf & Miller* in 1965 (FPF), and *Brown* in 1965 (FPF), on *P. balfouriana*, *Miller & Bynum* in 1964 (FPF), *Scharpf & Miller* in 1965 (FPF) and *Brown* in 1965 (FPF). COUNTY UNCERTAIN: Tenderfoot Lake, Siskiyou Nat. For., on *P. monticola*, *Lewis* in 1916 (ILL).

COLORADO

BOULDER CO.: 3 mi. S of Ward, *H & Gill 195* in 1958 (FPF); Brainard Lake rd. Jct. at Ward, *H 417* in 1963 (FPF); Ward, *Bethel, Schmoll & Clokey 4314* (MO) and *4315* in 1921 (CAS, CS, COLO, JEPS, MO, POM, RM, UC, US, WTU), *Bethel* in 1921 (CS), and *W 2926* in 1961 (COLO); Allenspark, *Johnston & Thompson FP 24883* in 1917 (FPF); 1.3 mi. E of Eldora, *H 689** in 1964 (FPF); 3 mi. S of Ward on Rte. 160, on *P. contorta*, *H &*

Gill 194 in 1958 (FPF) and on *P. ponderosa*, *H & Gill 198* in 1958 (FPF) and *H & W 565* in 1964 (FPF). CLEAR CREEK CO.: Hamlin Gulch rd. 1.4 mi from Fall River rd., ca. 7 air mi. NW of Idaho Springs, *H 1057* and *1058* on *P. ponderosa*, in 1967 (FPF). EL PASO CO.: Ridge rd., *Christ 1877* in 1935 (CS); Rock Cr. (T. 15 S, R. 67 W, Sec. 1), *Hill FP 68276* in 1932 (FPF); 5 mi. S of Bruin Inn on Gold Camp rd., *H 540** in 1963 (FPF); Pikes Peak, Lake Moraine, *Ewan 15154* in 1943 (COLO); Pikes Peak, *Hedgcock FP 1614* in 1909 (FPF) and *FP 19185* in 1911 (FPF); *Macbride 2677* in 1913 (MO); Fremont Exp. For. (2 mi. W of Manitou Springs), *Hedgcock FP 22706* and *22707* in 1916 (FPF) and *Hedgcock, Payson & Johnston FP 24852* in 1917 (FPF); Pikes Peak, Minnehaha, *Hedgcock FP 635* in 1909 (FPF); Pikes Peak For. Reserve, *Flintham* in 1903 (US); Pikes Peak, Halfway, *Hartley FP 1774* in 1909 (FPF) and *Hedgcock FP 15909* in 1914 (FPF, RSA); Rampart Range rd., 3 mi. SE of Woodland Park, *Schacht* in 1964 (FPF). Crystal Park, *Gill FP 68235* in 1932 (FPF). GILPIN CO.: 1 mi. SW of Tolland, *H 827* in 1965 (FPF). (FPF). FREMONT CO: Sangre de Cristo Range, 8 mi. SW of Coaldale on Hayden Pass rd., *H & Laut 1317* in 1970 (FPF). LARIMER CO.: Eaton Reservoir, *Douglass* in 1957 (CS); 4 mi. W of Eaton Reservoir, *Hinds** in 1962 (FPF); Estes Park, *Cooper 65* in 1904 (RM); Boulder Ridge, 0.5 mi. S of Sand Cr. rd., *H 82* in 1961 (FPF); 1.6 mi. E of Pingree Park on main rd., *H 1055* in 1967 (FPF); Rocky Mtn. Nat. Park, Gem Lake Trail, *Ashton 66* in 1930 (RMNP); Rocky Mtn. Nat. Park, Glacier Gorge, *Loll FP 11832* in 1924 (FPF); Boulder Ridge, *H 196* in 1961 (FPF); Boulder Ridge, 0.5 mi. S of Wyoming bdy., *H 84* in 1961 (FPF); 6.5 mi. S of Estes Park on Rte. 7, *H & Staley 288* in 1962 (FPF); Pennock Cr., 2 mi. S of Pingree Park rd., *H 562* in 1964 (FPF); Medicine Bow Mtns., 4.3 mi. S of Wyoming bdy. on Roach rd., *H 829* in 1965 (FPF). COUNTY UNCERTAIN: La Sal Mtns., col.? in 1915 (FPF, ILL).

IDAHO

BEAR LAKE CO.: Ridge S of Bloomington Lake, W of Bloomington, *Peterson 65–370* in 1965 (FPF). BUTTE CO.: Craters-of-the-Moon Nat. Mon., *Peterson 62–53** in 1962 (FPF) and *Mahoney* in 1965 (FPF). LEMHI CO.: Near Salmon, *Wolpert* in 1917 (FPF, ILL).

MONTANA

BEAVERHEAD CO.: Big Hole Valley, on *P. albicaulis*, *Weir 3216* n.d. (FPF, ILL). BIG HORN CO.: Crow Res., Bighorn Mtns., Rotten Grass drainage, *Gregory* in 1969 (FPF). CARBON CO.: Rock Cr. Ranger Sta., *Hedgcock FP 11147* in 1911

(FPF); 5 mi. W of Red Lodge on Rock Cr. rd., *W 3865* in 1965 (FPF, UT). Pryor Mtns., Crooked Cr., *Brown* in 1969 (FPF). DEERLODGE CO.: French Gulch near Anaconda, *Weir 3246* in 1913 (FPF, ILL); Mt. Haggin near Anaconda, *Weir 3218* in 1914 (FPF, ILL); near Anaconda, *Weir 8254* in 1914 (ILL). GALLATIN CO.: Rocky Can., near Bozeman, *Blankinship 436* in 1905 (POM, RM, US): 7 mi. E of Bozeman, *W 3257** in 1962 (COLO, FPF): Bozeman, *Brandegee* in 1883 (UC) and *Langohr* in 1917 (ILL). COUNTY UNCERTAIN: Mt. Powell, *Weir 8345* in 1914 (ILL).

OREGON

COUNTY UNCERTAIN: Obsidian Cliff, on *P. albicaulis, Gorman 1753* in 1903 (US).

NEVADA

CLARK CO.: Charleston Mtns.: On *P. aristata, Coville & Funston 311* in 1891 (US); head of Tractor Lane, Lee Can. *Train 2150* in 1938 (UC). Peak Trail, *Clokey 5430* in 1935 (CAS, DS, FPF, RM, RSA, UC, US, WTU), and on *P. aristata, Clokey 5429* in 1935 (CAS, DS, FPF, JEPS, UC, WTU) and *Clokey 5492* in 1935 (CAS, DS, JEPS, RM, RSA, WTU). ELKO CO.: Ruby Mtns.: *Grover* in 1958 (FPF) and Lamoille Can., 12 mi. SE of Lamoille, *H & W 575** in 1964 (FPF).

UTAH

CACHE CO.: Logan Can., near Jardine Juniper, *Krebill 454* in 1967 (FPF); Tony Grove Lake, *Maguire & Maguire 20377* in 1939 (RM, WTU) and *20378* in 1939 (RM); 0.25 mi. NW of Tony Grove Lake, *Peterson 62–75* in 1962 (FPF); Mt. Naomi, 1 mi. from Tony Grove, *Snell 1047* in 1938 (UC, WTU). DAGGETT CO.: 2 mi. W of Utah, Wyo., and Colo. corner on Loop rd. from Clay Basin, *Bleazard* in 1965 (FPF, UT). DUCHESNE CO.: Indian Can., 25.5 mi. SW of Duchesne on Rte. 33, *H 571* in 1964 (FPF). GARFIELD CO.: 10 mi. W of Bryce Can. Lodge, *Dorn* in 1947 (POM); near Escalante, *Peterson 52–61* in 1961 (FPF); Bryce Can. Nat. Park; Headquarters area, *Gill FP 68144* in 1932 (FPF) and on *P. aristata, FP 68143* in 1932 (FPF); *Garrett FP 38107** in 1921 (FPF) and on *P. aristata, FP 38106* in 1921 (FPF); *H 255* in 1962 (FPF) and on *P. aristata, 256* in 1962 (FPF); Bryce Point, *W 3034* and *3178* in 1962 (COLO, FPF), *Howell & Eastwood 7204* n.d. (CAS). IRON CO.: 16.5 mi. E of Cedar City on Rte. 14, *H 679* in 1964 (FPF) and on *P. aristata, H 680* in 1964 (FPF); 1 mi. W of Summit on Rte. 14, *W 4127* in 1966 (FPF, UT) and on *P. aristata, W 4125* in 1966 (FPF, UT). KANE CO.: 1 mi. N of Navajo Lake on Rte. 14, *W 4124* in 1966 (FPF, UT). UTE CO.: 8 mi. S of

Belknap Guard Sta., above Deep Cr., *Peterson 65–339* in 1965 (FPF). COUNTY UNCERTAIN: Charles Peak, southern part of State, *Siler* in 1879 (MO).

WYOMING

ALBANY CO.: 1.0 mi. N of Albany rd. on Cinnabar Park rd., *H & Hinds 197* in 1961 (FPF); Centennial Mt., *Nelson* in 1915 (RM); Laramie Mtns., *Nelson 8247* in 1901 (ARIZ, MO, RM, US): Pilot Knob, *Nelson* in 1905 (MO, RM); Boulder Ridge, 7 mi. SW of Tie Siding, *H 85* in 1961 (FPF); Sheep Mtn., *Nelson 3320* in 1897 (RM, US); Hermosa, *Garrett FP 38174* in 1921 (FPF); Centennial, Mullin Cr., *Garrett FP 15833* in 1914 (FPF); Dale Cr. Bridge near Sherman, col.? n.d. (MO); Laramie Mtns., *Weir 9872* in 1918 (FPF, ILL), 2 mi. SW of Pilot Hill, *H & Bailey 1008* in 1966 (FPF); Boulder Ridge, 10 feet N of Colorado bdy., 7 mi. SW of Tie Siding, on *P. ponderosa, H 284* in 1962 (FPF). CARBON CO.: Medicine Bow Mtns.: 3 mi. S of Pennock Mtn., *Landgraf* in 1965 (FPF) and Cooper Cr., 12 air mi. N of Centennial, *Landgraf* in 1965 (FPF); Ferris Mtns., NE slope of Whiskey Gap, *Dunder* in 1969 (FPF); Shirley Mtns., Lower Prior Flat, *Dunder* in 1969 (FPF); N side of Elk Mtn., Rattlesnake Cr., *Dunder* in 1969 (FPF). CONVERSE CO.: Laramie Mtns., Cold Springs, *Simmons* in 1917 (ILL). FREMONT CO.: Slate Cr., SE Lander District, *Peterson* in 1960 (FPF); Fossil Hill, ca. 10 air mi. SW of Lander, *Stewart* in 1967 (FPF); W fork of Long Cr., 21 mi. WNW of Dubois, *H 277* in 1962 (FPF); 4 mi. WNW of South Pass City, *Landgraf & Davel* in 1965 (FPF); Green Mtns., Crook Gap, *H & Landgraf 279** in 1962 (FPF). LINCOLN CO.: Alpine, along Snake River, *Payson & Armstrong 3406* in 1923 (MO, PH, RM);E of Alpine, *Graham*, in 1965 (FPF). PARK CO.: "Cody," *Weir FP 91249** in 1918 (FPF, OSC, ILL); Cody Can., 44 mi. W of Cody, *W 3258* in 1962 (COLO); Rattlesnake Cr., ca. 15 air mi. WNW of Cody, *Bailey* in 1966 (FPF); Dry Fork, ca. 19 air mi. NW of Cody, *Stewart* in 1967 (FPF); along switchbacks E of Dead Indian Campground, ca. 22 air mi. NW of Cody, *Stewart* in 1967 (FPF). YELLOWSTONE NAT. PARK: "Yellowstone For. Reserve," *Hapeman* in 1906 (RM).

10. *ARCEUTHOBIUM DIVARICATUM*

Specimens Examined: On *Pinus edulis* except as noted.

UNITED STATES

ARIZONA

APACHE CO.: Carisso, *Brandegee 1226* in 1875 (PH, UC); 2 mi. S of Eagar, *H & L 208* in 1962

(FPF); 17 mi. NW of Sawmill on Can. de Chelly rd., *L & Weiss 66–45* in 1966 (FPF); 3 mi. E of Lukachukai, *L & Weiss 66–47* in 1966 (FPF); 8 mi. SW of Red Rock on Lukachukai rd., *L & Weiss 66–52* in 1966 (FPF). Can. de Chelly: 6 mi. SE of Chin Lee, *Ferris 10183* in 1940 (UC) and 5 mi. W of Tsalie Dam on N Rim of Can. del Muerto, *L, Ela & Lampi 65–54* in 1965 (FPF); 19 mi. W of Maverick on White River rd., *H & L 904* in 1966 (FPF). COCONINO CO.: Grand Can. Nat. Park: South Rim: *Toumey* in 1894 (UC), *MacDougal 190* in 1898 (ARIZ, UC, US), *Knowlton 295* in 1889 (US), *Spaulding FP 303* in 1909 (FPF), *Hedgcock FP 4907* in 1910 (FPF), *Hitchcock 25* in 1913 (US), *Batram 435* in 1920 (US), *Gill FP 68232* and *FP 68233* in 1932 (FPF); Desert View: *Cronquist* in 1938 (RM), *Gill FP 68234* in 1932 (FPF), and *H & Scharpf 701* in 1964 (FPF); 1 mi. SW of Bright Angel Camp, *Gill FP 68132* in 1932 (FPF); Bright Angel Trail, *Gill FP 68230* in 1932 (FPF); Grandview, *Dachnowski-Stokes* in 1913 (US); El Tovar, *Setschell* in 1907 (UC); Duck-on-a-Rock, *H 35* in 1954 (FPF) and *H & Scharpf 703* in 1964 (FPF). Flagstaff, *Jones 3973* in 1884 (ARIZ, DS, POM, RM, UC); 14 mi. N of Frazier Well, *H & L 187* in 1962 (FPF); between Flagstaff and Grand Can., 14 mi. SE of Rte. 64 on Rte. 164, *H 246* in 1962 (FPF); NE of Long Valley, *Ellis FP 89426* in 1939 (FPF); Sedona, *Hedgcock FP 4917* in 1910 (FPF); North Kaibab Plateau on US 89, *Gill FP 68300* in 1934 (FPF); 6 mi. E of Jacob Lake on US 89, *W 3185* in 1962 (COLO, FPF); Kaibab For., *Richards* in 1938 (WTC); Jacob Lake to Fredonia, *Kearney & Peebles 13761* in 1937 (ARIZ, US); 30 mi. SW of Winslow on Rte. 65, *H & L 915* in 1966 (FPF); 34 mi. S of Winslow on Chevlon rd., *H & L 916* in 1966 (FPF). Walnut Can. Nat. Mon., *L 66–22* in 1966 (FPF); 15 mi. S of Page on US 89, *L & Weiss 69–4* in 1969 (FPF). GILA CO.: 6 mi. SE of Cedar Cr. on Rte. 73, *H & L 906* in 1966 (FPF). GRAHAM CO.: San Carlos Indian Res., 3 mi. W of Eagle Cr. on Malay Gap rd., *H & L 1114* in 1968 (FPF). GREENLEE CO.: Red Hill near Blue, *Ellis FP 89331* in 1939 (FPF). MOHAVE CO.: Mt. Trumbull, *Hevly* in 1959 (MNA); Grand Can. Nat. Mon., 5 mi. S of Nixon Spring, *H, L & Laut 1165* in 1969 (FPF); 4 mi. E of Mt. Trumbull P. O., *H & L 1168* in 1969 (FPF); 10 mi. W of Wolf Hole on Black Rock Mtn. rd., on *P. monophylla, H, L & Laut 1171* in 1969 (FPF). NAVAJO CO.: 4.5 mi. S of Rte. 264 on Rte. 77, ca. 12 air mi. SE of Keams Can., *H & L 1084* in 1967 (FPF), 15 mi. E of Heber, *Ellis FP 89337* in 1939 (FPF); 2 mi. W of Heber, *L 64–19* in 1964; between Snowflake and Show Low, *Hevly* in 1959 (MNA); 7 mi. W of US 60 on Mogollon Rim rd., *H & L 922* in 1966 (FPF); Navajo Nat. Mon., Betatakin Can., *Wetherill 919/3149* in 1937 (ARIZ, MNA) and *Howell 24505* in 1948 (CAS); Pinon, *Whiting 854/*

2825 in 1937 (ARIZ, MNA); 4 mi. SE of Fort Apache on Maverick rd., *H & L 905* in 1966 (FPF). YAVAPAI CO.: Mingus Mtn., 5 mi. W of Jerome on US 89, *H & L 245* in 1962 (FPF). COUNTY UNCERTAIN: Mahogany Range, Point Daguerre, *Palmer 2* in 1869 (UC).

CALIFORNIA

All California Collections on *Pinus monophylla*

INYO CO.: 8.5 mi. W of Lone Pine on Mt. Whitney trail, *Gill & Wright FP 68061* in 1931 (FPF); 10 mi. "above" Lone Pine, *Schrieber 1017* in 1934 (UC); SE side of Mt. Whitney, *Armstrong 1024* in 1934 (UC); 3 mi. W of Lone Pine, *Kuijt 1389* in 1957 (UC); Inyo Mtns., Whippoorwill Flats on Saline Valley rd., *W 2740* in 1960 (RSA). Death Valley Nat. Mon.: Wildrose Can., *Stewart* in 1935 (US) and head of Death Valley Can., *Coville & Gilman 120* in 1931 (US). LOS ANGELES CO.: San Gabriel Mtns.: Mescal Cr., *Ewan 9941* in 1936 (MO) and Swarthout Can., *Putnam n.d.,* (ILL). MONO CO.: 6 mi. S of Coleville, *Wagener FP 89604* in 1936 (FPF) and *Kuijt 1413* in 1957 (UC); 0.5 mi. S of Coleville, *Peterson 63–131** in 1963 (FPF). VENTURA CO.: Mt. Pinos, Seymour Cr., *Peirson 3251* in 1922 (POM, RSA); Mt. Pinos area, *W 3217** in 1962 (COLO, FPF); E edge of Fraser Mtn., *Putnam FP 98054* in 1919 (FPB); Fraser Mtn., *Root* in 1919 (ILL). SAN BERNARDINO CO.: San Bernardino Mtns.: Johnson Grade, Little Bear, *Gill FP 89420* in 1939 (FPF); Big Bear Ranger Sta., *Gill & Wright FP 68089* in 1931 (FPF); Dobel Mine, Bear Lake, *Gill & Wright FP 68064* in 1931 (FPF); Arrastre Cr., T. 2 N, R. 2 E, Sec. 11, *Miller FP 68024* in 1962 (FPB); Arrastre Cr., 3 mi. SE of Baldwin Lake, *Jaeger* in 1938 (POM); NE slope San Bernardino Mtns., *Parish & Parish 1442* in 1882 (MO, UC, US); N side of Sugarloaf, *Munz 10771* in 1926 (POM); 1 mi. N of Baldwin Lake, *H 733* in 1965 (FPF); Bear Valley, *Lieberg 3312* in 1898 (US). New York Mtns., 5 mi. SE of Ivanpah, *Gill & Wright FP 68238* in 1931 (FPF). Providence Mtns.: *Brandegee* in 1902 (UC); S fork of N fork of Fountain Can., *Beal 660* in 1939 (JEPS); near Bonanza King Mine, *Munz et al.* in 1920 (POM) and *Shields* in 1965 (FPF). COUNTY UNKNOWN: *Bigelow* in 1853–54 (US).

COLORADO

DELTA CO.: S of Delta, *Hedgcock FP 9299* in 1911 (FPF). DOLORES CO.: T. 39 N, R. 17 W, Sec. 9 [ca. 4 mi. E of Cahone], *Hinds 63–10* in 1963 (FPF). GARFIELD CO.: West Elk Guard Sta., N of Newcastle, *Hinds* in 1961 (FPF). LA PLATA CO.: Without locality, *Curran* in 1914 (US); Durango, *Tweedy 595* in 1896 (US); N of Durango, *Hunt & Bethel FP 24428* in 1917 (FPF); Bayfield, *Hedgcock &*

Bethel FP 24674 in 1917 (FPF). MESA CO.: Colorado Nat. Mon.: *Wilford* in 1961 (FPF); 2 mi. S of Fruita, *W 3168* in 1962 (COLO, FPF). MONTE-ZUMA CO.: Mancos: *Baker, Earle & Tracy 94* in 1898 (CAS, MO, POM, RM, US), *Tracy, Earle & Baker 388* in 1898 (DS), and *Eastwood* in 1891 (COLO); 3 mi. S of Mancos, *Peterson 30–61* in 1961 (FPF); 1 mi. NE of Mancos, *Hinds* in 1965 (FPF). Mesa Verde Nat. Park: *Erdman 120* in 1959 (COLO, WTU), *Weber 6065* in 1951 (COLO), and *Bethel & Hunt FP 29261* in 1918 (FPF); N entrance, *H & Scharpf 691** in 1964 (FPF); Spruce Tree House, *Mathias 652* in 1929 (MO). MONTROSE CO.: 13 mi. SW of Montrose, *Hinds* in 1960 (FPF); T. 48 N, R. 70 W, Sec. 9 [5 mi. W of Cimarron], *Hinds 63–14* in 1963 (FPF); 20 mi. N of Placerville, *Pesman* in 1960 (CS); T. 46 N, R. 12 W, Sec. 7 [1 mi. E of Ute], *Hinds 63–17** in 1963 (FPF); 11 mi. E of Naturita on Rte. 90, *H 1087* in 1967 (FPF); 8 mi. W of Bedrock on Rte. 90, *H 713* in 1965 (FPF). OURAY CO.: 2 mi. SE of Ridgway, *Payson FP 26016* in 1917 (FPF).

NEVADA

All Nevada Collections on *Pinus monophylla*

CHURCHILL CO.: Carroll Summit, 10 mi. E of Eastgate on US 50; *H & W 835* in 1966 (FPF). CLARK CO.: Charleston Mtns.: *Coville & Funston 308* in 1891 (US); Deer Cr. Campground, *W 3207* in 1962 (COLO, FPF); Kyle Can., *Clokey 8565* in 1939 (ARIZ, CAS, CS, MO, POM, RM, RSA, UC, WTU); 2 mi. E of Nat. For. bdy. on Rte. 58, *H & Scharpf 672* in 1964 (FPF). Sheep Mtns., Spring Can., *Johnson* in 1969 (FPF). DOUGLAS CO.: Pine Nuts Hills, S of Carson City, *Peterson* in 1960 (FPF); 9 mi. S of Gardnerville, *Wagener FP 89603* in 1936 (FPF); near Minden, *McKlevey 1464* in 1930 (US); ca. 7 mi. N of Topaz Lake on US 395, *Krebill & Nelson 467* in 1967 (FPF). ELKO CO.: Big Springs near Cave Cr. P. O., *Mason 4748* in 1928 (UC). ESMERALDA CO.: White Mtns., *Roos 1028* in 1937 (POM). LANDER CO.: 10 mi. E of Austin on US 50, *H & W 833* in 1966 (FPF); Austin, *Weir* in 1916 (FPF, ILL, UC) and *Jones* in 1882 (POM); Big Cr., *Linsdale & Linsdale 264* in 1931 (CAS). LINCOLN CO.: Deer Lodge, E part of co. [near Fay], *Train 2521* in 1938 (ARIZ, UC). LYON CO.: Wassuk Range, Coal Valley, *Alexander & Kellogg 5328* in 1947 (UC, WTU); 6 mi. SE of Wellington, *McMillan 197* in 1941 (RSA, UT) MINERAL CO.: Alum Cr. S of Hawthorn, *Peterson 63–327** in 1963 (FPF). NYE CO.: Grant Range, Irwin Can. near Timber Mtn., *Peterson 63–329** in 1963 (FPF); E side of Pahute Mesa, *Bostick 5237* in 1967 (DS, FPF). WHITE PINE CO.: E of Lehman Caves Nat. Mon., *Peterson 63–338** in 1963 (FPF) and *Maguire & Becraft 2535a* in 1933 (UC).

NEW MEXICO

BERNALILLO CO.: Manzano Mtns., Cedro Can., *Ellis FP 89502* in 1939 (FPF); Sandia Mtns., 0.5 mi. W of Doc Long Campground, *H 36* in 1956 (FPF) and *L* in 1962 (FPF). CATRON CO.: Mogollon, *Hedgcock and Long FP 9936* in 1911 (FPF); Mogollon Cr., *Metcalfe 288* in 1902 (ARIZ, DS, FPF, MO, POM, UC, US); 2 mi. W of Mogollon, *H & L 133* in 1962 (FPF); Adams Diggins, 18 mi. NW of Pie Town, *L 65–5* in 1965 (FPF); 6.5 mi. S of Luna on Rte. 180, *H 817* in 1965 (FPF); Diamond Cr., 13 mi. S of Beaverhead on Rte. 61, *L 65–41* in 1965 (FPF); 20 mi. N of Rte. 78 on Apache Springs rd. *L 65–44* in 1965 (FPF); 11 mi. SE of Reserve on new rd. to Beaverhead, *H & L 899* in 1966 (FPF); 1 mi. W of Red Hill on US 60, *H & L 926* in 1966 (FPF); 11 mi. S of US 60 on Rte. 32, *H & L 927* in 1966 (FPF). GRANT CO.: Telegraph Mtns., *Wooton* in 1902 (POM, RM, US); Walnut Cr., near Silver City, *Gill FP 68301* in 1934 (FPF); Fort Bayard, *Johnson FP 15106* in 1913 (FPF), *Hedrick FP 41* and *FP 286* in 1908 (FPF); Stephens Ranch, Fort Bayard Watershed, *Blumer 110* in 1905 (US); 5 mi. W of Mimbres River on Rte. 180, *H & L 125* in 1962 (FPF); 21 mi. N of Mimbres on Rte. 61, *L 65–38* in 1965 (FPF). LINCOLN CO.: 1 mi. S of Nogal on Rte. 37, *H & L 101* in 1962 (FPF); Gallina Mtns., SW of Corona, *Riffle* in 1964 (FPF) and *H & L 1078* in 1967 (FPF); 3 mi. SE of Ancho, *L 64–30* in 1964 (FPF). MCKINLEY CO.: Continental Divide, 25 mi. E of Gallup on US 66, *Ellis FP 89503* in 1939 (FPF) and *L 64–12* in 1964 (FPF); 2 mi. NE of San Mateo, *L 63–29* in 1963 (FPF); 0.5 mi. S of Old Fort Wingate, *L 63–36** in 1963 (FPF). OTERO CO.: Pinon, *Wyman FP 1838* in 1914 (FPF); Box Can. near Highrolls, *Viereck* in 1902 (PH). RIO ARRIBA CO.: 5 mi. W of Coyote on US 84, *L 63–18* in 1963 (FPF); 15 mi. NW of Espanola, *L 63–136* in 1963 (FPF); 2.5 mi. W of Canjilon, *L 63–6* in 1963 (FPF); near Gobernador, *L 64–9* in 1964 (FPF); Carson Nat. For., La Jara Cr., on Rte. 17, *L 64–11* in 1964 (FPF). SANDOVAL CO.: Sandia Mtns., N side, *Gill & Long FP 68137* in 1932 (FPF) and *Ellis FP 89411* in 1939 (FPF); 14 mi. NW of Cuba on Rte. 44, *H & Scharpf 692** in 1962 (FPF). SAN JUAN CO.: Near Cedar Hill, *Standley 7979* in 1911 (US); Navajo Res., Tunitcha [Chuska] Mtns., *Standley 7810* in 1911 (US); 5 mi. SW of Sheep Springs, *L & Weiss 66–41* in 1966 (FPF). SAN MIGUEL CO.: 3 mi. N of Pecos on Rte. 63, *L 65–30* in 1965 (FPF). SANTA FE CO.: Santa Fe, *Heller & Heller 3533* in 1897 (FPF, MO, US); Mesa NE of Santa Fe, *Hedgcock & Bethel FP 24730* in 1917 (FPF, ILL); Mtns. E of Santa Fe, *Fendler 312* 1847 (MO); 20 mi. E of Espanola, *L 63–16* in 1963 (FPF); near Rio en Media, *H & Hinds 1077* in 1967 (FPF); Canoncito, *Brandegee* in 1879 (UC);

vicinity of Santa Fe, *Rose & Fitch 17765* in 1913 (US). SIERRA CO.: Rhodes Pass, 20 mi. E of Engle, *Cutler 2047* in 1938 (CAS, MO, UC); 2 mi. W of Kingston on Rte. 90, *H & L 889* in 1966 (FPF). SOCORRO CO.: San Mateo Mtns., 10 mi. S of US 60 on Rte. 52, *L 65–33* in 1965 (FPF); 5 mi. W of Magdalena on US 60, *L 63–41* in 1963 (FPF); 25 mi. W of Carrizozo on US 380, *L 65–1* in 1965 (FPF); 7.5 mi. W of Claunch, *L 65–20* in 1965 (FPF). TAOS CO.: Taos, *Greene* in 1877 (MO); Penasco, *von Schrenk* in 1907 (MO); 19 mi. S of Tres Piedras on US 285, *L 63–11* in 1963 (FPF); 11 mi. N of Taos on Rte. 3 at San Cristobal Jct., *L 65–45* in 1965 (FPF); 12 mi. S of Tres Piedras on US 285, *H 1011* in 1967 (FPF). VALENCIA CO.: 2.3 mi. W of Cebolleta, *L 65–6* in 1965 (FPF); 3 mi. NW of Trechado on Rte. 36, *L 65–4* in 1965 (FPF); 10 mi. E of Grants on rd. to La Mosca Lookout, *L 65–50* in 1965 (FPF). COUNTY UNCERTAIN: Alamo Nat. For., *Long FP 19634* in 1915 (FPF); Embudo to Rio Pueblo, *O'Bryne & Long FP 18678* in 1914 (FPF).

TEXAS

JEFF DAVIS CO.: Davis Mtns.: *Young 63* in 1914 (MO); Mt. Livermore, *Andresen & Andresen 1824** in 1962 (FPF); Wood Can., Jones Ranch, *Hinckley* in 1936 (ARIZ); north slope of Sawtooth Mtn., on *P. cembroides*, *Little & Correll 19033* in 1963 (FPF); Mt. Livermore, Goat Can., on *P. cembroides*, *Hinckley* in 1935 (SRSC); H. O. Can., on *P. cembroides*, *Hinckley* in 1935 (SRSC); H. O. Can., on *P. cembroides*, *Hinckley 3163* in 1944 (SRSC); H. O. Can., 1 mi. S of summit on Rte. 166, on *P. cembroides*, *H, L & Lampi 1050* in 1967 (FPF).

UTAH

CARBON CO.: Price, *Flowers* in 1934 (FPF, UT); Sunnyside, *Jones* in 1907 (POM). DUCHESNE CO.: 11 mi. W of Duchesne on US 40, *H 1052* in 1967 (FPF). GARFIELD CO.: 5 mi. SW of Panguitch, *Peterson 62-107* in 1962 (FPF); 2 mi. W of Tropic, *Buchanan 527* in 1959 (UT, WTU); SE of Table Cliffs, *Peterson 64-87* in 1964 (FPF); 21 mi. SW of Escalante on Rte. 54, *H 682** in 1964 (FPF); Henry Mtns., NW slope of Bull Mtn., *Harrison 11184* in 1947 (UC). IRON CO.: Near Cedar City, *Parry* in 1874 (MO). JUAB CO.: Deep Cr. Range, Stewarts Cabin, on *P. monophylla*, *Holmgren 3748* in 1944 (UC, WTU). KANE CO.: 0.5 mi. N of Glendale, *W 3179* in 1962 (COLO, FPF); 4 mi. SE of Mt. Carmel on US 89, *H & Laut 1164* in 1969 (FPF). MILLARD CO.: House Mtns. col.? in 1938 (UT). PIUTE CO.: 3 mi. SW of Marysvale, *W 4168* in 1967 (FPF, UT). SAN JUAN CO.: 5 mi. N of Blanding on Rte. 47, *Peterson 65-69* in 1965 (FPF); 8 mi. N of Blanding on Rte.

47, *H 1089* in 1967 (FPF). SANPETE CO.: SE of Ephraim, *Hedgcock FP 8142* in 1912 (FPF); W of Ephraim, *Hedgcock FP 8135* and *FP 8139* in 1912 (FPF) and on *P. monophylla*, *Tidestrom 1300* in 1908 (US). WASHINGTON CO.: Zion Nat. Park, on *P. monophylla*, *Nelson & Nelson 2697* in 1938 (RM); 10 mi. N of Beaver Dam Summit, on *P. monophylla*, *W 3913* in 1966 (FPF, UT); 1 mi. N of Pine Park, ca. 16 air mi. W of Enterprise, *H, L & Laut 1174* in 1969 (FPF). WAYNE CO.: Aquarius Plateau, Head of Poison Cr., *Rydberg & Carlton 7371* in 1905 (RM, US); 2 mi. S of Grover, *W 3171* in 1962 (COLO, FPF). COUNTY UNCERTAIN: La Sal Mtns., Little Springs on W slope, *Rydberg & Garrett 8542* in 1911 (RM, US).

MEXICO

BAJA CALIFORNIA: Sierra Juárez: 21 mi. S of La Rumorosa on rd. to Laguna Hanson, on *P. quadrifolia*, *L & Gill 64-34* in 1964 (FPF); 16.5 mi. N of Laguna Hanson, on *P. quadrifolia*, *H & Scharpf 786* in 1965 (FPF).

11. ARCEUTHOBIUM DOUGLASII

Specimens Examined: on *Pseudotsuga menziesii* except as noted.

CANADA

BRITISH COLUMBIA: 1 mi. S of Sirdar, N of Creston, *Calder & Savile 11413* in 1953 (WTU); Summerland Exp. Sta., *Calder & Savile 11536* in 1953 (UC, US); Similkameen River, *Macoun 79522* in 1905 (MO); 10 mi. SE of Kelowna, *Kuijt 588* in 1954 (DAVFP, FPF); Beaver Lake rd., near Wood Lake, *Kuijt 581* in 1954 (DAVFP, FPF); 10 mi. N of Sirdar, *Kuijt 650* in 1954 (DAVFP, FPF).

MEXICO

COAHUILA: Sierra del Carmen, *H, L & Muñoz 1027* in 1967 (FPF). DURANGO: 47 mi. S of Durango on La Flor rd., *H & W 514* in 1963 (FPF). NUEVO LEON: Cerro Potosí, 11 mi. from village "18 de Marzo" on rd. to relay tower, *H & W 395** in 1963 (FPF).

UNITED STATES

ARIZONA

APACHE CO.: 4 mi. S of Eagar, *H & L 209* in 1962 (FPF); Alpine, *Goodding FP 26737* in 1917 (FPF); 4.7 mi. SW of Alpine on Rte. 666, *H & Scharpf 699* in 1964 (FPF); Milk Can., 8 mi. E of Nutrioso, *Parker & McClintock 7587* in 1951 (ARIZ); 5 mi. E of Lukachukai on Red Rock rd., *L & Weiss 66–48* in 1966 (FPF); 11 mi. SW of Red Rock on Lukachukai rd., *L & Weiss 66–50* in 1966 (FPF); 2 mi. E of Big Lake, *H 820* in 1965 (FPF); 3 mi. NE of Maverick on Fort Apache rd., *H & L 902* in 1966 (FPF); 13 mi. E of McNary on Rte. 73, *H & L 924* in 1966 (FPF). COCHISE CO.: Chiricahua Mtns.: Pinery Can. rd., *Gill & Ellis FP 89497* in 1939 (FPF); Pinery Can. rd., 7 mi. E of Nat. For. bdy., *H & L 152** in 1962 (FPF); Rustler Park, *Gill FP 68056* in 1935 (FPF). Huachuca Mtns., Carr Can., *Goodding FP 33284* in 1919 (FPF) and *Goodding 2088* in 1915 (ARIZ). COCONINO CO.: "Kaibab For.," *Richards* in 1938 (ARIZ, RM, WTU); San Francisco Peaks, *Knowlton 40* in 1889 (US); San Francisco Peaks, Interior Basin, *H & L 251* in 1962 (FPF); Grand Can., South Rim, 1 mi. E of Grandview Point, *H 39* in 1954 (FPF) and *H & L 183* in 1962 (FPF); Oak Cr. Can., *Ellis FP 89504* in 1939 (FPF); Jacob Lake, *Moberg & Gill FP 68299* in 1934 (FPF); Mt. Eldon, near Flagstaff, *Drake FP 15122* in 1913 (FPF); San Francisco Peaks, Spruce Cabin, *Gill FP 68134* in 1932 (FPF); Flagstaff, *Purpus* in 1900 (UC); N slope, Mt. Eldon, *Whiting 1053/5338* in 1941 (ARIZ); Grand Can., Grandview Trail, *Thornber & Hockdoerffer 2944* in 1907 (ARIZ); San Francisco Peaks, *Goodding* in 1917 (ARIZ); Baker Butte, *Andrews, Ellis & Gill FP 89229* in 1937 (FPF); Rim rd., 5 mi. SE of W bdy. of Sitgreaves Nat. For., *L 64–16* in 1964 (FPF); 3 mi. E of Long Valley, *L 64–14* in 1964 (FPF); North Kaibab Plateau, 7 mi. W of Kaibab Lodge, on *Picea engelmannii, Peterson 45–61* in 1961 (FPF); San Francisco Peaks, 7 mi. NE of Schultz Pass on Interior Basin rd., on *Abies lasiocarpa* var. *arizonica, H & L 250* in 1962 (FPF); near Weimer Springs, W of Mormon Lake, *H & L 913* in 1966 (FPF); 11 mi. S of Chevlon Ranger Sta., *H & L 918* in 1966 (FPF). GILA CO.: Sierra Ancha, Workman Cr., *H 44* in 1956 (FPF) and *L & Lampi 64–15* in 1965 (FPF); 26 mi. E of Payson on Rte. 160, *L 63–55* in 1963 (FPF). GRAHAM CO.: Graham Mtns.: 1 mi. above Arcadia Guard Sta., *H & L 142* in 1962 (FPF); Hospital Flat, *H & L 226* in 1962 (FPF); Turkey Flat, *Gill FP 68037* in 1936 (FPF); Treasure Park, *Mielke & Ellis FP 89694* in 1944 (FPF); Grant Cr., on *Abies lasiocarpa* var. *arizonica, Stouffer FP 68239* in 1934 (FPF). GREENLEE CO.: 47 mi. S of Springerville on US 666, *Gill FP 68303* in 1934 (FPF); Blue Summit, *Gill FP 68307* in 1934 (FPF); 3 mi. S of Hannagan Meadows on Rte. 666, *Andrews* in 1963 (FPF). NAVAJO CO.: 6 mi. E of Rte. 160 on Mogollon Rim rd., *H & L 920* in 1966 (FPF). PIMA CO.: Santa Catalina Mtns.: *Toumey* in 1896 (US); Soldier Camp, *Gill FP 68127* and *FP 68263* in 1932 (FPF); Bear Wallow Campground, *H & L*

166 in 1962 (FPF). YAVAPAI CO.: Spruce Mtn., *Hedgcock FP 4856* and *FP 4871* in 1910 (FPF); 0.5 mi. N of Spruce Mtn., *H & L 239* in 1962 (FPF).

CALIFORNIA

PLUMAS CO.: Providence Hill, ca. 4 mi. N of Twaiai, T. 26 N., R. 8 E., Sec. 35, *Henson* in 1970 (FPF). SHASTA CO.: Near Pondosa Jct., *Kuijt 1367* in 1957 (UC); 2 mi. SW of Pondosa Jct., *H & W 645* in 1964 (FPF). SISKIYOU CO.: Sisson, *Hedgcock, Meinecke & Long FP 9669* in 1911 (FPF); Dry Lake Lookout, Oak Knoll [4 mi. SE of Cowdry Mtn.], *Gill & Sargent FP 68179* in 1932 (FPF); N side Cascade Gulch, Mt. Shasta, *Cooke 17729* in 1947 (WTU); Upton, Mt. Shasta, *Hall & Babcock 4078* in 1903 (UC) and *Cooke 13920* in? (DS); Joe Cr., 7 mi. S of Copper, Oregon, *H & W 634* in 1964 (FPF); West base of Black Butte, 5 mi. S of Weed on US 99, *H & W 639* in 1964 (FPF,; Siskiyou Mtns., W fork Cottonwood Cr. [SW of Hilts], *Wheeler 2783* in 1934 (MO, POM, US, Z); rd. to Gumboot Lake [ca. 12 mi. W of Dunsmuir], *Smith & Bacigalupi* in 1957 (UC).

COLORADO

ARCHULETA CO.: Pagosa Springs, *Hedgcock & Bethel FP 24654* in 1917 (FPF); 3 mi. N of Piedra, *Hinds 63–6* in 1963 (FPF). CHAFFEE CO.: 6.8 mi. S of US 285 on Bassam Park rd., *H 446* in 1963 (FPF). CONEJOS CO.: 2 mi. SW of Conejos River on Rte. 17, *L 63–2* in 1963 (FPF) and *Hinds 63–2* in 1963 (FPF). CUSTER CO.: 3.8 mi. NW of Isabel Lake on Rte. 165, *H 429* in 1963 (FPF) and on *Picea engelmannii, H 430* in 1963 (FPF); 4.7 mi. W of Hillside, *H 434* in 1963 (FPF). DOUGLAS CO.: 5.5 mi. W of Rte. 105 on Jackson Cr. rd., *H 206* in 1962 (FPF). EAGLE CO.: 8 mi. SW of Gypsum on Cottonwood Pass rd., *H 946* in 1966 (FPF). EL PASO CO.: Palmer Lake, *Bethel* in 1912 (US) and in 1919 (CS); Clifton Park, *Hill FP 68280* in 1932 (FPF); Palmer Lake, *Hedgcock FP 15900* in 1914 (FPF, RSA, WTU); W of Palmer Lake, *Hedgcock, Thompson & Gayman FP 24901* in 1917 (FPF); 5 mi. W of Monument, *W 2984* in 1962 (COLO, FPF); 1.7 mi. above Cascade on Pikes Peak rd., *H & Hinds 425* in 1963 (FPF); 0.3 mi. E of Bruin Inn, N Cheyenne Can., *H 538** in 1963 (FPF); Air Force Academy, 0.5 mi. S of Cadet Area, *H 541* in 1963 (FPF); Crystal Park, *Gill FP 68141* in 1932 (FPF); Mt. Manitou, *Gill FP 68256* in 1932 (FPF); Halfway, Pikes Peak, *Hedgcock FP 905* in 1909 (FPF); Palmer Lake Reservoir, *Gill FP 68139* in 1932 (FPF). FREMONT CO.: Sangre de Cristo Mtns., Hayden Pass rd. ca. 5 mi. SW of Coaldale,

Schacht in 1969 (FPF). GARFIELD CO.: 0.5 mi. S of Douglas Pass, *H 686* in 1964 (FPF); 14 mi. NNE of Rifle, *Hinds* in 1965 (FPF). GUNNISON CO.: Elk Mtns., Coal Cr. Can., *Brandegee* in 1881 (MO, PH, UC); near Marble, *W 3618* in 1964 (FPF, UT). HINSDALE CO.: Little Sand Cr., 21 air mi. NW of Pagosa Springs, *Landgraf* in 1965 FPF). HUERFANO CO.: Williams Cr., ca. 10 mi. N of Gardner, *H 432* in 1963 (FPF); N of Black Mtn., ca. 10 mi. NNW of Gardner, *Stewart* in 1964 (FPF). LA PLATA CO.: Hills N of Durango, *Hunt & Bethel FP 24429* in 1917 (FPF); W of Trimble, *Hedgcock & Bethel FP 24639 and FP 24689* in 1917 (FPF); Dry Fork Cr., 8 air mi. NW of Durango, *Landgraf* in 1965 (FPF). LAS ANIMAS CO.: Near Stonewall Gap, *Hedgcock & Johnston FP 24945 in 1917* (FPF). MINERAL CO.: 4.2 mi. N of Archuleta co. line on US 160, *Hinds 63–4* in 1963 (FPF). MOFFAT CO.: Dinosaur Nat. Mon., Can. Overlook, *W 4129* in 1967 (FPF, UT). MONTEZUMA CO.: W Mancos Can., *Baker, Earle & Tracy 388* in 1898 (ARIZ, MO, RM, POM, US); Priest Gulch, 8 mi. E of Stoner, *Landgraf* in 1965 (FPF); 14 mi. NE of Dolores on Rico rd., *Hinds 63–12* in 1963 (FPF); Aspen Guard Sta., 10 mi. NNE of Mancos, *Hinds* in 1965 (FPF); MONTROSE CO.: Uncompahgre Plateau, Windy Point, *Peterson 51–61* in 1961 (FPF); 5.5 mi. N of Rte. 90 on Transfer rd., *Hinds 63–15* in 1963 (FPF). OURAY CO.: Ouray, *Gayman FP 26521* in 1917 (FPF) and *Hedgcock FP 15915* in 1914 (FPF). PUEBLO CO.: Beulah, *Edmonston FP 295* in 1909 (FPF). SAGUACHE CO.: 5 mi. E of N Cochetopa Pass, *H 440* in 1963 (FPF); 2 mi. S of Poncha Pass on US 285, *H 444* in 1963 (FPF); 4 mi. SW of Rte. 114 on Dry Gulch rd., *H & L 442* in 1963 (FPF); near Cochetopa Pass, on *Picea engelmannii*, *L & Schacht 63–26* in 1963 (FPF). SAN MIGUEL CO.: 7.9 mi. W of Dallas Divide on Rte. 62, *Hinds* in 1965 (FPF); 2 mi. W of Placerville, *Payson FP 26026* in 1917 (FPF). TELLER CO.: Hotel Gulch, 1.5 mi. E of Manitou Exp. For. headquarters, *H 260* in 1962 (FPF).

IDAHO

ADAMS CO.: Evergreen, *Hedgcock FP 988* in 1909 (FPF); 13 mi. N of Council on US 95, *H 977* in 1966 (FPF). BLAINE CO.: Bald Mtn. near Ketchum, *Mielke* in 1957 (FPF). BONNER CO.: Hope, *Sandberg & Lieberg 4443* in 1893 (MO, POM, RM, US); Lake Pend Oreille, *Sandberg, MacDougal & Heller 744* in 1892 (MO, US, Z); Priest River *Weir 9995* in 1917 (ILL); Smiths Peak, Priest Lake, on *Abies lasiocarpa*, *Weir 2419* in 1913 (ILL). BOUNDARY CO.: Pack River, on *Abies lasiocarpa*, *Weir 2415* n.d. (ILL). CAMAS CO.: Boise River, 1 mi. E of Elmore Co. bdy., *Peterson 62–50* in 1962 (FPF).

CLARK CO.: Spencer, *Hurtt FP 20583* in 1912 (FPF). CUSTER CO.: Challis, *Gill FP 68206** in 1932 (FPF); 8 mi. W of Challis, *Benlow* in 1917 (ILL); Garden Cr. near Challis, on *Abies lasiocarpa*, *Gill FP 68207* in 1932 (FPF). FRANKLIN CO.: Cub River near Franklin Basin, *Peterson 63–364* in 1963 (FPF). IDAHO CO.: 5 mi. S of Grangeville, *Krebill 159* in 1964 (FPF), and *H 968* in 1966 (FPF); 15 mi. N of Burgdorf on Salmon River rd., *H 971* in 1966 (FPF); Salmon River at Fern Cr., ca. 23 mi. W of Shoup, *W 4127a* in 1966 (FPF, UT). KOOTENAI CO.: Lakeside, col.? in 1889 (UC); Canfield Mtn. [4 mi. NW of Coeur d' Alene], *Weir 2412* in 1916 (ILL). LATAH CO.: 3 mi. E of Viola, *Wicker* in 1959 (WSP). LEMHI CO.: SW of Salmon on N fork of Williams Cr., *Krebill 126* in 1964 (FPF); 4 mi. N of Gibbonsville on US 93, *H & Hinds 1123* in 1968 (FPF); Wagonheimer, 3 mi. SE of North Fork, *Hedgcock FP 4457* in 1910 (FPF); 2.5 mi. E of Tendoy, *H & Hinds 1122* in 1968 (FPF). LEWIS CO.: 3 mi. N of Winchester on US 95, *H 967* in 1966 (FPF). MADISON CO.: Hawley Ranger Sta., *Peterson 62–16* in 1962 (FPF). SHOSHONE CO.: Marble Mtn., on *Abies lasiocarpa*, *Weir 2418* in 1914 (ILL). TETON CO.: Near Driggs, *Peterson 62–11* in 1962 (FPF). VALLEY CO.: W of Cascade, *Thompson 13844* in 1937 (MO, UC, WTU); McCall, *Weir* in 1914 (ILL); 3 mi. NE of McCall, *H 975* in 1966 (FPF). WASHINGTON CO.: Weiser, *Oman* in 1912 (RM). COUNTY UNCERTAIN: St. Joe Nat. For., on *Abies lasiocarpa*, *Weir 2416* n.d. (ILL).

MONTANA

FLATHEAD CO.: FLATHEAD LAKE: Yellow Bay, *Clemens* in 1908 (DS); Mainland opposite Bull Island, *Clemens* in 1908 (MO, PH); Bull Island, *Jones 9307* in 1908 (POM, US); Bigfork, *Jones 9380* in 1908 (MO, POM). LINCOLN CO.: Sylvanite [18 mi. N of Troy], on *Picea engelmannii*, *Weir 2400* in 1916 (FPF, ILL). MISSOULA CO.: Norman Valley, *Barkley & Barkley 3504* in 1938 (ARIZ, COLO, MO, POM, UC, US); Pattee Cr., near Missoula, *Weir FP 91207* in 1918 (FPF, OSC); "Paddy" Can., *Barkley 1999* in 1937 (POM); Pattee Can., *Spaulding FP 15107* in 1913 (FPF) and *Hedgcock FP 4556* in 1910 (FPF); Missoula, *Weir 9986* in 1915 (ILL) and *7426* in 1917 (ILL). RAVALLI CO.: Blogett Cr. [W of Hamilton], *Hedgcock FP 9519* in 1911 (FPF); Spoon Cr. near Darby, *Hughes* in 1917 (FPF, ILL); 10 mi. E of Hamilton on Skalkaho Pass rd., *H & Wicker 953* in 1966 (FPF).

NEVADA

WHITE PINE CO.: NE slope of Wheeler Peak, *Peterson 63–337* in 1963 (FPF).

NEW MEXICO

BERNALILLO CO.: Sandia Mtns.: *Hedgcock FP 172, FP 185, FP 1538* and *FP 1539* in 1908 (FPF); *Long & Seay FP 21275* in 1916 (FPF): La Luz, Juan Tabo Trail, *H 15* in 1954 (FPF); 2 mi. E of La Madera Ski Area, on *Abies concolor, H 56* in 1956 (FPF). CATRON CO.: 0.5 mi. W of Mogollon, *H & L 131* in 1962 (FPF); 6 mi. S of Luna on US 260, *H & L 213* in 1962 (FPF); Mangas Mtn., *H & Scharpf 697* in 1964 (FPF): Tularosa Summit, 11.5 mi. N of Rte. 78 on Apache Springs rd., *L 65–43* in 1965 (FPF); 7 mi. E of Mogollon, on *Abies lasiocarpa* var. *arizonica, Hedgcock FP 9899* in 1911 (FPF) and *H & L 216* in 1962 (FPF); 2 mi. E of Bursum Campground on Rte. 78, on *Abies lasiocarpa* var. *arizonica, H & L 218* in 1962 (FPF); 1.5 mi. E of Bursum Campground on Rte. 78, on *Abies concolor, H & L 217* in 1962 (FPF); 2 mi. W of Rte. 78 on Bearwallow Lookout rd., *H & L 898* in 1966 (FPF). COLFAX CO.: 8 mi. SE of Black Lake on Rte. 120, *L 65–48* in 1965 (FPF); 1 mi. E of Eagle Nest Lake, *H FP 89958* in 1951 (FPF) and on *Abies concolor, H FP 89957* in 1951 (FPF); 9.5 mi. W of Cimarron on US 64, *L 65–21* in 1965 (FPF). GRANT CO.: Emory Pass, *H & L 120* in 1962 (FPF); 2 mi. N of Red stone, *H & L 127** in 1962 (FPF); 22 mi. N of Mimbres on Rte. 61, *L 65–39* in 1965 (FPF). LINCOLN CO.: Capitan Mtns.: 2 mi. E of Capitan Gap, *H & L 106* in 1962 (FPF) and 1 mi. E, *1099* in 1968 (FPF); West Capitan Mtn. *L 66–20* in 1966 (FPF); Seven Cabins Can., *Ellis, Hackleman & Gill FP 89491* in 1938 (FPF). E side of Gallinas Peak, 10 mi. W of Corona, *L & Riffle 63–43* in 1963 (FPF) and *H & L 1079* in 1967 (FPF). LOS ALAMOS CO.: 1 mi. N of W gate to Los Alamos, *L 65–31* in 1965 (FPF); 5 mi. W of Los Alamos on Rte. 4, *L & Gill 65–24* in 1965 (FPF); McKINLEY CO.: Zuni Mtns., Stinking Springs rd., *L 63–34* in 1963 (FPF); Chuska Mtns., 1 mi. S of Camp Ayassi [ca. 6 mi. S of Crystal], *L 64–1** in 1964 (FPF). MORA CO.: 3 mi. NW of Holman on Rte. 3, *L 65–49* in 1965 (FPF). OTERO CO.: Mescalero Indian Res.: Summit Can., *H 26* in 1954 (FPF); Goat Can., *H FP 89992* in 1952 (FPF); Whitetail Well, *H 23* in 1954 (FPF); 1 mi. E of Apache Summit, *H & Scharpf 694* in 1964 (FPF). Silver Springs Can., 7.5 mi. NE of Cloudcroft, *H & L 878* in 1966 (FPF). Curtis Can., 5 mi. W of State Rte. 130, W of Mayhill, *H & L 880* in 1966 (FPF); 10 mi. S of Cloudcroft on Sacramento Peak rd., *H & L 886* in 1966 (FPF). Sixteen Springs Can., 7 mi. E of Cloudcroft, *H 1080* in 1967 (FPF). RIO ARRIBA CO.: 12.5 mi. E of Canjilon on Rte. 110 *L 63–7* in 1963 (FPF); 6 mi. W of Vallecitos, *L63–8* in 1963 (FPF). SANDOVAL CO.: 5 mi. SE of Fenton Lake *L 63–22* in 1963 (FPF); N end Sandia Mtns., *Gill & Long FP 68136* in 1932 (FPF); Placitas, *Hedgcock FP 650* n.d., (FPF); 2 mi. N of Sulphur Springs Jct. on Rte. 126, *L & Gill 65–25* in 1965 (FPF). SAN JUAN CO.: 6.5 mi. SW of Sheep Springs, *L & Weiss 66–43* in 1966 (FPF); Tunitcha [Chuska] Mtns., *Standley 7664* in 1911 (US). SANTA FE CO.: Hyde State Park, *L 63–39* in 1963 (FPF); 8 mi. E of Chimayo, *L 63–24* in 1963 (FPF); 9 mi. E of Santa Fe, *Heller & Heller 3527* in 1897 (ARIZ, DS, MO, US, Z). SAN MIGUEL CO.: 15 mi. E of Pecos, *L 63–23* in 1963 (FPF); 4 mi. S of Cowles on Rte. 63, *L 65–28* in 1965 (FPF). SOCORRO CO.: Magdalena Mtns., 3 mi. above campground in Water Can., *W 2994* in 1962 (COLO, FPF); San Mateo Mtns.: Hughes Sawmill, *Long FP 21126* in 1915 (FPF) and 11 mi. S of US 60 on Rte. 52, *L 65–34* in 1965 (FPF). TAOS CO.: Penasco, near U.S. Hill, *Long FP 19340* in 1914 (FPF); 1 mi. W of Colfax co. bdy. on US 64, *L 65–23* in 1965 (FPF); Cienega Ranger Sta., *Korstian FP 19276* in 1914 (FPF); 3 mi. E of Questa, *L 65–46* in 1965 (FPF); Santa Barbara Can., on *Abies concolor, Thorne* in 1963 (FPF); Taos Can., 7 mi. E of Taos on US 64, *H 876* in 1966 (FPF). TORRANCE CO.: Manzano Mtns., 3 mi. NW of Manzano, *Riffle* in 1963 (FPF). VALENCIA CO.: Mt. Taylor, Marquez Can., *L 63–31* in 1963 (FPF); Mt. Sedgwick, ca. 17 mi. W of Grants, *L 65–7* in 1965 (FPF). COUNTY UNCERTAIN: Front Cr. Basin, Gila Nat. For., *Hedgcock & Long FP 9847* in 1911 (FPF).

OREGON

BAKER CO.: Lily White Guard Sta., 7 mi. NE of Sparta, *Steward & Jackman 6499* in 1953 (WTU); 22 mi. S of Baker on Rte. 7, *H & W 584* in 1964 (FPF). CLACKAMAS CO.: Clackamas River, T. 7 S, R. 8 E, Sec. 32, ca. 4 mi. W of the Cascade Crest, ca. 12 air mi. NE of Breitenbush, *Nicholson* in 1968 (FPF). DESCHUTES CO.: 14 mi. NW of Sisters on Rte. 126, *H & W 616* in 1964 (FPF). GRANT CO.: 20 mi. N of John Day, *Graham* in 1964 (FPF); Prairie City, Peebles Mill, *Boyce FP 40121* in 1920 (FPF); Dixie Butte, *H 980* in 1966 (FPF) and on *Abies lasiocarpa, H 982* in 1966 (FPF); 4 mi. S of Seneca on Rte. 395, *H & W 576* in 1964 (FPF); Skookum Cr., 25 air mi. ESE of Seneca, *H & Scharpf 1268* in 1969 (FPF). JACKSON CO.: Rogue River Nat. For., Yale Cr., [ca. 14 mi. SSW of Medford], *Bedwell & Childs** in 1950 (FPF, OSC) and Childs in 1948 (OSC); 20 mi. SW of Ashland, *Graham* in 1963 (FPF); 10 mi. E of Butte Falls, *Graham* in 1964 (FPF); 11 mi. E of Ashland on Lake of the Woods rd., *H & W 870* in 1966 (FPF); 20 mi. W of Ashland, *H & W 636* in 1964 (FPF); Fish Lake rd., 12 mi. SE of Butte Falls, *Graham* in 1965 (FPF); Huckleberry Mtn., 9 mi. NE of Prospect, *Graham* in 1965 (FPF). JEFFERSON CO.: Suttle Lake, *Gill FP 68192* in 1932 (FPF). JOSEPHINE CO.: 16 mi. E of Cave

Jct. on Oregon Caves rd., *H & W 868* in 1966 (FPF); 13 mi. E of O'Brien on Happy Camp rd., *H & Hinds 997* in 1966 (FPF). KLAMATH CO.: Kirk, Pelican Bay Camp, *Boyce FP 40165* in 1921 (OSC); Pelican Bay, *Peck* in 1920 (PH); 20 mi. W of Klamath Falls on Rte. 66, *H & W 628* in 1964 (FPF); between Lake of the Woods and Pelican Bay, *Daniels* in 1914 (ILL). MORROW CO.: 35 mi. S of Heppner, *Steward & Steward 7329 in 1957* (RSA, US). UNION CO.: 1 mi. NE of Kamela, *H & W 587* in 1964 (FPF); 4 mi. W of Elgin on Rte. 204, *H & W 590* in 1964 (FPF). WALLOWA CO.: 6 air mi. SW of Jct. of Snake and Salmon Rivers, *Graham* in 1964 (FPF); Billy Meadows [5 mi. E of Kirkland Spring], *Colville 2478a* in 1907 (PH); Kirkland area, 30 mi. N of Enterprise, *Graham* in 1965 (FPF). WASCO CO.: Bear Springs For. Campground, *Childs & Hansbrough FP 68261* in 1931 (FPF) and *Childs & Hansbrough (Childs 69)* in 1931 (OSC); 3 mi. E of Bear Springs, *Childs 57* in 1948 (OSC); 4 mi. W of Bear Springs, *H & W 610* in 1964 (FPF). WHEELER CO.: 1 mi. N of Nat. For. bdy., on Derr Meadows rd., 12 mi. SSE of Mitchell, *H 984* in 1966 (FPF); 0.25 mi. N of Ochoco Divide on US 26, on *Abies concolor*, *H & Scharpf 1264* in 1969 (FPF); 1 mi. N of Ochoco Divide, 11 air mi. W of Mitchell, *H 986* in 1966 (FPF); 26 mi. S of Hardman on Rte. 207, *H & Scharpf 1272* in 1969 (FPF). COUNTY UNCERTAIN: White Pine, *Starker* in 1916 (FPF, ILL).

UTAH

CACHE CO.: Logan Can., near Jardine Juniper, *Krebill 453* in 1967 (FPF). DAGGETT CO.: Big Springs outlet, 11 mi. SW of Manila on Rte. 44, *H 567* in 1964 (FPF); Sheep Can. SW of Manila, *W 4128* in 1966 (FPF, UT); Palisades Campground, *Peterson 64–217* in 1964 (FPF). DUCHESNE CO.: 25.5 mi. SW of Duchesne on Rte. 33, *H 570* in 1964 (FPF). GARFIELD CO.: S of Grover, near Wildcat Ranger Sta., *Peterson 64–92* in 1964 (FPF); 14 mi. SE of Panguitch, *Peterson 63–87* in 1963 (FPF); Bryce Nat. Park, 3 mi. N of Far View Point, *Buchanan 310* in 1957 (RSA); 23 mi. N of Boulder on Rte. 117, *H 685* in 1964 (FPF). IRON CO.: 14 mi. N of Panguitch Lake, *Peterson 62–67* in 1962 (FPF); 12 mi. E of Cedar City on Rte. 14, *H 678* in 1964 (FPF); 13 mi. N of Panguitch Lake, on *Abies lasiocarpa*, *Peterson 62–28* in 1962 (FPF). KANE Co.: Without locality, *Siler* in 1878 (MO); 10.4 mi. W of Rte. 89 on Rte. 14, *H 681* in 1964 (FPF); Panguitch Lake Jct. on Rte. 14, *W 4121* in 1967 (FPF, UT); 2 mi. above old Seegmiller Ranch on lower Kanab Cr., E of Alton, *W 4120* in 1967 (FPF, UT); Cougar Hollow, S end Bryce Can. Nat. Park, on *Picea pungens*, *Peterson 62–111* in 1962 (FPF);

MILLARD CO.: Willow Cr. rd., W of Salina, *Peterson 64–63** in 1964 (FPF) on *Abies concolor*, *Peterson 64–64* in 1964 (FPF). PIUTE CO.: 2 mi. W of Nat. For. bdy. on Marysvale—Mt. Belknap rd., *W 3036* in 1962 (COLO); Puffer Lake rd., W of Jct., *Peterson 64–83* in 1964 (FPF); Marysvale, Tote Mine, *Jones 5911c* in 1894 (POM, US); Marysvale, *Jones 5395* in 1894 (MO, POM US). SALT LAKE CO.: Big Cottonwood Can., *Hartley FP 17865* in 1915 (FPF, ILL). SAN JUAN CO.: Abajo Mtns., near Spring Cr., *Rydberg & Garrett 9864* in 1911 (RM, US); Elk Ridge, SW of Kigalia Guard Sta., *Peterson 65–76* in 1965 (FPF); N slope Abajo Mtns., *Krebill 288* in 1964 (FPF). SANPETE CO.: Ephraim Can., SE of Ephraim, *Hedgcock FP 8126* in 1912 (FPF); Great Basin Exp. Sta., *Gill FP 68262* in 1932 (FPF); 8.7 mi. E of Ephraim on Great Basin Exp. Sta. rd., *H 574* in 1964 (FPF). SEVIER CO.: 4 mi. NW of Joseph, *Harris* in 1914 (ILL); S end of Fish Lake, *H & Laut 1161* in 1969 (FPF). SUMMIT CO.: Kamas, *Hedgcock FP 93222* in 1911 (FPF). UTAH CO.: 5 mi. SW of Rte. 50 on Skyline rd., *H 572* in 1964 (FPF); Spring Lake, *Parry* in 1875 (MO) and on *Abies concolor*, *Parry 86* in 1875 (MO, US). TOOELE CO.: Stansbury Mtns., end of rd. in south Willow Can., *W 3865B* in 1965 (FPF, UT). COUNTY UNCERTAIN: Ephraim Plateau, *Harris C2770B* in 1927 (PH); central Utah, on *Abies concolor*, *Parry 10659* in 1875 (ILL, MO).

WASHINGTON

CHELAN CO.: 8 mi. NW of Leavenworth on US 2, *H, Stewart & Thompson 1136* in 1968 (FPF); Fish Lake, *Hanzlik FP 68257* in 1932 (FPF); Tip Top Mtn., 13 mi. W of Wenatchee, Col.? in 1915 (ILL); Chelan Lake, *Weir 6162* in 1916 (ILL); Stehekin River at north end of Chelan Lake, *Graham* in 1964 (FPF); 8.5 mi. E of Stevens Pass on US 2, *H, Stewart & Thompson 1137* in 1968 (FPF). CLACKAMAS CO.: Clackamas River, T. 7 S., R. 8 E., Sec. 32, ca. 12 air mi. NE of Breitenbush, *Nicholson* in 1968 (FPF). COLUMBIA CO.: Wolf Fork of Touchet River, *St. John 6936* in 1925 (UC). FERRY CO.: Sherman Cr. near Growden, *Wicker* in 1964 (WSP); Republic, *Foster* in 1912 (MO). KLICKITAT CO.: 2 mi. NW of Satus Pass, *H & W 593* in 1964 (FPF). OKANOGAN CO.: Okanogan, *Weir?* in 1914 (ILL); 18 air mi. E of Tonasket, *Graham* in 1965 (FPF); 5 mi. SW of Methow, *Graham* in 1964 (FPF); 9 mi. W of Republic on Rte. 30, *H, Stewart & Thompson 1132* in 1968 (FPF); 12 mi. W of Okanogan on Rte. 20 *H, Stewart & Thompson 1134* in 1968 (FPF). YAKIMA CO.: 23 mi. E of White Pass on Rte. 14 [2 mi. W of Nat. For. bdy.], *H & W 596* in 1964 (FPF); Dog Lake, Tieton Can., *Wicker* in 1966 (FPF).

WYOMING

LINCOLN CO.: Wolf Cr. Campground on Snake River, Targhee Nat. For., *Peterson 62–64* in 1962 (FPF, RM). TETON CO.: 4 mi. E of Idaho bdy. on Teton Pass rd., *Peterson 62–12* in 1962 (FPF, RM).

12a. ARCEUTHOBIUM GILLII subsp. GILLII

Specimens Cited: on *Pinus leiophylla* var. *chihuahuana* unless as noted.

MEXICO

CHIHUAHUA: Continental Divide on Mexico NW Railroad on ridge between Río Chico and Río Caballo, on *P. leiophylla, Barlow* in 1911 (FPF); 1 km, S of Majalca, *Andresen & Andresen 1804* in 1961 (FPF); Majalca, *Sueur 599* in 1936 (UC); Mt. Mohinora, *Nelson 4887* in 1898 (F, US); 65 mi. E of Batopilas, *Goldman 184* in 1898 (F, US); 25 mi. SW of La Junta, *H & W 292** in 1963 (FPF); 34 mi. SW of La Junta, *H & W 294* in 1963 (FPF) and on *P. arizonica, H & W 293* in 1963 (FPF); 36 mi. SW of La Junta, *H & W 297* in 1963 (FPF); 14 mi. E of El Vergel, *H & W 307** in 1963 (FPF); 26 mi. SW of Col. Juárez, *H & W 460** in 1963 (FPF); 12 mi. SE of Mesa Huracán on Chico rd., *H & W 474* in 1963 (FPF); 18 mi. S of Las Varas on Madera rd., *H & W 481* in 1963 (FPF); 48 mi. SW of Matachic on Ocampo rd., on *P. lumholtzii, H & W 487* in 1963 (FPF); 43 mi. SW of Matachic on Ocampo rd., *H & W 484* in 1963 (FPF) and on *P. ponderosa, H & W 483* in 1963 (FPF); 29 mi. SW of Matachic on Ocampo rd., *H & W 497* in 1963 (FPF); 6 mi. W of Matachic on Ocampo rd., *H & W 499* in 1963 (FPF). SINALOA: Sierra Surutato, Municipio de Badiraguato, on *Pinus lumholtzii, Breedlove & Thorne 18617* in 1970 (CAS). SONORA: "Frosty Saddle," *Hartman 364* in 1890 (BM, F, ILL, K, Ny, PH, UC, US).

UNITED STATES

ARIZONA

COCHISE CO.: Chiricahua Mtns.: Pedestal Pass, *Blumer 1515* in 1906 (ARIZ, ILL, K, MO, RM, US, Z); Pine Can., *Blumer 2394* in 1907 (ARIZ, DS, RM, Z); 6 mi. from Faraway Ranch, Portal, *Gill FP 68036* in 1936 (FPF); Portal, near Southwestern Research Sta., *H & L 157* in 1962 (FPF); Rustler Park, *Ellis & Gill FP 89500* in 1939 (FPF); Parker Can. *Long FP 318* in 1909 (FPF); Pinery Can., *H & L 153** in 1962 (FPF); Pinery Can. at Jct. of N and S forks, *Stone 201* in 1919 (PH). Huachuca Mtns.: Reef, *Gill & Ellis FP 89496* in

1939 (FPF). PIMA CO.: Santa Catalina Mtns.: General Hitchcock Campground, *H & L 164** in 1962 (FPF) and *H & Scharpf 705* in 1964 (FPF); Oracle rd., *Peterson 62–148* in 1962 (FPF) and *H & L 1111* in 1968 (FPF); Mt. Lemmon, *Peebles, Harrison & Peebles 2565* in 1926 (ARIZ, US): Mud Springs, *Harris C16354B* in 1916 (US). Rincon Mtns., *Blumer 3362* in 1909 (ARIZ, MO, UC). SANTA CRUZ CO.: W side Huachuca Mtns., T. 24 S, R. 18 E, *H & L 161** in 1962 (FPF); Santa Rita Mtns., SE side of Mt. Wrightson, 1 mi. up trail from end of Tunnel Springs rd., *L 65–26* in 1965 (FPF). COUNTY UNCERTAIN: Santa Rita Mtns., *Pringle 13876* in 1881 (FPF).

12b. ARCEUTHOBIUM GILLII subsp. NIGRUM

Specimens Examined:

MEXICO

DURANGO: 30 mi. E of El Salto on Rte. 40, on *P. leiophylla* var. *chihuahuana, H & W 337* and *519* in 1963 (COLO, FPF), on *P. lumholtzii, H & W 336* in 1963 (COLO, FPF), and on *P. teocote, H & W 520* in 1963 (COLO, FPF); 32 mi. E of El Salto on Rte. 40, on *P. teocote, H & W 334** in 1963 (COLO, FPF): 5 mi. E of El Salto on Rte. 40, on *P. leiophylla, H & W 1244* in 1969 (FPF); 2 mi. E of El Salto on Rte. 40, on *P. leiophylla, H & W 343** and *525* in 1963 (COLO, FPF); 33 mi. S of Durango on La Flor rd., on *P. leiophylla* var. *chihuahuana, H & W 510* in 1963 (COLO, FPF), on *P. lumholtzii, H & W 509* in 1963 (COLO, FPF), and on *P. teocote, H & W 508** in 1963 (COLO, FPF); 15 mi. W of Santiago Papasquiaro, on *P. leiophylla* var. *chihuahuana, H & W 533* in 1963 (COLO, FPF) and on *P. lumholtzii, H & W 534* in 1963 (COLO, FPF); 18 mi. W of Santiago Papasquiaro, on *P. leiophylla, H & W 535* in 1963 (COLO, FPF). HIDALGO: 20 mi. N of Zimapan on Rte. 85, on *P. teocote, H & W 385** in 1963 (COLO, FPF) and on *P. montezumae, H & W 386* in 1963 (COLO, FPF). OAXACA: Dist. de Teotitlán, Camino de Huaulla, on *Pinus* sp., *Conzatti 4123* in 1921 (US). VERACRUZ: Cofre de Perote, 3 mi. SE of Perote, on *P. teocote, H & W 382** in 1963 (COLO, FPF) and on *Pinus* sp., probably *P. teocote, W 2574* in 1959 (FPF, RSA).

13. ARCEUTHOBIUM GLOBOSUM

Specimens Examined:

MEXICO

CHIAPAS: On *Pinus* sp., *Seler 2190* in 1896 (US); near Siltepec, on *Pinus* sp., *Matuda 4408* in 1941 (MO, NY); Mt. Male, near Porvenir, on *Pinus* sp.,

Matuda 4630 in 1941 (F, NY) and on "oak tree" (probably in error; no host material with collection), *Matuda 4601* in 1941 (F, MO, NY, UC, US); between Cristobal de las Casas and Buenavista on rd. to Tenejapa, on *Pinus* sp., *Langman 3712* in 1948 (EAP, PH, US); Trail to Pokolum, near Tenejapa Center, on *Pinus* sp., *Breedlove 6974* in 1964 (DS, FPF); on old rd. to Comitán from Mitzitón, Municip. Chamula, on *Pinus* sp., *Breedlove 8016* in 1964 (F); E of San Cristobal de las Casas on Rte. 90, on *P. pseudostrobus, Andresen & Steinhoff A2008* in 1962 (FPF); Valle cut SE of Las Casas, on *Pinus* sp., *Alexander 1199* in 1945 (NY). CHIHUAHUA: Mesa Colorado, on *Pinus* sp., *Gentry 587M* in 1933 (MICH); 19 mi. W of Mesa Huracán, on *P. arizonica, H & W 466* in 1963 (COLO, FPF), and on *P. engelmannii, H & W 467** in 1963 (COLO, FPF). DISTRICT FEDERAL: Desierto de los Leones, on *Pinus* sp., *Roldan* in 1919 (FPF, ILL). DURANGO: 20 mi. W of El Salto on Rte. 40, on *Pinus* sp., *McVaugh 11518* in 1951 (MICH); N slopes of Cerro Huehueto, on *Pinus* sp., *Maysilles 7260* in 1950 (MICH); San Luis del Río, 51 mi. NW of Coyotes, on *Pinus* sp., *Maysilles 7977* in 1955 (NY); 1.5 mi. E of El Salto on Rte. 40, on *P. cooperi, H & W 344** and *524* in 1963 (COLO, FPF); 13 mi. W of El Salto on Rte. 40, on *P. cooperi, H & W 349* in 1963 (COLO, FPT); 24 mi. W of El Salto on Rte. 40, on *P. durangensis, H & W 351* in 1963 (COLO, FPF), 33 mi. W of El Salto on Rte. 40, on *P. durangensis, H & W 526** in 1963 (FPF); 35 mi. W of El Salto on Rte. 40, on *P. durangensis, H & W 1246* in 1969 (FPF). JALISCO: Mamatlán, 15 mi. SSE of Autlán by way of Chante, on *Pinus* sp., *Wilbur & Wilbur 1837* and *1982* in 1949 (MICH). MEXICO: Ojos de Agua, Nevado de Toluca, on *Pinus* sp., *Balls B4089* in 1938 (BM, K, UC, US); 40 km W of Toluca, on *Pinus* sp., *Frye & Frye 2590* in 1939 (ARIZ, DS, MO, NY, RSA, UC, WTU); Ixtacchiuatl, on *Pinus* sp., *Purpus 1778* in 1905 (F, ILL, MO, NY, UC, US); Amalacaxo, on *Pinus* sp., *Miranda 872* in 1940 (MEXU); Crucero Agua Blanco, Temascaltepec, on *Pinus* sp., *Hinton 8901* in 1936 (ARIZ, K, US); Valley of Mexico, on *Pinus* sp., *Borglav 1115* in 1866 (K, US); Nevado de Toluca, on *Pinus* sp., N slope, (4,120 m.), *Iltis, Iltis & Flores 1701* in 1963 (WIS), on *P. hartwegii, Andresen & Steinhoff A2035* in 1962 (FPF) and on *P. rudis, H & W 369** in 1963 (COLO, FPF); 6 mi. E of Michoacán bdy. on Rte. 15, on *P. michoacana, H & W 368* in 1963 (COLO, FPF): 32 mi. W of Toluca on Rte. 15, on *P. montezumae, H 49* in 1956 (FPF); 3 mi. W of Río Frío on Rte. 190, on *P. montezumae, H & W 371** in 1963 (COLO, FPF): 1.5 mi. E of Michoacán bdy. on Rte. 15, on *P. pseudostrobus, H & W 367* in 1963 (COLO, FPF). MICHOACAN: Cerro Tancitaro, on *Pinus* sp.,

Leavenworth 710 in 1940 (F, MO); and on *P. rudis, Leavenworth & Hoogstraal 1126* in 1941 (F, MO); 18 mi. S of Patzcuaro, on *Pinus* sp., *King & Soderstrom 5174* in 1961 (MICH, NY, UC, US); NW of Cuidad Hidalgo, on *Pinus* sp., *McVaugh 9952* in 1949 (MICH); San Alejo: on *P. lawsonii, Valdivia & Soloranzo 648* in 1963 (FPF); on *P. rudis, Valdivia & Soloranzo 649* in 1963 (FPF); on *P. michoacana, Valdivia & Soloranzo 650* in 1963 (FPF); on *P. montezumae, Valdivia & Soloranzo 646* in 1963 (FPF); and on *P. tenuifolia, Valdivia & Soloranzo 637* in 1963 (FPF). 26 mi. E of Morelia on Rte. 15, on *P. pseudostrobus, H 51* in 1956 (FPF) and *H & W 361** in 1963 (COLO, FPF); 29 mi. E of Morelia, on *P. pseudostrobus, Valdivia & Soloranzo 634* in 1963 (FPF) and on *P. tenuifolia, Valdivia & Soloranzo 633* in 1963 (FPF). OAXACA: Sierra de San Felipe, on *Pinus* sp., *Pringle 4727* in 1894 (BM, K, MEXU, MO, NY, PH, US, Z); 21 mi. S of Tuxtepec on rd. to Oaxaca de Juarez, on *P. rudis, Andresen & Steinhoff A1983* in 1962 (FPF); 8 mi. S of Suchixtepec, on *P. michoacana, Peterson 68–105* in 1968 (FPF). PUEBLA: Near Río Frío, on *Pinus* sp., *Kenoyer* in 1938 (ARIZ). SONORA: "Pine Ridge Pass," on *Pinus* sp., *Hartman 340* in 1890 (ILL, K, NY, UC, US). VERACRUZ: Mt. Orizaba, on *Pinus* sp., *Balls B4399* in 1938 (BM, K, UC, US); Cofre de Perote, on *P. hartwegii, Beaman 2214* in 1958 (RM, UC, US).

GUATEMALA

DEPT. ALTA VERAPAZ: Cobán, on *P. tenuifolia, von Turckheim II1815* in 1907 (ILL, MO, NY, US). DEPT. BAJA VERAPAZ: Purulha, on *Pinus* sp., *Cook 7* in 1906 (FPF, ILL, US). DEPT. CHEMALTENANGO: between Tecpan and Encuentros, *Aguilar* in 1955 (EAP). DEPT. HUEHUETENANGO: Sierra Cuchumatanes: Cerra Cananá, between Nucapula and Cananá, on *Cupressus* sp. (no host with collection), *Steyermark 49044* in 1942 (F); Chemal, on *Pinus* sp., *Johnston 1777* in 1940 (EAP, F); Km. 36, Chemal, on *Pinus* sp., *Standley 81637* in 1940 (EAP, F, NY), *81642* in 1940 (F), and *81683* in 1940 (F); vicinity of Touquia, on *P. rudis, Steyermark 50130* in 1942 (MO, NY, US); between Paquix and San Miguel, on *P. pseudostrobus, Molina, Burgur & Wallenta 16483* in 1966 (EAP, NY); 33 km. N of Huehuetenango near Chemal, on *P. rudis, H & W 1219* in 1969 (FPF); 10 km N of Santa Eulalia on road to Barillas, on *P. rudis, H & W 1223* in 1969 (FPF). DEPT. SAN MARCOS: Volcan Tajumulco, on *Pinus* sp., *Schmidt* in 1934 (F) and *Steyermark 36940* ("on roots and branches") in 1940 (MICH). DEPT. ZACAPA: Sierra de las Minas, on *Pinus* sp., *Steyermark 29788* in 1939 (MICH) and *42524* in 1942 (MICH, NY).

EL CAYO DIST.: Mtn. Pine Ridge, Granite Carin rd., 6 mi. E of Augustine, ca. 30 mi. W of Stann Cr., *Hunt 286* in 1959 (US) [Host on sheet labeled as *Pinus* sp., but Hunt (1962) gives it as *P. caribaea*]; Mtn. Pine Ridge, Raspa rd., on *P. caribaea, Etheridge BFDS 26* in 1965 (DAVFP, FPF).

14. ARCEUTHOBIUM GUATEMALENSE

GUATEMALA

DEPT. HUEHUETENANGO: Sierra Cuchumatanes: 2 km. N of Santa Eulalia on Barillas rd., on *Pinus ayacahuite, H & W 1222* in 1969 (FPF); 54 km. N of Huehuetenango on Santa Eulalia rd., on *Pinus ayacahuite, H & W 1221** in 1969 (FPF). DEPT. TOTONICAPAN: Near km. 170 on Pan American Highway, 15 km. W of Nahualá, on *Pinus ayacahuite, H & W 1226** in 1969 (FPF).

15. ARCEUTHOBIUM HONDURENSE

HONDURAS

DEPT. FRANCISCO MORAZAN: Near Piedra Herrada: Rio Yeguare drainage, Lat. 14°N, Long. 87°W., on *Pinus oocarpa, Williams 15964** in 1969 (BM, EAP, F); 22 km. SE of Tegucigalpa on rd. to Escuela Agrícola Panamericana, on *P. oocarpa, H, W & Molina 1203** in 1969 (FPF); 7 km. W of Zamorano on Tegucigalpa rd., on *P. oocarpa, H & W 1209* in 1969 (FPF).

16. ARCEUTHOBIUM LARICIS

Specimens Examined: On *Larix occidentalis* unless noted otherwise.

CANADA

BRITISH COLUMBIA: Burton, *Kuijt 566* in 1953 DAVFP, FPF); Balfour, *Kuijt 563* in 1953 (DAVFP, FPF); Slocan Lake, *Kuijt* in 1953 (DAVFP, FPF); Christina Cr., *Kuijt 553* in 1953 (DAVFP, FPF); Grand Forks, *Kuijt 556* in 1953 (DAVFP, FPF); Salmo, *Kuijt 547** in 1953 (DAVFP, FPF); Castlegar, *Kuijt 546* in 1953 (DAVFP, FPF); Fruitvale, *Kuijt* in 1953 (DAVFP, FPF); Creston, *Kuijt* in 1953 (DAVFP, FPF); St. Mary's Lake, *Kuijt 544* in 1953 (DAVFP, FPF); 3 mi. N of Moyie on Cranbrook rd., *Calder & Saville 11415* in 1953 (CAS, UC, WTU); 6 mi. W of Jct. west of Rossland, *Calder & Saville 11465* in 1953 (US); Owens Lake, *Weir 8362* in 1913 (ILL); Salmon Arm, *Weir 8364* in 1913 (FPF, ILL).

ADAMS CO.: Evergreen, *Hedgcock FP 997* in 1909 (FPF). BENEWAH CO.: St. Maries, *Hedgcock FP 9526* in 1911 (FPF) and *Weir 659* in 1911 (ILL). BOISE CO.: Idaho City, *Weir 8371* in 1917 (ILL). BONNER CO.: Priest River, *Weir 8373* in 1917 (FPF, RM, US); Sandpoint, *Wehmeyer* in 1922 (US); Priest River Exp. For. Headquarters, on *Picea abies, H & Wicker 963* in 1966 (FPF); on *Pinus banksiana, Graham* in 1958 (FPF) and *H & Wicker 964* in 1966 (FPF), and on *Pinus resinosa, H & Wicker 965* in 1966 (FPF); 4 mi. N of Priest River on rd. to For. Exp. Sta., *H & Wicker 961** in 1966 (FPF) and on *Pinus contorta, H & Wicker 962* in 1966 (FPF). Coolin, on *Pinus contorta, Weir 8385* in 1917 (ILL) and on *Abies lasiocarpa, Weir 8391* in 1916 (ILL); Blue Lake, on *Abies grandis, Weir 8392* in 1917 (ILL); Priest River, on *Abies grandis, Weir 3252* in 1917 (ILL). BOUNDARY CO.: Above Upper Priest Lake, *Boyce 1225* in 1924 (FPF, OSC). IDAHO CO.: 6 mi. S of Grangeville on Snow Haven rd., *H 969* in 1966 (FPF). KOOTENAI CO.: Clark's Fork, Coeur d' Alene Mtns., *Lieberg 1672* in 1895 (MO, POM, RM, UC, US); 4th of July Summit, *W 3255** in 1962 (COLO, FPF); Granite Sta., *Sandberg, MacDougal & Heller 787* in 1892 (CAS, US); Coeur d' Alene, on *Pinus ponderosa, Weir 3271* in 1916 (ILL). LATAH CO.: Moscow Mtn., *Piper 1882* in 1894 (MO, RM). SHOSHONE CO.: Lick Cr. Lookout [ca. 6 mi. SSW of Avery], *Gill FP 68291* in 1932 (FPF) and on *P. monticola, Gill FP 68202* in 1932 (FPF); 3 mi. W of Montana bdy. on US 10, *W 3256* in 1962 (COLO, FPF); Monumental Butte, St. Joe Nat. For., on *Pinus monticola, Weir* in 1914 (FPF, ILL); ¼ mi. W of Thompson Pass, on *Tsuga mertensiana, H & Wicker 957* in 1966 (FPF) and on *Abies lasiocarpa, H & Wicker 958* in 1966 (FPF); 1 mi. S of Jack Waite Mine on Woodchuck Pass rd., on *Tsuga mertensiana, H & Wicker 959* in 1966 (FPF). VALLEY CO.: McCall, col.? in 1915 (ILL); 3 mi. NE of McCall on shore of Payette Lake, *H 973* in 1966 (FPF) and on *Abies lasiocarpa, H 974* in 1966 (FPF).

UNITED STATES

MONTANA

FLATHEAD CO.: Somers, Flathead Lake, *Weir 3258* in 1916 (ILL); Big Fork, Flathead Lake, *Jones 9312* in 1908 (DS, POM) and *9309* in 1908 (POM); Columbia Falls, *Williams 897* in 1892 (US). GRANITE CO.: Phillipsburg, *Weir 8374* in 1917 (ILL). LAKE CO.: Yellow Bay, Flathead Lake, *Jones 9313* in 1908 (POM) and *Butler 182* in 1908 (FPF); 4 mi. N of Dunton, *Krebill 136* in 1964

(FPF); E of St. Ignatius near St. Mary's Lake, *Krebill 133* in 1964 (FPF). LINCOLN CO.: Cabinet Mtns. near Scotchmans Peak, on *Larix lyalli*, *Weir 3250* n.d. (FPF, ILL) and on *Tsuga mertensiana*, *Johns* in 1914 (FPF, ILL). MINERAL CO.: 6 mi. W of St. Regis on US 10, *H & Wicker 956** in 1966 (FPF) and on *Pinus contorta*, *H & Wicker 955* in 1966 (FPF). MISSOULA CO.: Missoula, *Weir FP 17048* in 1914 (FPF); Blue Cr., 35 mi. NW of Missoula, on *Picea engelmannii*, *Toko & Pinney 65–34* in 1965 (FPF); Pattee Can. near Missoula, on *Pinus contorta*, *Paulson* in 1916 (FPF, ILL) and *Weir 3267* in 1916 (ILL); Bitterroot Mtns. near Lolo, on *Larix lyalli*, *Weir 8366* in 1914 (FPF, ILL); Lolo, on *Pinus ponderosa*, *Weir 8337* in 1916 (FPF, ILL). RAVALLI CO.: One Horse Cr. near Florence, col.? in 1915 (ILL); Victor: on *Picea engelmannii*, *Weir 7196* in 1917 (FPF); on *Pinus albicaulis*, *Weir 8334* in 1917 (ILL); on *Pinus contorta*, *Weir 8336* and *8384* in 1917 (ILL); and on *Abies lasiocarpa*, *Weir 8390* in 1917 (ILL). SANDERS CO.: Thompson Falls, *Hedgcock & Weir FP 9442* in 1911 (FPF); and on *Pinus ponderosa*, *Hedgcock & Weir FP 9444* in 1911 (FPF); 8 mi. N of Plains, on *Pinus ponderosa*, *Sieminski* in 1964 (FPF); 2 mi. E of Noxon on US 10A, *H & Wicker 960* in 1966 (FPF).

OREGON

BAKER CO.: 6 mi. E of Medical Springs, *Peterson 63–236** in 1963 (FPF); 12 mi. S of Baker on Rte. 7, *H & W 585** in 1964 (FPF); Jim Cr. Fork of Eagle Cr., 30 mi. NE of Baker, *Graham* in 1965 (FPF) and, on *Pinus albicaulis*, *Graham* in 1965 (FPF). CROOK CO.: Ochoco, Can. Cr., *Donnelly* in 1920 (FPF). GRANT CO.: 16 mi. S of John Day on Rte. 395, *H & W 579* in 1964 (FPF) and on *Pinus ponderosa*, *H & W 578* in 1964 (FPF); 6 mi. E of Dixie Pass on US 26, *H & W 582** in 1964 (FPF); Elkhorn Spring rd. [ca. 16 mi. E of Prairie City], *Childs 212* in 1952 (OSC); Dixie Butte, *Weir 2421* 1915 (FPF, ILL) and on *Abies grandis* (as *A. "concolor"*), *Weir 2425* in 1915 (FPF, ILL); 4 mi. N of US 26 on Dixie Butte rd., on *Abies grandis*, *H 981* in 1966 (FPF); Big Canyon, 9 air mi. NE of Seneca, *H & Scharpf 1270* in 1969 (FPF). JEFFERSON CO.: Metolius area, *Gill FP 68189** in 1932 (FPF); Metolius River near Camp Sherman, *Graham* in 1964 (FPF). MORROW CO.: Alder Cr., 35 mi. S of Heppner, *Steward & Steward 7328* in 1957 (CAS, DS, RSA, US, WTU). UMATILLA CO.: 13 mi. E of Kamela, *H & W 588* in 1964 (FPF). UNION CO.: 12 mi. W of Elgin, *H & W 589* in 1964 (FPF); 15 air mi. NNE of Elgin, *Orr* in 1968 (FPF). WALLOWA CO.: Minam Meadows [12 mi. SW of Enterprise], *Sampson & Pearson 168* in 1907 (FPF, MO): Billy Meadows [30 mi. NNE of Enterprise], *Coville 2459* in 1907 (US); Wallowa Mtns., Bear Cr.,

Coville 2363 in 1907 (US); Wallowa Mtns., Bear Cr. sheep trail, *Coville 2480* in 1907 (US). WASCO CO.: Bear Springs Campground, Mt. Hood, *Childs & Hansbrough FP 68268* in 1931 (FPF) and *Childs 27* in 1940 (OSC); 5.7 mi. SE of Wapinita Pass on US 26, *H & W 609* in 1964 (FPF). WHEELER CO.: 3 mi. S of Nat. For. bdy. on Derr Meadows rd., ca. 12 mi. SSE of Mitchell, *H 985* in 1966 (FPF); 26 mi. S of Hardman on Rte. 207, *H & Scharpf 1273* in 1969 (FPF); Ochoco Summit on US 26, *H & Scharpf 1262* in 1969 (FPF).

WASHINGTON

CHELAN CO.: Chelan Lake, *Weir 8363* in 1916 (ILL); Leavenworth, *Bunder* n.d. (ILL). FERRY CO.: Growden, *Wicker* in 1963 (FPF); Fritz Cr. near Growden, *Wicker** in 1963 (FPF); 16 mi. E of Republic on Rte. 30, *H, Stewart & Thompson 1129* in 1968 (FPF) and on *Abies lasiocarpa*, *H, Stewart & Thompson 1130* in 1968 (FPF). GARFIELD CO.: 7 air mi. SSW of Peola, *Orr* in 1968 (FPF). KITTITAS CO.: N of Ellensburg, *Brandegee 1071* in 1883 (PH, US); Wenatchee Mtns., *Coville 1881* in 1901 (US); Peoh Point, ca. 3 mi. S of Cle Elum, *Will* in 1968 (FPF). OKANOGAN CO.: 9 mi. W of Republic on Rte. 30, on *Pinus contorta*, *H, Stewart & Thompson 1133* in 1968 (FPF); Loup Cr., 12 mi. W of Okanogan on Rte. 20, *H, Stewart & Thompson 1134* in 1968 (FPF). PEND OREILLE CO.: Metaline Falls, *Weir 8365* in 1916 (FPF, ILL). STEVENS CO.: 3 mi. W of Park Rapids, *Krebill 147* in 1964 (FPF). WHITMAN CO.: N side of Kamiak Butte, *St. John 6359* in 1924 (MO, UC). YAKIMA CO.: Havens Ranch, SE of Mt. Adams, *Henderson 2535* in 1892 (WTU); Tieton Basin, *Tweedy* in 1882 (DS); "Yakima Region," *Brandegee* in 1882 (UC); 2.5 mi. E of White Pass on Rte. 5, *H & W 597* in 1964 (FPF) and on *Pinus monticola*, *H & W 598* in 1964 (FPF); 6.5 mi. E of White Pass, on Rte. 5, *H & W 603* in 1964 (FPF); Tieton Cr., 2 mi. SW of Tieton Lake, on *Abies grandis*, *H & W 600* in 1964 (FPF); 7 mi. S of Ticton, *Graham* in 1966 (FPF); 4 mi. E of Dog Lake, *Wicker* in 1966 (FPF); 1 mi. W of Rimrock, *Stewart* in 1968 (FPF). COUNTY UNCERTAIN: Cascade Mtns., *Tweedy* in 1882 (MO).

17. *ARCEUTHOBIUM MICROCARPUM*

Specimens Examined: Host is *Picea engelmannii*, except as noted.

UNITED STATES

ARIZONA

APACHE CO.: Mt. Baldy, *Woolsey FP 12566* in 1914 (FPF); 20 mi. W of Eagar on Rte. 73, *H & L 207** in 1962 (FPF); 4.7 mi. SW of Alpine on US 666, on *Picea pungens*, *H & Scharpf 700** in 1964

(FPF); 2 mi. E of Big Lake, on *Picea pungens*, *H 819* in 1965 (FPF); 1 mi. S of Horseshoe Cienega, 10 mi. E of McNary, on *P. pungens*, *H & Gilbertson 1083* in 1967 (FPF); 6 mi. NE of Maverick, on *Picea pungens*, *H & L 900* in 1966 (FPF); 5 mi. SW of Rte. 373 on Big Lake rd., 2 air mi. SW of Greer, on *P. pungens*, *H & L 925* in 1966 (FPF). COCONINO CO.: "Kaibab Forest," *Richards* in 1938 (RM, UC, WTU); San Francisco Peaks: Flagstaff Water Camp, *H & L 249** in 1962 (FPF) and Interior Basin, *Long FP 21671* in 1916 (FPF). Grand Can. Nat. Park, North Rim: *Gill & Andrews FP 87301* in 1935 (FPF); near entrance, *Gill FP 68298* in 1934 (FPF); 2.0 mi. E of Rte. 64, on Point Imperial rd., *H 253** in 1962 (FPF); Telephone Can., *W 3183* in 1962 (COLO); 2.4 mi. E of Rte. 64 on Point Royal rd., on *Picea pungens*, *Peterson 43–61* in 1961 (FPF). GRAHAM CO.: Graham Mtns.: *Kearney & Peebles 9971* in 1934 (ARIZ, US) and *Ellis FP 89430* in 1939 (FPF); Hospital Flat, *Gill FP 68310* in 1934 (FPF) and *Kearney & Peebles 14135* in 1938 (ARIZ); Columbine, *Gill FP 68290* in 1934 (FPF), *Maynard* in 1963 (FPF) and on *Abies lasiocarpa* var. *arizonica*, *Stouffer & Gill FP 68291* in 1934 (FPF); High Peak rd., 3 mi. N of main rd., *H & L 224** in 1962 (FPF); Soldier Cr. Campground, *H & L 225** in 1962 (FPF); Webb Peak, *Darrow, Phillips & Pultz 1173* in 1944 (ARIZ). GREENLEE CO.: 1 mi. S of Blue Summit on US 666, *Gill FP 68302* and *FP 68305* in 1934 (FPF); US 666 N of Jct. of Gobbler Point rd., *Peterson 62–165* in 1962 (FPF); 3 mi. N of Hannagan Meadows on US 666, *Andrews* in 1963 (FPF) and *L 64–20* in 1964 (FPF).; Hannagan Cr. N of Hannagan Meadows on US 666, on *P. pungens*, *H 1082* in 1967 (FPF)

NEW MEXICO

CATRON CO.: Mogollon Mtns.: On or near W fork of Gila River, *Metcalfe 493* in 1903 (ARIZ, FPF, ILL, MO, POM, UC, US); Willow Cr. Campground, on *Picea pungens*, *H & L 219** in 1962 (FPF); 4 mi. W of Rte. 78 on Bearwallow Lookout rd., *H & L 897** in 1966 (FPF).

18. *ARCEUTHOBIUM OCCIDENTALE*

Specimens Examined: on *Pinus sabiniana* except as noted.

UNITED STATES

CALIFORNIA

ALAMEDA CO.: Berkeley, on planted *P. radiata*, *Offord & Scharpf* in 1964 (FPF). AMADOR CO.: 6 mi. E of Jackson, *Gill FP 68255* in 1932 (FPF); 1 mi. S of Jackson, *W 3224* in 1962 (COLO, FPF); near Ione, *Braunton* in 1904 (MO); 1 mi. S of Ione, *Kuijt 1208* in 1956 (UC); Pine Grove, *Hanson 718* in 1895 (MO, US). BUTTE CO.: Big Chico Cr.

E of Chico, *Heller 11144* in 1913 (DS, MO, PH, US); Magalia, *Howell 37436* in 1962 (CAS); near Magalia, *W 2728* in 1960 (RSA); Chico, *Griffiths* in 1912 (MO); Paradise, *Wall* in 1935 (CAS); Bangor, *Rose* in 1931 (CAS). CALAVERAS CO.: 1.5 mi. E of Copperopolis on Rte. 4, *Kuijt 1410* in 1957 (UC); rd. from Vallecito to Columbia, *Quick 53–141* in 1953 (CAS). CONTRA COSTA CO.: Mt. Diablo: *Bethel FP 26266* in 1918 (FPF, ILL); *Scharpf** in 1963 (FPF); N slope, *Hicks 110* in 1917 (UC); Mitchell Can., *Jepson* in 1898 (JEPS, MO) and on *P. coulteri*, *Bacigalupi* in 1922 (DS); Little Rock City, *Kuijt 1444* in 1958 (UC); Rock City, *Kuijt 1425a* in 1957 (UC); Ranger Headquarters near S entrance, *H & Scharpf 856* in 1966 (FPF) and on *P. coulteri*, *H & Scharpf 857* in 1966 (FPF). EL DORADO CO.: Smith Flat, *Benson 47* in 1924 (DS); Placerville, *W 2335** in 1962 (COLO, FPF); 2–3 mi. E of Placerville on Rte. 550, *Robbins 1403* in 1943 (UC); 1.7 mi. SW of Garden Valley, *Kuijt 1257* in 1957 (UC); 3 mi. NW of Placerville on Rte. 49, *H & W 841* in 1966 (FPF); S fork of American River, N of Placerville, *Kuijt 1274* in 1957 (UC). FRESNO CO.: Auberry, *Stillinger* in 1920 (FPF, ILL); 10 mi. SW of Auberry on Friant rd., *H 843* in 1966 (FPF); 5 mi. N of Auberry on North Fork rd., *H 844* in 1966 (FPF). GLENN CO.: 2.1 mi. N of Stonyford, *Kuijt 1506* in 1958 (UC). KERN CO.: Walker Basin, *Rothrock 429* in 1875 (MO, US); Calienti, *Gill FP 68089* in 1932 (FPF); Havilah, *Coville & Funston 1073* in 1891 (DS, FPF, US); Greenhorn Pass, 4 mi. W of Kernville, *Gould 1010* in 1940 (DS, MO, UC, US); 1 mi. E of Isabella Res. on Rte. 178, *Kuijt 1437* in 1957 (UC); head of Tejon Cr., *Twisselmann 8832* in 1963 (CAS); between Glenville and Sierra Alta, 7 mi. W of Summit Guard Sta., *W 3605** in 1964 (FPF); Kernville, *Kerr* in 1938 (CAS); Tehachipai Mtns., Upper Cottonwood Cr., W of White Oak Lodge, *Tucker 3444* in 1938 (ARIZ); 2.5 mi. W of Wofford, *Howell 38710* in 1962 (CAS). LAKE CO.: without locality, *Bolander 2671* in 1863 (UC, US); near Jct. of Rtes. 53 and 20, SE of Clear Lake, *Rossbach 236* in 1955 (UC); Siegler Springs, *Blankinship* in 1924 (CAS); Lakeside, Clear Lake, *Abrams 6297* in 1916 (DS); Kelseyville, *Blankinship* in 1924 (RSA) and *Jussel* in 1931 (CAS); Kelseyville, Rincon School, *Benson 726* in 1928 (POM); Mt. Konocti, *Blankinship* in 1923 (MO); 3 mi. N of Middletown on Rte. 29, *Scharpf* in 1965 (FPF). LASSEN CO.: 10 mi. S of Pittville, *Wagener FP 97951* in 1928 (FPB). LOS ANGELES CO.: Liebre Mtns.: Elizabeth Lake Can., *Dudley & Lamb 4411* in 1896 (DS); Collins Ranch, *Peirson 4302* in 1921 (RSA); Sandbergs, *Munz 4423* in 1921 (POM). MADERA CO.: Raymond, *Hedgcock FP 4837* in 1910 (FPF, ILL); 9 mi. W of Oakhurst, *Kuijt 1254* in 1957 (UC); 18 mi. N of Pinedale on Rte. 41, *H 1144* in 1968 (FPF); 1 mi. W of North Fork, *H 658** in 1964 (FPF) and *H** in 1964 (FPF); Hogue Ranch, 16 mi. from North Fork, on Mammoth rd., *H 847* in 1966 (FPF); 1.5 mi. N of Oakhurst, *Howell 41197* in 1965 (CAS); Peckinpah Cr., *Howell & Barneby 29387* in 1954 (CAS). MARIN CO.: Inverness Ridge, on *P. muricata*, *Howell 19686* in 1944 (CAS, UC); Mt. Vision rd., Inverness, on *P. muricata*, *Schreiber 853* in 1933 (UC). MARIPOSA CO.: Bear Valley Mtn., *Ward 51* in 1895 (US); El Portal, *Posey* in 1919 (ILL); 3 mi. W of Mt. Bullion, *Kuijt 1253* in 1957 (UC); near Bootjack, *Howell 8135* in 1931 (CAS, US); Mariposa, *Congdon* in 1903 (MO, US). MENDOCINO CO.: Fort Bragg, on *P. muricata*, *Mason 5639* in 1930 (UC); Mouth of Gualala River, on *P. muricata*, *Bacigalupi 1808* in 1921 (DS); Van Damme State Park, on *P. muricata*, *Kuijt 1214* in 1957 (UC); Pine barrens near Fort Bragg, on *P. muricata*, *Johnson 1420* in 1929 (RSA); 3 mi. E of Fort Bragg, on *P. muricata*, *H & Scharpf 849* in 1966 (FPF); Point Arena, on *P. contorta* subsp. *bolanderi*, *Mason 7168* in 1932 (UC); Van Damme State Park, on *P. contorta* subsp. *bolanderi*, *Kuijt 1215* in 1957 (UC); just east of airport near Albion, on *P. contorta* subsp. *bolanderi*, *Peterson 65–116* in 1965 (FPF); White Sands near Mendocino City, on *P. muricata*, *Eastwood 18836* in 1912 (CAS); 4 mi. SE of Fort Bragg, on *P. contorta* subsp. *bolanderi*, *H & Scharpf 854* in 1966 (FPF). MONTEREY CO.: Pebble Beach, Carmel, on *P. radiata*, *Boyce 33* in 1915 (FPF); between Pacific Grove and Carmel, on *P. radiata*, *Gill FP 68145* in 1932 (FPF); Carmel, on *P. radiata*, *von Schrenk* in 1920 (MO); Carmel highlands above Yankee Point, on *P. radiata*, *Balls 23608* in 1958 (WTU); Point Lobos State Park, on *P. radiata*, *Lee & Mason 9153* in 1935 (UC); Point Lobos, on *P. radiata*, *Kuijt 1213* in 1957 (UC); near Point Pinos, on *P. radiata*, *Dudley* in 1893 (DS); Gibson Cr., on *P. radiata*, *Wheeler 4452* in 1936 (POM). Monterey: on *P. radiata*, *Parry* in 1850 (MO), *Brewer 700* in 1861 (US), *Engelmann* in 1880 (MO), *Meehan* in 1883 (PH), *Elmer 4031* in 1902 (POM), *Meinecke FP 9059* in 1910 (FPF, ILL), *Bethel FP 26279* in 1918 (FPF, ILL) and *H & Scharpf 1151* in 1968 (FPF). Pacific Grove: on *P. radiata*, *Davy 7064* in 1900 (UC), *Heller 6776* in 1903 (COLO, MO, RM, UC, US), *Smith 955* in 1905 (MICH), *Condit* in 1909 (UC), *Beattie 5281* in 1916 (FPF), *Guppy FP 96959* in 1924 (FPB), *Gill FP 68076*, *FP 68093* and *FP 68103* in 1932 (FPF), *W 3220* in 1962 (COLO, FPF), and *Peterson 63–156** in 1963 (FPF). Cypress Point: on *P. radiata*, *Abrams 7660* in 1920 (RM, US), and *Mason 3987* in 1927 (UC). Between Monterey and Carmel, on *P. muricata*, *Mason 5888* in 1931 (UC); Huckleberry Hill, Carmel, on *P. muricata*, *Mason 5515* in 1929 (UC) and

Wheeler 4428 in 1936 (POM); 7.2 mi. NE of Gonzales, *W 3219* in 1962 (COLO, FPF). Santa Lucia Mtns.: San Antonio River, *Brewer 582* in 1861 (US); Pine Can., *Duncan 90* in 1920 (DS, POM); Miller Can., on *P. coulteri*, *Ferris 12158* in 1929 (DS, RM, RSA, WTU); Miller Can., Chews Ridge, on *P. coulteri*, *Ray 1565* in 1949 (US); Tassajara rd. at Chews Ridge Lookout Jct., on *P. coulteri*, *Kuijt 1401* in 1957 (UC) and *H & Scharpf 1152* in 1968 (FPF); Marble Peak, 0.5 mi. NW of Anderson Peak, on *P. coulteri*, *Offord FP 98091* in 1963 (FPB); Junipero Serra Peak, on *P. coulteri*, *Howell 30162* in 1955 (CAS); near Cone Peak, on *P. coulteri*, *Ferris 3649* in 1923 (DS, POM) and *H & Scharpf 1158* in 1968 (FPF); Monterey For. Reserve, on *P. coulteri*, *von Schrenk* in 1920 (MO); 5 mi. W of Jolon on Nacimiento rd., *H & Scharpf 1153* in 1968 (FPF). NAPA CO.: Conn Valley, *Jepson* in 1895 (JEPS, US) and *Raven 3928* in 1951 (CAS); Moore Cr., Howell Mtn., col.? in 1902 (UC); 3 mi. from Aetna Springs on Middletown rd., *Howell 5618* in 1930 (CAS); 14 mi. SE of Middletown on Aetna Springs rd., *H & W 859* in 1966 (FPF). PLACER CO.: Auburn, *Loran* in 1886 (UC) and *Engelmann* in 1880 (ILL, MO). SAN BENITO CO.: Pinnacles Nat. Mon., *W 3218* in 1962 (COLO, FPF) and *Gill FP 68078* in 1932 (FPF); 20 mi. S (E?) of Bitterwater on New Idria rd., *Kuijt 1313* in 1957 (UC); rd. to New Idria, 4.5 mi. S of Jct. N of Bitterwater, *Kuijt 1300* in 1957 (UC); near New Idria, on *P. coulteri*, *Quibell 1658a* in 1953 (RSA) and *Kuijt 1310* in 1957 (UC). SAN LUIS OBISPO CO.: Paso de Robles, *Summers 926* in 1886 (UC); Santa Margarita, *Mason 525* in 1923 (UC); Mariana Cr., E side La Panza Range, *Hoover 6310* in 1946 (CAS); Cambria, on *P. radiata*, *Gill FP 68079* and *FP 68253** in 1932 (FPF), *Hoover 6448* in 1946 (CAS), and *H & Scharpf 1159* in 1968 (FPF). SANTA BARBARA CO.: San Rafael Mtns., Yellow Gate, *Meinecke FP 97947* (FPB) and *FP 17026* (FPF, ILL) in 1914; Pine Can., Roosevelt, *Hunt FP 97958* in 1912 (FPB); Figueroa Mtn., *Pollard* in 1950 (CAS) and 1956 (CAS); 8 mi. E of Los Olivos on Figueroa Mtn. rd., *H 935* in 1966 (FPF); 12 mi. E of Los Olivos on Figueroa Mtn. rd., on *Pinus coulteri*, *H 936* in 1966 (FPF). SANTA CLARA CO.: Mt. Hamilton Range: E slope of Mt. Hamilton, *Beane 225* in 1949 (RM); Mt. Hamilton, *Chanser 6022* in 1906 (UC); Long Branch Cr., Mt. Day, *Sharsmith 3848b* in 1936 (DS, UC); E slope Mt. Hamilton, *Beane & James 2079* in 1949 (DS, RSA, WTU); 1 mi. above Alum Rock, Mt. Hamilton, *Dutton* in 1899 (DS); 2 mi. below summit of Mt. Hamilton, *Solbig* in 1957 (UC); 2 mi. E of Mt. Hamilton on Livermore rd., *H & Scharpf 1149* in 1968 (FPF) and on *P. coulteri*, *H & Scharpf 1148* in 1968 (FPF); near Mt. Hamilton Observatory, on planted *P. radiata*,

H & Scharpf 1150 in 1968 (FPF); Summit Copernicus Peak, *Sharsmith 1406a & b* in 1934 (UC). Mt. Umunhum, *Thomas 5519* in 1956 (DS, FPF, RSA); Loma Prieta, on *P. attenuata, Dudley* in 1895 (DS). Stanford Arboretum, on planted *P. radiata, Wight 47* in 1900 (US). SHASTA CO.: Morleys, *Baker* in 1898 (UC); 2.5 mi. W of Round Mtn., *Kuijt 1374* in 1957 (UC); Black Butte, *Anderson* in 1949 (CAS). SONOMA CO.: Fort Ross, on *P. muricata, Mason 4285* in 1928 (UC); 2 mi. S of Anchor Cover, on *P. muricata, Wolf 1342* in 1927 (DS). TEHAMA CO.: Manton, *Kuijt 1362* in 1957 (UC) and *Root* in 1919 (ILL); 12 mi. W of Mineral, *Kuijt 1361* in 1957 (UC). TRINITY CO.: Trinity River near Swede Cr. [ca. 6 mi. W of Big Bar], *Tracy 6912* in 1924 (UC); near Weaverville, *Kleeberger* in 1879 (CAS). TULARE CO.: 6 mi. E of Roads End P. O., *Howell 33147* in 1958 (CAS); Kern River Can., 7.6 mi. N of Kernville, *Twisselmann* n.d. (CAS). TUOLUMNE CO.: 5 mi. E of Sonora, *Wright FP 68054** in 1931 (FPF); 2 mi. E of Sonora, *W 3221* in 1962 (COLO, FPF); E side Sonora, *Gill & Wright FP 68066* in 1932 (FPF); 1 mi. W of Columbia, *Peterson 63–136* in 1963 (FPF); Long Barn, *Gill FP 68080* and *FP 68099* in 1932 (FPF) and *Wright FP 68119* in 1932 (FPF); Confidence, *Bóyce FP 97953* in 1915 (FPB); 2 mi. W of Rte. 49 Jct. on Rte. 120, *Kuijt 1427* in 1957 (UC); 4 mi. NE of Columbia, *Smith* in 1956 (UC); Sonora, *Bigelow 4* in 1854 (MO).

19. ARCEUTHOBIUM PUSILLUM

Specimens Examined: on *Picea mariana*, except as noted.

CANADA

MANITOBA

Freshford, *Laut* in 1968 (FPF, WINF) and on *Pinus banksiana, Laut* in 1968 (FPF, WINF). Belaire Provincial For., *Lawrence* in 1967 (FPF, WINF); Amana Bay, 40 mi. E of Gypsumville, on *P. glauca, Lawrence* in 1967 (FPF, WINF); Sandilands For. Reserve, *Campbell* in 1966 (FPF, WINF) and on *Pinus banksiana, Laut* in 1967 (FPF, WINF); Glenboro, on *P. glauca, Campbell* in 1965 (FPF, WINF); East Braintree, on *P. glauca, Campbell* in 1966 and *Lawrence* in 1967 (FPF, WINF); Long Point, SE of Grand Rapids, *Shepherd* in 1968 (FPF, WINF).

NEW BRUNSWICK

Grand Mann, *Weatherby & Weatherby 5770* in 1927 (UC, US) and *6685* in 1934 (US); 10 mi. W of Napadogan, *Bonga** in 1964 (FPF); Acadia For. Exp. Sta., *Bonga* in 1965 (FPF); Deer Island, near Johnson Lake, on *Picea* sp., *Malte 731/29* in 1929 (US, WTU).

NEWFOUNDLAND

Wild Cover, near Humbermouth, White Cliff, Humber Dist., *Rouleau 612* in 1950 (RM, UC, US); Bay of Islands, *Howe & Lang 1141* in 1901 (GH); Deer Arm, Bonne Bay; McIver's Cove, *Fernald et al. 1655* in 1929 (GH, PH), Deer Brook, *Fernald et al. 1656* in 1929 (GH, PH), and Main River, *Fernald et al.* in 1929 (PH, US). Port a Port, on *Picea* sp., *Fernald & St. John 10830* in 1914 (GH).

NOVA SCOTIA

Cape Breton Island: Creignish, *Bonga* in 1965 (FPF); 2 mi. E of Margaree For., *von Schrenk* in 1928 (MO, PH, POM, UC); Ingonish, on *Picea* sp., *Pease 20948* in 1929 (GH). Lower Argyle, *Fernald et al. 21045* in 1920 (MO, UC, US); Gold Lake, Birchton Branch, *Fernald & Long 23788* in 1921 (GH, NY, PH); Hectanooga, *Fernald & Pease 21041* in 1920 (GH, PH); Pictou, *Howe & Lang* (GH, NY, PH, RM) and on *P. glauca, von Schrenk* in 1929 (MO); Tefry's Lake, Arcadia, *Fernald & Pease 21043* in 1920 (GH): East Jordan, *Fernald & Pease 23878* in 1921 (GH); Mt. Uniache, *Jack 3225* in 1924 (GH); Woliamakeh Beach, Port Mouton, *Jack 3473* in 1924 (GH). Yarmouth Co.: Tusket, on *P. glauca, Jack 3759* in 1924 (UC) and *Long & Fernald 21042* in 1920 (GH, PH); Eel Lake, on *P. glauca, Fernald et al. 21044* in 1920 (GH, PH). Shelburne Co.: *Jack 3468* in 1924 (US).

ONTARIO

Snelgrove, *White* in 1918 (FPF, ILL); 7 mi. SW of Killarney, Georgian Bay, on *P. glauca, Coville* in 1915 (US); near Cloche, McGregor Bay, N side Georgian Bay, on *P. glauca, Coville* in 1915 (US); Bruce Peninsula, Stokes Bay, on *Larix laricina, Hamai* in 1964 (FPF); White Otter Lake, on *Pinus banksiana, McPhee & Miller,* in 1955 (FPF, FPT, WINF); Temagami For. Reserve, *Watson 6762* in 1922 (WIS).

PRINCE EDWARD ISLAND

Tracadie Beach, *Churchill* in 1901 (MO, PH): Tignish, *Fernald et al. 7327* in 1912 (NY, PH, UC, US).

QUEBEC

Richelieu, *Rouleau* in 1945 (UC, WIS). Lac-Aux-Atocas, Parc de Mont Tremblant, *Rolland-Germain 220* in 1956 (UC, US); Riv. Ste. Anne des Monts, *Fernald & Collins 218* in 1906 (US); St. Adolphe, Comte d' Argenteuil, Riv. du Lac. St. Joseph, on *Picea* sp., *Rolland-Germain 7512* in 1949 (DS); Cap Chat River, below Pirian River, Matane Co., on *Picea* sp., *Fernald & Pease 25031* in 1922 (GH); St.

Adolphe, Argenteuil, on *P. glauca, Rolland-Germain 3061* in 1949 (RM); Ste. Anne de la Pocatiere, on *P. glauca, Marie-Victorin 28456* in 1928 (RM, US, WIS), on *Picea* sp., *Cody et al. 676* in 1947 (MO) and *Campagna 34173* in 1930 (GH); near Lake Ouimet, Tierbonne Co., *Pease 19055* in 1922 (GH); Lac Monroe, on ?, *Rolland-Germain 361* in 1957 (US); Mont Tremblant, on *Picea* sp., *Louis-Alphonse* in 1952 (MO, US).

SASKATCHEWAN

Otosquen, *Crawford* in 1967 (FPF, WINF): Mi. 30 on Cumberland rd., on *P. glauca, McLeod* in 1968 (FPF, WINF); on Highway 123, on *P. glauca* at Mi. 20, *McLeod* in 1968 (FPF, WINF) and Mi. 37, *McLeod* in 1968 (FPF, WINF).

UNITED STATES

CONNECTICUT

LITCHFIELD CO.: North side Bear Mtn., *Greenman 2492* in 1910 (GH, MO); Bigham Pond, near Salisbury, *Mann* in 1906 (US); South Spectacle Pond, near Kent, *Gill et al. FP 68284** in 1933 (FPF) and *Harger 45859* in 1909 (PH), and on *Larix laricina, Gill et al. FP 68285* in 1933 (FPF); Norfolk, *Weatherby 3906* in 1916 (PH, US) and *Bissell* in 1904 (GH).

MAINE

AROOSTOOK CO.: Fort Kent, *Fernald* in 1899 (UC); Monticello, *Fernald & Long 13521* in 1916 (PH). CUMBERLAND CO.: Great Chebeague Island, on *Picea* sp., *Fernald 1741* in 1909 (GH). FRANKLIN CO.: New Sharon, *Knowlton* in 1903 (GH) and *Knowlton 23525* in 1905 (WIS). HANCOCK CO.: Mt. Desert Island, Great Head, on *P. glauca, Rand* in 1906 (UC); Acadia Nat. Park, *Cottam 11561* in 1938 (FPF, UT): Gouldsboro, *Nortan* in 1922 (WIS). KENNEBEC CO.: Belgrade, *Fassett 2527* in 1925 (GH, WIS). KNOX CO.: Isle au Haut, on *P. glauca, Arthur* in 1900 (GH); Matinicus Island, on *P. glauca, Norton & Chamberlain* in 1916 (GH). LINCOLN CO.: Bristol, on *P. glauca, Churchill 351* in 1903 (MO); Squirrel Island, Boothbay Harbor, on *P. glauca, Welch** in 1958 (FPF); Monhegan Island, on *P. glauca, von Schrenk** in 1899 (MO) and *Fernald* in 1933 (PH, US); Linekin, on *P. glauca, von Schrenk* in 1899 (MO); Georgetown, on *Picea* sp., *Morton 2063* in 1921 (WTU). Lighthouse Hill, host?, *Churchill* in 1921 (WIS); White Island, host?, *Fassett 2185* in 1925 (WIS); Ocean Point, *Fassett 3923* in 1922 (WIS). OXFORD CO.: Norway, *Bean 2241* in 1907 (GH). PENOBSCOT CO.: Alton, *Fernald 23322* in 1900 (GH, WIS). SOMERSET CO.: Baker Brook, Headwaters St.

John River, *St. John & Nichols 2281* in 1917 (US); Pleasant Ridge, *Murdoch 2010* in 1906 (F); Palmer Pond, *Fassett 14308* in 1931 (WIS). WASHINGTON CO.: Indian Township, Grand Lake Stream rd., *Gill FP 68313* in 1934 (FPF). COUNTY UNCERTAIN: Middle Cary Pond, *Spaulding & Collins* in 1920 (ILL); Deer River, *Weir 2394* n.d. (ILL).

MASSACHUSETTS

BERKSHIRE CO.: Becket, *Hoffmann* in 1904 (GH) and 1907 (MO). ESSEX CO.: Andover, *Pease 406* in 1902 (GH). HAMPDEN CO.: Springfield, *Clark & Seymour G586* in 1928 (WIS). MIDDLESEX CO.: Wilmington, *Moore 634* in 1903 (UC); Concord, *Eaton* in 1930 (RSA); Acton, on *Picea* sp., *Jack* in 1898 (GH). WORCHESTER CO.: Ashburnham, *Murdoch 5301* in 1914 (F); Lancaster, *Fassett 2345* in 1924 (GH); Clinton, on *P. glauca, Jack* in 1898 (F); Boylston, *Jack* in 1898 (MO) and on *P. glauca, Jack* in 1898 (F, MO).

MICHIGAN

(Information on the *A. pusillum* collections at the University of Michigan (MICH) and the Cranbrook Institute of Science (BLH) provided by Dr. E. G. Voss and at Michigan State University (MSC) by Dr. J. H. Hart). ALCONA CO.: N end of Milikin Lake, *Voss 4581* in 1957 (MICH). ALGER CO.: Chatham, on *Picea* sp., col.? in 1901 (NY, US) and *Wheeler* in 1900 (MSC); Rock River, *Kauffman* in 1927 (MICH). BENZIE CO.: Homstead Township, North Branch of Platte River, *Frohlich 61* in 1968 (MICH). CHARLEVOIX CO.: Beaver Island: Egg Lake, *Voss 7009* in 1958 (MICH); Green Bay, on *P. glauca, Voss 3935* in 1957 (MICH); and Donegal Bay, on *P. glauca, Voss 6986* in 1958 (MICH). CHEBOYGAN CO.: Little Lake 16, near Cheboygan, *Cutler* in 1937 (MO, US), *Voss 1539* in 1953 (MICH), and *Ehlers 6127* in 1936 (MICH). Mud Lake bog, *Gates & Gates 10682* in 1917 (RM), *Gates 14886* in 1927 (MO, UC) and *Erlanson 484* in 1924 (MICH). Douglas Lake, *Ehlers 1120* in 1920 (MICH, WIS). Bryans Bog, Univ. of Mich. Biol. Sta., *Gates 11116* in 1919 (WTU). CHIPPEWA CO.: 2.5 mi. N of Eckermann, *McVaugh 9781* in 1948 (BLH, MICH, MO). Munuskong Bay State Park, *Bessey* in 1927 (MSC). 3 mi. E of W Border of county on Rte. M-28, *Bourdo* in 1961 (MSC). Whitefish township at mouth of Toquamonon River, *Churchill* in 1957 (MSC). Drummond Island, Warners Cove, on *P. glauca, Voss 12239* in 1966 (MICH). EMMET CO.: Bliss Township, Waugoschance Point, on *P. glauca, Churchill* in 1955 (MSC) and *Voss 1048* in 1951 (MICH). Bliss Township, Sec. 18, on *P. glauca, Marshall 809* in 1949 (MSC). Galloway Lake, 1 mi. N of Levering, *Wood, Clover & Voss 8118* in 1953

(MICH) and *Voss 12076* in 1966 (MICH). GOGE-BIC CO.: Near Imp Lake, *Gillis 3007* in 1959 (MSC) and *Voss 7854* in 1958 (MICH). Banks Lake, *Voss 12467* in 1967 (MICH). Mud Lake, *Darlington 2749* in 1919 (MICH). Sylvania Recreation Area, *Voss 12712* in 1968 (MICH). HURON CO.: Island in Rush Lake, *Dodge* in 1908 (MICH, MSC). IRON CO.: Basswood Pond, ca. 3 mi. SE of Elmwood, *Voss 8602* in 1959 (MICH). KEWEE-NAW CO.: 1.5 mi. W of Eagle Harbor, *Voss 11870* in 1965 (MICH). LEELANAU CO.: Glenn Arbor Township, Sec. 13, bog near Crystal River, *Thompson L-1128* in 1948 (BLH). LUCE CO.: Barclay Lake, 9 mi. SW of Crisp Point on Lake Superior, *Voss 3169* in 1956 (MICH). MACKINAC CO.: 7 mi. E of Naubinway on US 2, on *P. glauca*, *H 687** in 1964 (FPF). Bois Blanc Island, on *P. glauca*, *Dodge* in 1913 (MICH, MSC) and *Ehlers 5144* in 1932 (MICH). MARQUETTE CO.: Turin, *Barlow 145** in 1901 (MSC, UC). Conway Lake, *Stoutamire 3013* in 1959 (BLH). MENOMINEE CO.: Bog NE of Wireglass Lake, ca. 5.5 mi. WSW of Carney, *Voss 12696* in 1968 (MICH, MSC). MONTMORENCY CO.: Ess Lake, 5 mi. N of Hillman, *Stewart* in 1966 (FPF). Lake 22 (Gaylanta Lake), *Case* in 1955 (MICH). SCHOOLCRAFT CO.: Long Lake, ca. 5.5 mi. NE of Melstrand, *Voss 2660* in 1955 (MICH).

MINNESOTA

AITKIN CO.: 6 mi. S of Aitkin, *Gill FP 68209* in 1932 (FPF); S of McGregor, *Rosendahl 4450* in 1924 (PH). BELTRAMI CO.: Waskish, *Anderson** in 1965 (FPF); W of Upper Red Lake, T. 135 N, R. 35 E, Sec. 5, *Anderson* in 1967 (FPF). CASS CO.: Cass Lake, *Weir* in 1916 (ILL, RM, UC) and on *Larix laricina*, *Weir* in 1916 (FPF, ILL). CHISAGO CO.: T. 37 N, R. 22 W, *Gill FP 68208** in 1932 (FPF). CLEARWATER CO.: Itasca State Park, *Green 9* in 1947 (WIS) and on *Larix laricina*, *French & Tainter* in 1967 (FPF); 2 mi. NW of Mississippi River headwaters, *Thorne 19860* in 1958 (RSA); Lake Itasca, on *P. glauca*, *Hedgcock & Freeman FP 4145* in 1910 (FPF); Lake Itasca, Floating Bog Bay, on *P. glauca*, *Thorne* in 1962 (RSA). COOK CO.: Superior Nat. For., T. 64 N, R. 1 W, Sec. 6, on Rte. 12 ca. 24 air mi. NNW of Grand Marais, *Skilling* in 1964 (FPF). HUBBARD CO.: Itasca Park, SE of Mary Lake, *Grant 3197* in 1929 (GH, MO, PH, WTU, US). ST. LOUIS CO.: 16 mi. N of Duluth, *Lakela 4503* in 1941 (MO): Floodwood, *Lakela 18527* in 1954 (US); Duluth, Normanna township, *Lakela 15555* in 1952 (WIS). COUNTY UNCERTAIN: Gnesen Township, N of Duluth, *Lakela 7912* in 1948 (RM).

NEW HAMPSHIRE

CARROL CO.: Ossipee, on *Picea* sp., *Grover* in 1896 (GH). COOS CO.: "White Trail," Shelburne, on ?, *von Schrenk* in 1938 (MO); Randolph, Brook Bank, *Pease 3258* in 1903 (UC); Round Pond, Errol, *Pease 32509* in 1946 (RSA); Fernway Region, Randolph, on *P. rubens*, *Moore 143* in 1901 (POM, UC). CHESHIRE CO.: Nelson, on *Picea* sp., *Batchelder* in 1931 (MO). GRAFTON CO.: Hanover, *Jesup & Eggelston* in 1893 (DS, PH, US) and on *Picea* sp., *Eggelston* in 1893 (PH, RM); Lebanon, *Jesup* in 1891 (MO). ROCKINGHAM CO.: Nottingham, on *Picea* sp., *Eaton 443* in 1900 (GH). COUNTY UNCERTAIN: White Mtn. Nat. For., SE of Blue Brook Ranger Sta., *Hedgcock FP 8640** in 1913 (FPF, ILL).

NEW JERSEY

SUSSEX CO.: Pine Swamp, Lake Mashipscong, *MacKenzie* in 1920 (PH) and *Cain & Svenson 6597* in 1935 (UC, WIS).

NEW YORK

CHENANGO CO.: Newcomb, *Hansbrough & Spaulding FP 68210* in 1932 (FPF); Plymouth, *Coville* in 1887 (US); Preston, *Coville* in 1885 (US). CLINTON CO.: Platsburg, Hotel Champlain, on *P. glauca*, *Schwartz FP 68288** in 1934 (FPF). COLUMBIA CO.: 1.5 mi. NW of Niverville, on *Picea* sp., *Wherry* in 1934 (UC). CORTLAND CO.: Labrador Swamp, *Wiegland* in 1893 (MO); Truxton, on *Picea* sp., *Wiegland* in 1894 (UC). ESSEX CO.: Newcomb, on *P. glauca*, *House 7186* in 1920 (UC); FRANKLIN CO.: Saranac Inn, *Spaulding FP 34543* in 1909 (FPF). HAMILTON CO.: Raquette Lake Village, *von Schrenk* in 1932 (PH, POM, RM, UC); Whitney Park, Sabattis, on *P. rubens*, *Spaulding & Eno FP 68312* in 1934 (FPF). HERKIMER CO.: Without locality, on *Picea* sp., *Haberer* n.d. (UC); Graefender Swamp, *Haberer* in 1881 (PH); Frankfort Hill, *Haberer 188* in 1892 (DS); Litchfield, *Haberer* in 1881 (GH). MONROE CO.: Mendon, *Baxter* in 1908 (UC) and *Killip* in 1917 (ARIZ, POM). ONEIDA CO.: Frankfort Hills, Utica, col.? in 1881 (MO). ONONDAGA CO.: Cicero, *Wiegland 6344* in 1916 (GH, MO); Syracuse, *Pennington* n.d. (ILL) and on *Larix laricina*, *Pennington* n.d. (ILL). OSWEGO CO.: Oswego, *Wibbe 11532* in 1878 (MO), *Killip 7816* in 1921 (US) and on *P. glauca*, *Sheldon 439* in 1881 (US); South New Haven, *Mathews 2663* in 1927 (RM); New Haven, *Rowlee* in 1891 (MO). RENSSELAER CO.: Without locality, *Wibbe* in 1891 (ARIZ, CS, RM, UC, US, WIS). SCHENEC-TADY CO.: Schenectady, *Wibbe* in 1891 (F, US). ST. LAWRENCE CO.: Bean Pond, Wanakena,

Benedict in 1918 (ILL). SULLIVAN CO.: Forestburg, *Peck* in 1873 (MO). THOMPKINS CO.: Franklin Hills, *Haberer* in 1882 (GH). WARREN CO.: E lake George Marsh, Brayton, *Burnham* in 1897 (PH); Warrensburgh, *Millington* in 1912 (MO). WEBB CO.: Big Moose Lake, on *P. rubens, von Schrenk* in 1932 (MO, POM, UC). WESTCHESTER CO.: Peekskill, on *Picea* sp., *LeRoy* n.d. (NY).

PENNSYLVANIA

LACKAWANA CO.: Moosic Mtn., NE of Scranton, col.? in 1886 (PH); Little Roaring Brook, Scranton, *Dudley* in 1886 (DS). MONROE CO.: Tannersville, *Williamson* in 1908 (PH); Cranberry Marsh near Tannersville, *Batram & Long* in 1907 (PH); 5 mi NE of Dresser, *Haas* in 1951 (PH). PIKE CO.: Pine Lake, Greentown, *Olday 240** in 1961 (FPF); Spruce Pond, *Brown & Saunders* in 1899 (PH). SULLIVAN CO.: Shadynook, *Brown* in 1901 (MO, PH); near Lopez, *Williamson* in 1908 (GH, PH). WAYNE CO.: 1.5 mi. E of Hamlin, *Glowenke 2468* in 1938 (WTU).

RHODE ISLAND

PROVIDENCE CO.: Bowdish Reservoir, Glochester, *Collins* in 1904 (PH, UC), in 1919 (US) and in 1927 (MO).

VERMONT

CHITTENDEN CO.: Near Burlington, on *Larix laricina, von Schrenk* in 1899 (MO). GRAND ISLE CO.: Alburgh, *Jones* in 1899 (GH). RUTLAND CO.: Pittsford, on *Picea* sp., *Eggelston 1561* in 1899 (US); Mendon, on *Picea* sp., *Eggelston 1562* in 1899 (GH); Brandon, *Dutton* in 1911 (MO).

WISCONSIN

(Information on the *A. pusillum* collections at the University of Wisconsin (WIS) provided by Dr. H. H. Iltis, 1969). ASHLAND CO.: Mellen, *Fassett 10093* in 1927 (WIS). BURNETT CO.: West Sweden, *Ninman & Thompson FP 38713* in 1922 (FPF); Gaslyn, *Davis* in 1911 (WIS). DOOR CO.: Sturgeon Bay, *Davis* in 1913 and 1929 (WIS). Baileys Harbor: *Davis* in 1918 and 1929 (WIS), and *Fassett & Sieker 14703* in 1932 (WIS) and, on *P. glauca, von Schrenk* in 1934 (FPF, WIS), *Pohl 1145* in 1938 (WIS), and *Iltis 17558* in 1961 (WIS). DOUGLAS CO.: Gordon, *Wadmond 1271* in 1907 (GH, WIS); Solon Springs, *Fassett 22395* in 1934 (WIS). FLORENCE CO.: Boot Lake, *Iltis, Iltis & Turner 22225* in 1964 (WIS); Long Lake, *Davis* in 1915 (WIS). FOREST CO.: Laona, *Davis* in 1915 (WIS). IRON CO.: Mercer, *Davis* in 1919 (WIS).

JACKSON CO.: Glacial Lake, *Hartley 3991* in 1958 (WIS). LANGLADE CO.: Phlox, *Davis* in 1914 (WIS). LINCOLN CO.: Lost Lake, *Seymour 11906* in 1950 (WIS); Gerbig Lake, *Seymour 15104* in 1952 (WIS); Corning, *Seymour 14645* in 1952 (WIS) and *Schlising 124* in 1952 (WIS). MANITOWOC CO.: W of Kellnersville, *Fassett, Hoffman & Staffield 18265* in 1934 (WIS). ONEIDA CO.: Rhinelander, *Anderson* in 1963 (FPF); 9 mi. W of Crandon on US 8, *H 688* in 1964 (FPF); W of Woodruff on Rte. 20, *Anderson** in 1965 (FPF). PRICE CO.: Camp Merrill, *Davis* in 1911 (WIS): Butternut Lake, *Davis* in 1911 (WIS). RUSK CO.: Hawkins, *Davis* in 1918 (FPF, ILL, WIS). SAWYER CO.: Hayward, *Davis* in 1924 (WIS) and *Gilbert & Davis* in 1932 (WIS). TAYLOR CO.: 3.5 mi. N of Rib Lake, *Anderson 265* in 1947 (WIS). VILLAS CO.: Trout Lake, *Spaulding* in 1915 (FPF), *Fassett 8996* in 1929 (WIS), and *Fassett 13767* in 1932 (WIS). Lake Louise, 5 mi. E of Boulder Jct., *Wilson & Wilson 3067* in 1932 (POM, WIS). WASHBURN CO.: Spooner, *Davis* in 1911 (WIS).

20. ARCEUTHOBIUM RUBRUM

Specimens Examined:

MEXICO

DURANGO· 29 mi. E of El Salto on Rte. 40, on *Pinus teocote, H & W 338** and *521** in 1963 (COLO, FPF); on *P. engelmanni, H & W 339** in 1963 (COLO, FPF); and on *P. cooperi, H & W 340* in 1963 (COLO, FPF). 24 mi. E of El Salto on Rte. 40, on *P. teocote, H & W 1243* in 1969 (FPF); 2 mi. W of El Salto on Rte. 40, on *P. teocote, H & W 345** in 1963 (COLO, FPF) and on *P. durangensis, H & W 346* in 1963 (COLO, FPF). 35 mi. S of Durango on La Flor rd., on *P. teocote, H & W 511** in 1963 (COLO, FPF); on *P. engelmannii, H & W 513** in 1963 (COLO, FPF); and on *P. cooperi, H & W 512* in 1963 (COLO, FPF); 49 mi. W of El Salto on Rte 40, on *P. herrerai, H & W 1248* in 1969 (FPF). 30 mi. NW of Santiago Papasquiaro, on *P. teocote, Straw & Forman 1777* in 1959 (RSA). SINALOA: Without locality or host, Comisión Catastral y de Estudio de los Recursos Naturales del Estado, *Gonzales 1717* in 1920 (K, US).

21. ARCEUTHOBIUM STRICTUM

Specimens Examined: On *Pinus leiophylla* var. *chihuahuana* except as noted.

MEXICO

DURANGO: City of Durango and vicinity, *Palmer 774* in 1896 (BM, F, ILL, MO, NY, UC, US); 38 mi. E of El Salto on Rte. 40, *H & W 329** in 1963

(COLO, FPF); 36 mi. E of El Salto on Rte. 40, *H & W 1242* in 1969 (FPF) and on *P. teocote, H & W 518** in 1963 (COLO, FPF); 16 mi. S of Durango on La Flor rd., *H & W 500** in 1963 (FPF); 24 mi. S of Durango on La Flor rd., on *P. teocote, H & W 505** in 1963 (COLO, FPF) and on *P. engelmannii, H & W 506** in 1963 (COLO, FPF).

22. ARCEUTHOBIUM TSUGENSE

Specimens Examined: All on *Tsuga heterophylla*, except as noted.

CANADA

BRITISH COLUMBIA: Vancouver Island: *Rosendahl & Brandegee 136* in 1901 (COLO, MO); Ucuelet, *Henry 1822* and *1881* in 1917 (RM); Pender Harbour, *Spaulding FP 41633** in 1923 (FPF); Sproat Lake, on *Pinus contorta, Rosendahl & Butters 1092* in 1906 (WTU) and *Rosendahl 1958* in 1907 (UC); 6 mi. E of Duncan Jct., *Kuijt* in 1954 (DAVFP, FPF); 6 mi. W of Nanaimo Lakes Jct., *Kuijt* in 1954 (DAVFP, FPF); Cowichan Lake, *Kuijt* in 1954 (DAVFP, FPF) and *Smith* in 1965 (DAVFP, FPF); Robertson River Valley, *Kuijt** in 1954 (DAVFP, FPF); 8 mi. W of Sooke, *Kuijt* in 1954 (DAVFP, FPF); Chemainus, *Porter* in 1954 (DAVFP, FPF) and on *Pinus contorta, Kuijt* in 1954 (DAVFP, FPF); Metchosin, on *P. contorta, Kuijt 602* in 1954 (DAVFP, FPF); Horne Lake rd., on *P. contorta, Kuijt* in 1954 (DAVFP, FPF); Goldstream summit of Mt. Finlayson, on *P. contorta, Ziller* in 1965 (DAVFP, FPF). Sechelt, *Kuijt 618* in 1954 (DAVFP, FPF) and on *P. contorta, Kuijt* in 1954 (DAVFP, FPF). Vancouver, Stanley Park, *Hopping FP 97939* in 1928 (FPB) and *Kuijt* in 1954 (DAVFP, FPF); Vancouver, Univ. of British Columbia Botanic Gardens, *Kuijt* in 1954 (DAVFP, FPF); Agassiz, *Weir 2449*, n.d. (ILL); Savary Island, on *Pinus contorta, Davidson* in 1918 (FPF, ILL); Daisy Lake, ca. 30 mi. N of Squamish, *Boyce 2122* in 1931 (FPF).

UNITED STATES

ALASKA

Juneau, *Anderson 6406* in 1941 (PH, RM); Eagle River, 25 mi. N of Juneau, *Laurent* in 1965 (FPF); Chicagof Island, Basket Bay, *Laurent & Labue** in 1965 (FPF); Kupreanof Island, 15 mi. SW of Petersburg, *Graham* in 1966 (FPF); 1 mi. S of Little Basket Bay, on *Picea sitchensis, Laurent* in 1965 (FPF); near Sitka, on *T. mertensiana, Weir* in 1913 (FPF, ILL); near Ketchikan, *Weir* in 1915 (ILL) and *Drake* in 1917 (FPF, ILL); Mt. Verstovia, Sitka, *Coville & Kearney 916* in 1899 (US); Sitka, *Anderson 232* in 1915 (US).

CALIFORNIA

ALPINE CO.: Mosquito Lake, 11 mi. NE of Alpine, on *Tsuga mertensiana, H & Scharpf 665** in 1964 (FPF) and on *Pinus monticola, H & Scharpf 666* in 1964 (FPF). MENDOCINO CO.: 3 mi. E of Mendocino, *H & Scharpf 850* in 1966 (FPF). PLACER CO.: Emigrant Gap, on *Tsuga mertensiana, Jones* in 1881 (POM). PLUMAS CO.: Mt. Elwell [6 mi. SW of Blairsden], on *Tsuga mertensiana, Lieberg 5363* in 1900 (ILL, US). SHASTA CO.: Lassen Nat. Park: 2.5 mi. N of S entrance, on *Tsuga mertensiana, W 3235* in 1962 (COLO, FPF); 23 mi. SE of N entrance, on main rd., on *Tsuga mertensiana, H & W 652* in 1964 (FPF); 1–2 mi. S of Helen Lake, on *Tsuga mertensiana, Scharpf FP 38027* n.d. (FPB). SISKIYOU CO.: Marble Mtns.: Kidder Cr., on *Tsuga mertensiana, Gill & Sargent FP 68180** in 1932 (FPF); Chimney Rock Lake, on *Tsuga mertensiana, Hemphill* in 1968 (FPF, UT) and on *Picea breweriana, Hemphill* in 1968 (FPF, UT); near Chimney Rock, on *Pinus monticola, Hemphill* in 1968 (FPF, UT). Siskiyou Mtns.: Applegate Cr. Divide, on *Tsuga mertensiana, Meinecke FP 97938* in 1913 (FPB) and on *Picea breweriana, Meinecke FP 97941* in 1913 (FPB). TEHAMA CO.: Mineral, on *Tsuga mertensiana, Lory FP 97940* in 1911 (FPB). COUNTY UNCERTAIN: Bald Mtn., *Hubert* in 1918 (ILL).

IDAHO

These Idaho records on *Tsuga heterophylla* are tentatively listed here pending confirmation (see text). LATAH CO.: Bovill, *Weir* in 1918 (FPF, ILL). COUNTY UNCERTAIN: St. Joe Nat. For., *Weir 2452* in 1914 (ILL) and *Weir 6838* in 1916 (FPF, ILL).

OREGON

BENTON CO.: Mary's Peak, on *Abies procera, Shea* in 1968 (FPF). CLACKAMAS CO.: Still Cr. Trail near Rhododendron, *Gill FP 68193** in 1932 (FPF), *Faull, Childs & Hansbrough FP 68266* in 1931 (FPF), and on *Pinus monticola, Langley & Goodding* in 1931 (RM); 4 mi. E of Rhododendron, *Mielke FP 58275* in 1930 (OSC); 2 mi. W of Government Camp on US 26, *H & W 605* in 1964 (FPF) and on *Abies amabilis, H & W 606* in 1964 (FPF); Twin Bridges [5 mi. W of Government Camp on US 26], *Thompson 9422* in 1928 (DS, MO). COOS CO.: Siskiyou Mtns., 10 air mi. NNE of Agness, on *T. mertensiana, Graham* in 1965 (FPF). Near S fork of Coos River, 38 air mi. W of Roseburg, *Stewart* in 1968 (FPF). DESCHUTES CO.: 11 mi. W of Sisters on McKenzie Pass rd., on *Tsuga mertensiana, H & Hinds 991* in 1966 (FPF) and on *Abies lasio-*

carpa, *H & Hinds 992* in 1966 (FPF). DOUGLAS CO.: Myrtle Cr.—Deadman Cr. divide, ca. 11 air mi. N of Tiller, *Graham* in 1965 (FPF); Just N of Crater Lake Nat. Park, Diamond Lake rd., on *T. mertensiana, Graham* in 1964 (FPF); 20 mi. NE of Union Cr. on Rte. 230, *H 1141* in 1968 (FPF) and on *Pinus monticola, H 1142* in 1968 (FPF). JACKSON CO.: Union Cr., on *T. mertensiana, Applegate 6038* in 1929 (DS); Huckleberry Mtn., 10 mi. NE of Prospect, on *T. mertensiana, Graham* in 1965 (FPF); 8 mi. NW of W entrance to Crater Lake Nat. Park, *Graham* in 1963 (FPF). KLAMATH CO.: Crater Lake Nat. Park: Anna Springs Ranger Sta., on *T. mertensiana, Gill FP 68184* in 1932 (FPF); Wineglass, on *Pinus albicaulis, Gill FP 68182* in 1932 (FPF); 0.5 mi. S of Wineglass, on *T. mertensiana, Gill FP 68183* in 1932 (FPF); 5 mi. E of main rd. on N rim of Crater Lake, on *T. mertensiana, H & W 624* in 1964 (FPF) and on *Pinus albicaulis, H & W 625* in 1964 (FPF); Crater Lake, Palisades, on *T. mertensiana, Coville 1478* in 1902 (US); 15 mi. SW of Crescent Lake, *Childs 65* in 1937 (OSC); 2 mi. N of Windigo Pass, on *T. mertensiana, H & W 621* in 1964 (FPF) and on *Pinus monticola, H & W 622* in 1964 (FPF). LANE CO.: E Fork of S Fork of McKenzie River, 8 mi. S of McKenzie Bridge, *Stewart & Orr* in 1968 (FPF); near head of Mosquito Cr., on *Abies amabilis, Stewart & Orr* in 1968 (FPF); Head of Olallie Cr., on *Abies amabilis, A. grandis,* and *A. lasiocarpa, Stewart & Orr* in 1968 (FPF). 19 mi. E of Oakridge on Rte. 58, *H 1140* in 1968 (FPF); near Foley Springs, on *Abies sp., Coville & Applegate 1090* and *1091* in 1898 (US); Brice Cr., 20 air mi. SE of Cottage Grove, *Graham* in 1965 (FPF); McKenzie Pass. On *Abies lasiocarpa, Childs FP 91561* in 1947 (OSC); on *Pinus albicaulis, Gill FP 68188** in 1932 (FPF), *Lachmund & Childs FP 68269* in 1930 (FPF), and *Childs FP 91560* in 1947 (OSC); on *T. mertensiana, Gill FP 68187** in 1932 (FPF) and *Childs FP 91562* in 1947 (OSC). 1 mi. W of McKenzie Pass: on *A. lasiocarpa, Boyce 2298* in 1930 (FPF); on *Pinus albicaulis, Boyce 2299* in 1930 (FPF); and on *T. mertensiana, Boyce 2300* in 1930 (FPF). 1.5 mi. W of McKenzie Pass: on *A. lasiocarpa, W 3241* in 1962 (COLO, FPF); on *P. albicaulis, W 3243* in 1962 (COLO, FPF) and on *T. mertensiana, W 3242* in 1962 (COLO, FPF). LINCOLN CO.: 3 mi. E of Yachats, *Graham* in 1966 (FPF); Dicks Fork Cr., 4 mi. S of Waldport, *H & Scharpf 1252* in 1969 (FPF); T 15 S, R 11 W, Sec. 7, ca. 3 air mi. SE of Yachats on *Picea sitchensis, Ferguson* in 1969 (FPF). LINN CO.: Minto Mtn., on *T. mertensiana, Mielke FP 40694* in 1931 (OSC); Marion Lake, on *T. mertensiana, Coville & Applegate 1156,* in 1898 (US); 12 mi. W of Santiam Pass on US 20, *H & Scharpf 1254* in 1969 (FPF), on *Abies amabilis, H & Scharpf 1255*

in 1969 (FPF), and on *Picea engelmannii, H & Scharpf 1256* in 1969 (FPF). TILLAMOOK CO.: Near Nehalem, *Childs FP 40545* in 1930 (OSC). WASCO CO.: 5.7 mi. SE of Government Camp on US 26, *H & W 607* in 1964 (FPF) and on *A. amabilis, H & W 608* in 1964 (FPF).

WASHINGTON

CHELAN CO.: Lyman Glacier W of Chelan Lake, on *T. mertensiana, Weir 2456* in 1916 (ILL); Chelan Lake, *Weir* n.d. (FPF, ILL): N of Chelan Lake, on *P. albicaulis, Weir 3242* in 1916 (FPF, ILL). CLALLAM CO.: Lake Crescent, on *Tsuga sp., Jones 3439* n.d. (WTU); Piedmont, Crescent Lake, *Boyce 608** in 1920 (FPF) and *FP 40065* in 1920 (OSC); near Blyn, *W 3240* in 1962 (COLO). GRAYS HARBOR CO.: Wesport, *Gill FP 68195* in 1932 (FPF); 3.5 mi. NW of Montesano, *H 1250* in 1969 (FPF). KING CO.: Seattle, *Piper* in 1883 (PH), and on *T. mertensiana?, Piper 663* in 1892 (DU, MO, US, WTU); Berlin [5 mi. WNW of Skykomish], *Hedgcock FP 4765* in 1910 (FPF); Ronald Bog, N of Seattle, *Gunther* in 1930 (WTU); Corea, *Otis 1036* in 1920 (US); 4 mi. W of Stevens Pass on US 2, *H, Stewart & Thompson 1138* in 1968 (FPF) and on *Abies amabilis, 1139* in 1968 (FPF). KITSAP CO.: Mountaineer's Cabin, on *Tsuga sp., Jones 4299* in 1931 (WTU). KITTITAS CO.: Near Ellensburg, *Brandegee 1070* in 1883 (PH, US); E side Snoqualmie Pass, *W 3252* in 1962 (COLO) and on *Abies amabilis, W 3251* in 1962 (COLO). LEWIS CO.: 5 mi. N of Cayuse Pass on Rte. 143, on *Abies grandis, H & W 602* in 1964 (FPF), 4 mi. W of White Pass on Rte. 14, *Wicker* in 1966 (FPF) and on *Abies amabilis Wicker* in 1966 (FPF). PACIFIC CO.: 3 mi. N of Nemah on Rte. 101, *H & W 604* in 1964 (FPF). PIERCE CO.: Mt. Rainier Nat. Park: Longmire: *Gill FP 68198* in 1932 (FPF), *Gill & Warren FP 68199* in 1932 (FPF), *Flett* in 1915 (ILL), *Bookman FP 68265* in 1931 (FPF), and on *A. amabilis, Flett* in 1916 (ILL) and *Gill & Warren FP 68197* in 1932 (FPF); 5 mi. E of Longmire, *W 3248* in 1962 (COLO, FPF) and on *A. amabilis, W 3249* in 1962 (COLO, FPF); White River entrance, *Gill FP 68196** in 1932 (FPF). Ashford, *Flett* in 1915 (FPF, ILL); Huckleberry Cr., 8 mi. S of Greenwater, *Stewart* in 1968 (FPF) and on *A. amabilis, Stewart* in 1968 (FPF); Silver Springs, 32.5 mi. SE of Enumclaw on US 410, *H & W 601* in 1964 (FPF). SAN JUAN CO.: Orcas Island, Mt. Constitution, *Graham & Thompson* in 1965 (FPF) and on *Pinus contorta: Foster* in 1907 (WTU), *Cowles 372* in 1907 (US), *Rigg & Frye* in 1908 (WTU), *Zeller & Zeller 1194* in 1907 (MO), *Wright* in 1914 (US), *Beattie 5801* in 1921 (FPF), *Barker 254* in 1926 (DS) and *Graham & Thompson* in 1965 (FPF). SKAGIT CO.: Near

Power Dam on Skagit River, col.? n.d. (WTU). SKAMANIA CO.: Government Soda Springs, *Boyce 596* in 1920 (FPF) and *Boyce FP 40057* in 1920 (OSC); 24 mi. SE of Randle on Trout Lake rd., *W 3247* in 1962 (COLO, FPF); Tillicum Cr., 18 air mi. ESE of Spirit Lake, *Graham* in 1965 (FPF) and on *Abies amabilis, Graham* in 1965 (FPF); Dry Cr., 20 air mi. N of Stevenson, *Graham* in 1965 (FPF). SNOKOMISH CO.: 15 mi. N of Seattle, *Wittrock 5097* in 1927 (WTU). THURSTON CO.: Black Hills, *Meyer 1685* in 1939 (MO). WHATCOM CO.: Twin Sister Range, on *T. mertensiana, Muenscher 10431* in 1939 (DS); Bellingham to Mt. Baker, on *T. mertensiana, Weir* in 1915 (ILL). COUNTY UNCERTAIN: Upper Nisqually Valley, on *T. mertensiana, Allen 303* in 1896 (DS, MO, UC).

23a. *ARCEUTHOBIUM VAGINATUM*
subsp. *VAGINATUM*

Specimens Examined:

MEXICO

CHIHUAHUA: Sierra Madre, on *Pinus* sp., *Nelson 6077* in 1899 (K, US); Sierra Madre near Guachochi, on *Pinus* sp., *Goldman 177* in 1898 (US); 36 mi. SW of La Junta, on *P. ponderosa* var. *scopulorum, H & W 295* in 1963 (COLO, FPF); 39 mi. SW of La Junta, on *P. ponderosa* var. *scopulorum, H & W 298** in 1963 (COLO, FPF); 6 mi. E of El Vergel, on *P. ponderosa* var. *scopulorum, H & W 310* in 1963 (COLO, FPF); 1 mi. W of El Vergel, on *P. ponderosa* var. *arizonica, H & W 311* in 1963 (COLO, FPF); 10 mi. W of El Vergel, on *P. ponderosa* var. *arizonica, H & W 313** in 1963 (COLO, FPF): 10 mi. E of El Vergel, on *P. ponderosa* var. *scopulorum, H & W 308* in 1963 (COLO, FPF); on Ocampo rd. SW of Matachic, on *P. ponderosa* var. *arizonica,* at 48 mi., *H & W 486* in 1963 (COLO, FPF); 63 mi. *H & W 494** in 1963 (COLO, FPF); and at 69 mi. *H & W 491* in 1963 (COLO, FPF). COAHUILA: General Cepeda, *Pinus* sp., *Nelson 6730* in 1890 (US). DISTRICTO FEDERAL: Desierto de los Leones, on *Pinus* sp., *Alexander & Hernandez 2333* in 1945 (BM). DURANGO: Cienega de Ibarra, on *Pinus* sp., *Martínez* in 1940 (F); 13 mi. W of El Salto on Rte. 40, on *P. cooperi, H & W 348** in 1963 (COLO, FPF): 15 mi. W of El Salto on Rte. 40, on *P. cooperi, H & W 531** in 1963 (COLO, FPF); 18 mi. W of El Salto on Rte. 40, on *P. durangensis, H & W 1245* in 1969 (FPF); 26 mi. S of Durango on La Flor rd., on *P. engelmannii, H & W 507** in 1963 (COLO, FPF); 47 mi. S of Durango on La Flor rd., on *P. cooperi, H & W 515* in 1963 (COLO, FPF). HIDALGO: Real del Monte, on *Pinus* sp., *Coulter 17,* n.d. (GH, K). JALISCO: Nevado de Colima, on *Pinus* sp., *Jones 487* in 1892 (ILL, MO, POM, US); *Pringle 4368* in 1893 (BM, ILL, K,

MEXU, MO, NY, PH, UC, Z); *Reiche* in 1913 (MEXU); *McVaugh 10071* in 1949 (MICH) and *12916* in 1952 (MICH). MEXICO: Nevado de Toluca, Ojos de Agua, on *Pinus* sp., *Balls B4086* in 1938 (BM, K, UC, US); Telapón Peak N of Río Frío, on *Pinus* sp., *Miranda 114* in 1940 (MEXU) and on *P. hartwegii, Beaman 2441* in 1958 (UC); Ixtacchiuatl, on *Pinus* sp., *Purpus 3836* in 1905 (POM); Río Frío, on *Pinus* sp., *Hartley FP 89795* in 1947 (FPF); 6 mi. W of Río Frío on Rte. 190, on *P. montezumae, H & W 370** in 1963 (COLO, FPF). NAYARIT: Sierra Madre, near Santa Teresa, on *Pinus* sp., *Rose 3460* in 1897 (US). NUEVO LEON: Cerro Linadero, on *Pinus* sp., *Meyer & Rogers 2932* in 1948 (MO); 15 mi. SW of Galeana, on *Pinus* sp., *Mueller & Mueller 1013* in 1934 (F, MEXU, MICH); Galeana, Hacienda Pablilio, on *Pinus* sp., *Taylor 182* in 1936 (ARIZ, F, MEXU, MICH, RSA); Pablilio, 15 mi. S of Galeana, on *Pinus ponderosa* var. *arizonica, Griffiths* in 1966 (FPF). Cerro Potosí: on *P. rudis, Andresen & Steinhoff A2050* in 1963 (FPF); 2 mi. from village "18 de Marzo" on rd. to Relay Tower, on *P. ponderosa* var. *arizonica, H & W 391** in 1963 (COLO, FPF); 10 mi. from village "18 de Marzo" on rd. to Relay Tower, on *P. ponderosa* var. *arizonica, H & W 393* in 1963 (COLO, FPF); near Relay Tower, on *P. rudis, H & W 397** in 1963 (COLO, FPF) and on *P. culminicola, H & W 398* in 1963 (COLO, FPF). OAXACA: 1 mi. N of Suchixtepec, on *P. lawsonii, Peterson 68–106* in 1968 (FPF). SINALOA: Sierra Surutato, Municipio de Badiraguato, 3 mi. SE of Los Ornos, on *Pinus herrerai, Breedlove & Thorne 18535* in 1970 (CAS). TAMAULIPAS: Rte. to Peña Nevada out of Hermosa, on *Pinus* sp., *Standord, Tauber & Taylor 2495* in 1949 (DS, UC, WTU). PUEBLA: 1.7 mi. E of Paso de Cortez, between Popocatepetl and Ixtacchiuatl, on *P. hartwegii, H & W 374** in 1963 (COLO, FPF). VERACRUZ: Cofre de Perote, 6 mi. SE of Perote, on *P. montezumae, H & W 378** in 1963 (COLO, FPF) and 5 mi. SE of Perote, on *P. montezumae, H & W 380* in 1963 (COLO, FPF). ZACATECAS: Sierra Madre, on *Pinus* sp., *Rose 3535* in 1897 (US).

23b. *ARCEUTHOBIUM VAGINATUM*
subsp. *CRYPTOPODUM*

Specimens Examined: on *Pinus ponderosa* var. *scopulorum* except as noted.

MEXICO

CHIHUAHUA: 5 mi. S of Garcia on El Largo rd., on *P. ponderosa* var. *arizonica, H & W 461** in 1963 (COLO, FPF); 17 mi. N of El Largo on García rd., *H & W 462* in 1963 (COLO, FPF); 9 mi. N of El Largo on García rd., on *P. engelmannii, H & W 464* in 1963 (COLO, FPF); 16 mi. W of Mesa Huracán, on Chico rd., on *P. engelmannii, H & W 471* in

1963 (COLO, FPF): 13 mi. SE of Mesa Huracán on Chico rd., *H & W 476* in 1963 (COLO, FPF): 5 mi. W of Las Varas on Mesa Huracán rd., on *P. engelmannii, H & W 479* in 1963 (COLO, FPF); 18 mi. S of Las Varas on Madera rd., *H & W 480** in 1963 (COLO, FPF); 45 mi. SW of Matachic on Ocampo rd., on *P. ponderosa* var. *arizonica, H & W 485* in 1963 (COLO, FPF); 66 mi. SW of Matachic on Ocampo rd., on *P. ponderosa* var. *arizonica, H & W 492* in 1963 (COLO, FPF). COAHUILA: Sierra del Carmen: 1 mi. W of Ocampo, *H, L & Munoz 1023**, on *P. ponderosa* var. *arizonica* in 1967 (FPF) and *1024* on *P. arizonica* var. *stormiae* in 1967 (FPF); 6 mi. W of Ocampo, on *P. ponderosa* var. *arizonica, H, L & Muñoz 1026* in 1967 (FPF). Sierra del Pino, on *P. ponderosa* var. *arizonica, Johnston & Mueller 591* in 1940 (GH). SONORA: 2.7 mi. N of La Mesa, on *P. engelmannii, Tucker 2563* in 1952 (ARIZ, UC).

UNITED STATES

ARIZONA

APACHE CO.: 6 mi. W of Window Rock, *H & L 188* in 1962 (FPF); 4 mi. S of Eagar, *H & L 211* in 1962 (FPF); 2 mi. E of Big Lake, *H 821* in 1965 (FPF); Lukachuikai Mtns., *Goodman & Payson 2927* in 1936 (WTU); Fort Apache Res., 5 mi. NE of Maverick, *H & L 901* in 1966 (FPF); Fort Apache Res., 14 mi. W of Maverick on Fort Apache rd., *H & L 903* in 1966 (FPF); 8 mi. E of McNary on Rte. 73, *H & L 923* in 1966 (FPF). Navajo Res., 6 mi. NW of Sawmill, *L & Weiss 66–44* in 1966 (FPF); 6 mi. E of Lukachuikai on Red Rock rd., *L & Weiss 66–49* in 1966 (FPF); 11 mi. SW of Red Rock on Lukachukai rd., *L & Weiss 66–51* in 1966 (FPF). COCHISE CO.: Chiricahua Mtns., *Burrall 55* in 1908 (FPF) and *Raue 50* in 1956 (ARIZ): Rustler Park, *Gill FP 68047* in 1935 (FPF); 1 mi. S of Rustler Park, *H 808* in 1965 (FPF); Onion Saddle, on *P. ponderosa* var. *arizonica, H & L 154* in 1962 (FPF) and on *P. engelmannii, H & L 155* in 1962 (FPF); Barfoot Peak on *P. ponderosa* var. *arizonica, Blumer 1452* in 1906 (ARIZ, FPF, ILL, RM, US); Rustler, on *P. ponderosa* var. *arizonica, Ferris 9953* in 1940 (DS, RM, RSA, UC, WTU); Gulching rd., on *P. engelmannii, Blumer 1557* in 1907 (ARIZ, FPF, ILL, RM, US, K); 10 mi. W of Portal, on *P. engelmannii, Gill FP 68038* in 1936 (FPF). Huachuca Mtns.: Carr Can., *Gill, Ellis & Sowell FP 89498* in 1939 (FPF) and *Goodding FP 33285** in 1919 (FPF); head of Carr Can., on *P. ponderosa* var. *arizonica, Gill, Ellis & Sowell FP 89499* in 1939 (FPF); Miller Can., *Goodding* in 1909 (ARIZ); head of Ramsey Can., *Doherty FP 15240* in 1914 (FPF, ILL); 1.5 mi. W of Reef, on *P. ponderosa* var. *arizonica, H & L 233* in 1962 (FPF). COCONINO CO.: Jacob Lake, *Reed & Barkley*

4381 in 1939 (POM); Flagstaff, *MacDougal 23* in 1898 (ARIZ, RM, UC); 15 mi. S of Williams, *Gill FP 68252* in 1932 (FPF); Williams, *Hedgcock & Bethel FP 24413* in 1917 (FPF); 2.5 mi. E of Fort Valley Exp. For., *Gill FP 68249* in 1932 (FPF); Fort Valley Exp. For., *Long FP 19724* in 1915 (FPF); Grand Can., S Rim, Grandview Point, *H & L 185* in 1962 (FPF); 3 mi. N of Weimer Springs, W of Mormon Lake, *H & L 912* in 1966 (FPF); 13 mi. NE of Clints Well on Rte. 65, *H & L 914* in 1966 (FPF); 3 mi. S of Chevlon Ranger Sta., 43 mi. S of Winslow, *H & L 917* in 1966 (FPF); Jacob Lake, *Gill FP 68296* in 1934 (FPF); Dry Park, NW of Kaibab Lodge, *Peterson 64–72** in 1964 (FPF); Kaibab Plateau, *Richards* in 1938 (UC); 4 mi. E of Grandview, Grand Can., *Newlon 856* in 1922 (JEPS); Museum of Northern Arizona, N of Flagstaff, *Heiser 848* in 1944 (WTU); Grand Can., *Toumey 8* in 1893 (UC); 5 mi. E of Woods Can. Lake, *Mason, Mason & Phillips 2422* in *2422a* in 1964 (ARIZ); Oak Cr., *Goodding 17* in 1916 (ARIZ); Observatory Hill, Flagstaff, *Thornber* in 1930 (ARIZ); Hualapai Indian Res., ca. 5 mi. NW of Frazier's Well, *Truesdell* in 1965 (FPF); Coconino Rim rd., 1 mi. SE of Sitgreaves Nat. For. bdy., *L 64–15* in 1964 (FPF) and 0.5 mi. N of Jct. with Payson-Heber rd., *L 64–17* in 1964 (FPF); 16 mi. S of Happy Jack, *L 64–13* in 1964 (FPF). GILA CO.: Pinal Mtns.: Ice House Can., *Kirby & Long FP 18735* in 1914 (FPF) and *Kirby FP 12673* in 1914 (FPF); Bob Tail Ridge, *Gill FP 68295* in 1934 (FPF); 5 mi. above Sulphide del Rey, *Gill & L 63–51* in 1963 (FPF). 21 mi. E of Payson (3 mi. E of Indian Gardens), *L 63–54* in 1963 (FPF); 2 mi. W of Pine, *W 2705* in 1960 (RSA); 17 mi. NE of Young, *L & Lampi 65–16* in 1965 (FPF). Sierra Ancha: Aztec Peak, *Johnson* n.d. (ARIZ); Sierra Ancha Summit, between Roosevelt and Pleasant Valley, *Harrison, Kearney & Peebles 5979* in 1929 (ARIZ, US); Baker Mtn., *Harrison 7868* in 1931 (ARIZ); Sierra Ancha, *Peebles & Smith 13264* in 1937 (ARIZ, US); Sierra Ancha, Workman Cr., *L & Lampi 65–14* in 1965 (FPF). GRAHAM CO.: Graham Mtns.: Pine Crest, *Maguire 12138* in 1935 (RM); 1 mi. above Arcadia Guard Sta., *H & L 140b* in 1962 (FPF) and on *P. ponderosa* var. *arizonica, H & L 140a* in 1962 (FPF); Tripp Can., 8 mi. S of Nat. For. bdy., *H & L 146* in 1962 (FPF); Hospital Flat, *H & L 227* in 1962 (FPF) and *Gill FP 68309* in 1934 (FPF); Columbine, *Shreve 5239* in 1917 (DS); Swift Trail, *Peebles 12981* in 1936 (ARIZ, US). San Carlos Apache Res., Malay Gap, *H & L 1115* in 1968 (FPF). GREENLEE CO.: 3 mi. N of Nat. For. bdy. on US 666 (17 mi. N of Clifton), *H & L 136* in 1962 (FPF); 47 mi. S of Springerville on US 666, *Gill FP 68304* in 1934 (FPF); 10 mi. S of Mogollon Rim on US 666, *L 64–22* in 1964 (FPF). MOHAVE CO.: Hualapai

Mtn. Park, *Gill & Andrews* in 1959 (FPF), *W 3029* in 1962 (COLO), and *H 715* in 1965 (FPF); Hualapai Mtn., *Kearney & Peebles 12724* in 1935 (ARIZ, US). NAVAJO CO.: 1 mi. W of Show Low on Rte. 60, *L 63–45* in 1963 (FPF); 4 mi. E of Rte. 160 on Mogollon Rim rd., *H & L 919* in 1966 (FPF); near Deer Springs, 26 mi. E of Rte. 160 on Mogollon Rim rd., *H & L 921* in 1966 (FPF). PIMA CO.: Santa Catalina Mtns.: *Loran* in 1881 (UC) and *Thornber* in 1930 (ARIZ); Soldier Camp, *Gill FP 68129* and *FP 68251* in 1932 (FPF), and on *P. ponderosa* var. *arizonica, Hedgcock & Long FP 9759* in 1911 (FPF); Summerhaven, *Loomis, Peebles & Harrison 2179* in 1926 (ARIZ) and *H & L 168* in 1962 (FPF); Mt. Lemmon, *Nichol* in 1925 (ARIZ); Palisade Ranger Sta., *H & L 172* in 1962 (FPF) and on *P. ponderosa* var. *arizonica, H & L 171* in 1962 (FPF); Mt. Lemmon Ski Lodge, *H & L 169* in 1962 (FPF); Summit of Marshall Can., *Gill FP 68131* in 1932 (FPF); 1 mi. S of Rose Lake Jct., on *P. ponderosa* var. *arizonica, H & L 165* in 1962 (FPF); Sabino Can., on *P. ponderosa* var. *arizonica, Hedgcock & Long FP 9781* in 1911 (FPF, ILL). Rincon Mtns., Mt. Oeboa, on *P. ponderosa* var. *arizonica, Blumer 3563* in 1909 (ARIZ, DS, FPF, ILL); Mica Mt., on *P. ponderosa* var. *arizonica, Ela* in 1968 (FPF). SANTA CRUZ CO.: Santa Rita Mtns., Mt. Wrightson trail: 4 mi. from end of rd., *H 795* in 1965 (FPF); 1.5 mi. from end of rd., on *P. ponderosa* var. *arizonica, H 797* in 1965 (FPF). YAVAPAI CO.: Groom Cr., *H & L 177* in 1962 (FPF) and *Taylor FP 18641* in 1914 (FPF); Mingus Mtn., ca. 2 mi. S of US 89A, *H & L 243* in 1962 (FPF); Beaver Cr. Ranger Sta. *Drake FP 15119* in 1914 (FPF); Crown King, *Ancona & Long 12829* in 1914 (FPF); Horsethief Basin, 7 mi. S of Crown King, *H & Laut 1180* in 1969 (FPF); Prescott, *Hedgcock FP 4856* in 1910 (FPF, ILL); near Prescott, *Hedgcock FP 4854* and *FP 4855* in 1910 (FPF); Copper Basin, *Toumey 292* in 1892 (ARIZ); Santa Maria Mtns., 5 air mi. WNW of Camp Wood, *H & Laut 1179* in 1969 (FPF).

COLORADO

ARCHULETA CO.: Pagosa Springs, *Bethel* in 1897 (CS) and *Smith* in 1894 (PH); 20 mi. S of Pagosa Springs on US 84, *H & L 1051* in 1967 (FPF); S of Pagosa Springs, *Hedgcock & Bethel FP 24656* in 1917 (FPF); 10 mi. W of Pagosa Springs, *Hinds 63–5* in 1963 (FPF). BOULDER CO.: Sugarloaf Mtn., *Ramaley & Robbins 1784* in 1906 (COLO, RM); between Sunset and Ward, *Tweedy 4973* in 1902 (RM); Mt. Alto, *Ramaley 824* in 1901 (COLO, RM); S Boulder Peak, *Ewan 12721* in 1941 (COLO); Tucker's Meadow, *Wolcott* n.d. (COLO); Lyons, *Thomson FP 26558* in 1917 (FPF); SW of Boulder, *Hedgcock FP 22571* in 1916 (FPF, UC); 1 mi. E of Rte. 160 on Left Hand Can. rd., *H 203* in 1962 (FPF) and on *P. contorta* subsp. *latifolia, H 204* in 1962 (FPF); Boulder, *Hedgcock, Thompson & Gayman FP 24755* in 1917 (FPF); near Boulder, *W 2802* in 1961 (COLO); between Nederland and Rollinsville, *Jones 23161* in 1962 (ILL); 5 mi. N of Nederland on Rte. 160, on *P. flexilis, H 202* in 1958 (FPF); Ridge S of Left Hand Can., 2 mi. SE of Ward, on *Pinus flexilis, Sprakling & Plumb* in 1966 (FPF). CLEAR CREEK CO.: Mill Cr., Brookvale, *Churchill* in 1918 (RM); 0.5 mi. S of divide between Idaho Springs and Central City, *H & Staley 280* in 1962 (FPF); Empire, *Weir 6163* in 1918 (ILL); Hamlin Gulch rd., 1.4 mi. from Fall River rd., 7 air mi. NW of Idaho Springs, *H 1056* in 1967 (FPF). CONEJOS CO.: River Springs Ranger Sta., ca. 15 mi. W of Antonito, *Hinds 63–3* in 1963 (FPF); 3.1 mi. W of Nat. For. bdy. on Rte. 17, *L 63–1* in 1963 (FPF). COSTILLA CO.: Costilla Estate at New Mexico bdy., *Edmonston FP 1511* in 1908 (FPF). CUSTER CO.: Greenwood, *Edmonston FP 561* in 1909 (FPF); Alvarado Campground, 9 mi. SW of Westcliffe, *H 433* in 1963 (FPF); 4.5 mi. W of Hillside, *H 435* in 1963 (FPF); 3.5 mi. W of Hillside on Spruce Cr. rd., on *P. contorta* subsp. *latifolia, H 436* in 1963 (FPF); Westcliffe, Clay Ranger Sta., *Hedgcock, Thompson & Johnson FP 24828* in 1917 (FPF). DENVER CO.: Denver, Case Golf Course, *H & Stewart 832* in 1965 (FPF). DOLORES CO.: Doe Springs rd., T. 40 N, R. 17 W, Sec. 25, [12 mi. ESE of Dove Cr.], *Hinds 63–11* in 1963 (FPF). DOUGLAS CO.: 1.5 mi. E of Franktown on Rte. 86, *H 544* in 1963 (FPF); Missouri Ridge rd., Manitou Exp. For., *H 257* in 1962 (FPF). ELBERT CO.: 5.5 mi. S of Elbert on Rte. 157, *H 420* in 1963 (FPF); 6 mi. W of Kiowa on Rte. 86, *H 543* in 1963 (FPF). EL PASO CO.: Cheyenne Can., *Christ 1864* in 1935 (CS); Colorado Springs, *Jones 801* in 1878 (ARIZ, POM, RM); 14.5 mi. E of Monument, *H 419* in 1963 (FPF); 1.5 mi. E of Monument, *H 542* in 1963 (FPF), 1.7 mi. from Cascade on Pikes Peak rd., *H & Hinds 426* in 1963 (FPF); Bruin Inn, N Cheyenne Can., *H 539** in 1963 (FPF); Colorado Springs, *Saunders* in 1893 (RM); Pikes Peak, Halfway, *Hedgcock FP 903* in 1909 (FPF); Mt. Manitou, *Gill FP 68247* in 1932 (FPF); Palmer Park, Austin Bluff, *Gill FP 68248* in 1932 (FPF); NE of Manitou, *Hedgcock FP 22710* and *FP 22711* in 1916 (FPF); 5 mi. W of Monument, *W 2983* in 1962 (COLO, FPF). Monument; *Hedgcock FP 670* in 1909 (FPF), *Hartley FP 1613* in 1909 (FPF), *Hedgcock & Pierce FP 15951* in 1914 (FPF, ILL, RSA, UC, WTU), *Hedgcock FP 22550* in 1916 (FPF, UC), and *Hedgcock FP 24909* in 1917 (FPF). Fremont Exp. For. [2 mi. W of Manitou Springs], *Hedgcock FP 9174* and *FP 9175* in 1911 (FPF) and *FP 22704* and *FP 22705* in 1916 (FPF); Palmer Lake, *Hedgcock FP*

15898 in 1914 (FPF, UC), *Hedgcock, Thompson & Gayman FP 24902* in 1917 (FPF), and *Gill FP 68244* in 1932 (FPF). FREMONT CO.: "Canyon City," Sierra Majada, *Brandegee 11295* in 1877 (FPF, ILL). GILPIN CO.: Rollinsville, *Hedgcock FP 22599* in 1916 (FPF). HINSDALE CO.: Piedra River, T. 37 N, R. 3 W, Sec. 14, ca. 15 air mi. NW of Pagosa Springs, *Peterson 19–61* in 1961 (FPF). HUERFANO CO.: 10 mi. N of Gardner on Ophir Cr. rd., *H 431* in 1963 (FPF); La Veta, *Hedgcock & Thompson FP 24809* in 1917 (FPF). JEFFERSON CO.: Gunbarrel Cr., *Hill FP 68278* in 1932 (FPF); 10 mi. W of Deckers, *H 421* in 1963 (FPF); 8 mi. SW of Morrison on US 285, *H 453* in 1963 (FPF); Buffalo Cr., *Hill FP 68277* in 1932 (FPF); near Golden, *Weir 8958* in 1918 (ILL). LA PLATA CO.: Tacoma Power Plant, on *Pinus flexilis, Loughridge 273* in 1934 (CS); W of Trimble, *Hedgcock & Bethel FP 24688* in 1917 (FPF, UC); 10 mi. W of Durango on US 160, *H & Scharpf 690* in 1964 (FPF). LARIMER CO.: Estes Park, *Cooper 243* in 1904 (ARIZ, RM); Prospect Mtn. near Estes Park, *Maize* in 1966 (FPF); "Ft. Collins," *Buffum 5690* in 1896 (RM); "Mountains of Larimer Co.," *Crandal* in 1889 (RM); 4 mi. SW of Log Cabin, *H 200* in 1960 (FPF); Rist Can. Picnic Ground, *H 201* in 1961 (FPF); near Cherokee Park (lat. 40° 53′N-, northern limit?), *H 262* in 1962 (FPF); Poudre River 4 mi. E of Rustic, *H 410* in 1963 (FPF); Stove Prairie Hill, col.? *Plants of Colo. 2274* in 1896 (RM); Skyland Ranch, Rocky Mtn. Nat. Park, *Nelson 3205* in 1938 (RM); Rist Can., *Cameron, Pl. Colo. 2279* in 1897 (CS); Brinwood, Stove Prairie, col.? *Pl. Colo. 2277* in 1898 (FPF); 1 mi. SW of Glen Haven, *H & Staley 287* in 1962 (FPF); Assoc. Camp, Rocky Mtn. Park, *Case FP 38702* in 1922 (FPF); Rattlesnake (Pinewood) Park, *H 87* in 1961 (FPF); Rist Can., 7.2 mi. W of La Porte, *H 552* in 1964 (FPF); Rist Can., near Picnic Ground, on *P. contorta* subsp. *latifolia, H 199* in 1961 (FPF); Stove Prairie Hill, Pennock, on *P. contorta* subsp. *latifolia, Pl. Colo. 899* in 1892 (CS); 1 mi. E of Pennock Pass, on *P. contorta* subsp. *latifolia, H, Hinds & Staley 281* in 1962 (FPF) and *H 560* in 1964 (FPF); N of Stratton Park, 13 mi. WNW of Fort Collins, on *P. contorta* subsp. *latifolia, H 709* in 1962 (FPF); Bear Gulch, 5 mi. W of Masonville, on *P. contorta* subsp. *latifolia, H 710* in 1964 (FPF). LAS ANIMAS CO.: Mesa de Maya, Green Can. *Rogers 6089* in 1948 (COLO, US); Stonewall Gap, *Hedgcock & Johnson FP 24944* in 1917 (FPF); Monument Park, *H 1096* in 1968 (FPF). MESA CO.: Sawmill Mesa rd., 20 mi. SW of Delta, *Hinds 63–19* in 1963 (FPF). MONTEZUMA CO.: Water Can., T. 38 N, R. 13 W, Sec. 30, ca. 10 mi. N of Mancos, *Hinds 63–8* in 1963 (FPF). MONTROSE CO.: 10 mi. W of Paradox, *Harrington 4392* in 1949 (CS); Hanks Valley rd.,

T. 46 N, R. 11 W, Sec. 18, ca. 10 mi. NE of Norwood, *Hinds 63–16* in 1963 (FPF). PARK CO.: 1.5 mi. NW of Bailey, *H 282* in 1962 (FPF); 1.7 mi. S of 11 Mi. Reservoir rd. on Blue Mtn. rd., near Lake George, *H 424** in 1963 (FPF). PUEBLO CO.: 5 mi. W of Rye on Rte. 165, *H 427* in 1963 (FPF). SAGUACHE CO.: Spanish Cr., near N Cochetopa Pass, *H 438* in 1963 (FPF); E of North Cochetopa Pass, on *P. contorta* subsp. *latifolia, H 437* in 1963 (FPF) and on *P. aristata, H 439* in 1963 (FPF). SAN MIGUEL CO.: Iron Springs Mesa [7 mi. NW of Placerville], *Payson FP 26022* in 1917 (FPF). TELLER CO.: Florissant, *Ramaley 1333* in 1905 (RM); 6.2 mi. S of Divide on Rte. 67, *H & Hinds 423* in 1963 (FPF) and on *P. aristata, H & Hinds 422* in 1963 (FPF); Elklum (Elkton?), *Hedgcock & Johnston FP 26406* in 1917 (FPF); Woodland Park, *Gill FP 68138* and *FP 68246* in 1932 (FPF). COUNTY UNCERTAIN: Uncompahgre Divide, *Payson 396* in 1914 (COLO, RM); Trinchera Estate, E side San Luis Valley, *Edmonston FP 175* in 1908 (FPF); Rocky Ford, *Pool FP 20552* in 1912 (FPF).

NEW MEXICO

BERNALILLO CO.: Manzano Mtns.: 12 mi. S of US 66 on Rte. 10, *H 21* in 1954 (FPF). Sandia Mtns., Doc Long Campground, *Gill & Long FP 68250* and *FP 68258* in 1932 (FPF) and *Muenscher & Muenscher 14562* in 1939 (MO, UC, WTU). CATRON CO.: Datil Mtns., White House Can., 10.5 mi. NW of Datil on US 60, *H & L 1116* in 1968 (FPF); 1 mi. E of Mogollon, *H & L 132* in 1962 (FPF); 7 mi. E of Mogollon, *H & L 221* in 1962 (FPF); Mogollon Cr., *Woodrow & Long FP 18399* in 1914 (FPF); Mangas Mtn., *H & Scharpf 698* in 1964 (FPF); Tularosa Summit, 11.5 mi. N of Rte. 78 on Apache Springs rd., *L 65–42* in 1965 (FPF); 5 mi. E of Beaverhead Ranger Sta. on Rte. 59, *H & L 893* in 1966 (FPF); Can. Cr. Mtns., 12 air mi. W of Beaverhead Ranger Sta., *H & L 895* in 1966 (FPF); 1.5 mi. E of Rte. 78 on Loco Mtn. rd., *H & L 896* in 1966 (FPF); 1 mi. E of Fox Mtn., 20 mi. N of Apache Cr., *H & L 930* in 1966 (FPF). COLFAX CO.: 1 mi. E of Taos Co. line on US 64, *L 65–22* in 1965 (FPF). DONA ANA CO.: Organ Mtns., Fillmore Can., *Wooton* in 1903 (FPF). EDDY CO.: Guadalupe Mtns.: *Johnson FP 18638* in 1914 (FPF); Dark Can., *H & L 113** in 1962 (FPF). GRANT CO.: W side Emory Pass, *H & L 119* in 1962 (FPF); 1 mi. NW of Redstone, *H & L 126* in 1962 (FPF); Silver City, *Gaetz FP 182* in 1908 (FPF); N of Pinos Altos, *Hedgcock FP 813* in 1909 (FPF); 20 mi. N of Mimbres on Rte. 61, *L 65–37* in 1965 (FPF); Burro Mtns., near summit of Jack's Peak, *H & L 1103* in 1968 (FPF); Redstone Cr., on *P. ponderosa* var. *arizonica, Gill FP 68308* in 1934 (FPF); Snow cabin rd., 4 mi. W of Rte. 25, on *P. ponderosa* var. *arizonica*, *H & L 890* in 1966 (FPF). LINCOLN CO.: Ruidoso, *Fisher & Steyermark 38183* in 1938 (RM); Capitan Mtns., Capitan Gap, *H & L 104*** and *108* in 1962 (FPF); Capitan Mtns., west Capitan Peak, *L 66–21* in 1966 (FPF); Capitan Mtns., T. 7 S, R. 16 E, *Parks & Long FP 18383* in 1914 (FPF) and *Parks FP 18385* in 1914 (FPF); Capitan Mtns., E slope of Capitan Peak at Pine Lodge, *Martin 883* in 1945 (WTU); Gallinas Peak, 10 mi. W of Corona, *L & Riffle 63–42* in 1963 (FPF); White Mtns., Valley of Carrizo, *Wickens 2403* in 1932 (PH); S side of Capitan Mtns., 15 mi. E of Lincoln, *H & Scharpf 695* in 1964 (FPF); Jicarilla Mtns., 7 mi. SE of Ancho on White Oaks rd., *L 64–31* in 1964 (FPF); Tucson Mtn., NW of Capitan, *L 64–32* in 1964 (FPF). LOS ALAMOS CO.: Bandelier Nat. Mon., *L 65–55* in 1965 (FPF). MCKINLEY CO.: 2 mi. W of McGaffey, *L 63–37* in 1963 (FPF). MORA CO.: 17 mi. N of Mora on Rte. 38, *L 65–53* in 1965 (FPF). OTERO CO.: Avis, *Wyman FP 12815* in 1914 (FPF); Sierra Blanca Peak, *Wolf 2880* in 1928 (DS, RSA); Sacramento Mtns., James Can., *Wickens 2199* in 1932 (PH); Cloudcroft, *H & W 454* in 1963 (FPF). Mescalero Apache Res.: Carrizo, *H & L 103* in 1962 (FPF); Paul's Can., *H 24* in 1954 (FPF) Goat Can., *H FP 98511* in 1952 (FPF); above Ruidoso, *Hinckley* in 1963 (ARIZ); Whitetail area, on *P. strobiformis*, *L 64–2* in 1964 (FPF). 13 mi. SE of Cloudcroft on Rte. 23, *H & L 879* in 1966 (FPF), Tall Pines Camp, 2 mi. NW of Weed, *H & L 884* in 1966 (FPF), Upper Penasco Can., 13 mi. S of Cloudcroft, *H & L 885* in 1966 (FPF). RIO ARRIBA CO.: Chama, *Hedgcock & Bethel FP 29454* in 1917 (FPF); 12 mi. NW of Jct. of Lagunitas rd. and Rte. 285, *L 63–13a* in 1963 (FPF); 24 mi. E of Canjilon, *L 63–9* in 1963 (FPF); 2 mi. S of Tierra Amarilla, *L 63–4* in 1963 (FPF); 3 mi. SW of Tres Piedras, *L 63–25* in 1963 (FPF); 2.3 mi. N of Gallina, *L 63–21* in 1963 (FPF); 2 mi. W of Tres Piedras, *W 2986* in 1962 (COLO, FPF); 1 mi. N of S Jicarilla Res. bdy. on Rte. 95, *L 64–7* in 1964 (FPF); 18 mi. E of co. bdy. and 12 mi. S of Rte. 17, *L 64–8* in 1964 (FPF). SAN JUAN CO.: Chuska Mtns., 6 mi. SW of Sheep Springs, *L & Weiss 66–42* in 1966 (FPF). SAN MIGUEL CO.: Windsor's Ranch, Pecos Nat. For. *Standley 4173* in 1908 (FPF); Glorieta Mesa, 3.5 mi. S of Rowe, *H 1097* in 1968 (FPF). SANTA FE CO.: Sante Fe, *Hedgcock & Bethel FP 24712* in 1917 (FPF, ILL, UC); Borrega area E of Espanola, *L 63–27* in 1963 (FPF); Cañoncito, *Brandegee* in 1879 (UC); Can. 4 mi. E of Santa Fe, *Heller 3608* in 1897 (ARIZ, Z); near Santa Fe, *W 2988* in 1962 (COLO). SIERRA CO.: Kingston, *Metcalfe 964* in 1904 (FPF, POM, UC); near Boiler Peak on Rte. 59, 15 mi. E of Beaverhead Ranger Sta., *H & L 894* in 1966 (FPF). SOCORRO CO.: Magdalena Mtns.,

Mouth of Hop Can., *Diehl 878* in 1903 (POM); San Mateo Mtns.: N side of San Juan Peak, *L 65–32* in 1965 (FPF) and 11.5 mi. S of US 60 on Rte. 52, *L 65–35* in 1965 (FPF). TAOS CO.: 4 mi. E of Questa on Rte. 38, *L 65–47* in 1965 (FPF); 10 mi. S of Rancho de Taos on Rte. 3, *H 877* in 1966 (FPF). TORRANCE CO.: 5 mi. N of Tajique, *L & Riffle 63–56* in 1963 (FPF). VALENCIA CO.: Ojo Redondo, T. 11 N, R. 12 W, *L 63–38* in 1963 (FPF); S of San Mateo, Mt. Taylor, *L 63–32* in 1963 (FPF); 14 mi. E of Grants on rd. to La Mosca Lookout, *L 65–51* in 1965 (FPF). COUNTY UNCERTAIN: Front Cr. Basin, Gila Nat. For., *Hedgcock & Long FP 9835* in 1911 (FPF); Gila Nat. For., *Munro FP 15114* in 1914 (FPF).

TEXAS

CULBERSON CO.: Guadalupe Mtns.: *Johnston 3185* in 1958 (SRSC); Ridge above McKittrick Can., *Moore & Steyermark 3470* in 1931 (DS, PH, UC, US); the Bowl, *Warnock & McVaugh 5452* in 1947 (SRSC); above Frijole, *McVaugh 8156* in 1947 (DS, SRSC). JEFF DAVIS CO.: Davis Mtns.: Upper Madera Can., *Palmer 33429* in 1928 (PH); Mt. Livermore, *Hinckley* in 1937 (ARIZ), SR), *Hinckley 2650* in 1943 (SRSC) and *Warnock* in 1936 (SRSC); N slope of Mt. Livermore, *H, L & Lampi 1046*** in 1967 (FPF).

UTAH

GARFIELD CO.: Bryce Can. Nat. Park: Bryce Point, *W 3035* in 1962 (COLO, FPF) and Mistletoe Ridge, *Buchanan 99* in 1956 (ARIZ). Ruby's Inn, *Harris C2912813* in 1929 (UC); Aquarius Plateau, *Vickery 616* in 1960 (RSA, UT); 20 mi. N of Boulder on Rte. 117, *H 684* in 1964 (FPF). KANE CO.: N of Navajo Lake, *Peterson 49–61* in 1961 (FPF); 8 mi. S of Navajo Lake on Zion rd., *W 4123* in 1966 (FPF, UT). SAN JUAN CO.: Elk Mtns.: *Rydberg & Garrett 9328* in 1911 (RM, US); Elk Ridge, 2 mi. E of Kigalia Guard Sta., *Peterson 65–74* in 1965 (FPF). La Sal Mtns., Pine Ridge near Rte. 46, *Peterson 65–83* in 1965 (FPF). Abajo Mtns., S side of Abajo Mtn., *Krebill 235* in 1964 (FPF). SEVIER CO.: Wildcat Knolls, W of Emery, *Peterson 64–96*** in 1964 (FPF); Emery, *Williams* in 1918 (FPF, ILL). WAYNE CO.: Near Grover, *Peterson 64–93*** in 1964 (FPF); Wayne Wonderland, *Milner 7250a* in 1935 (UT). COUNTY UNCERTAIN: La Sal Mtns., *Stithem* in 1960 (FPF); Muddy Watershed, Manti Nat. For., *Korstian* in 1918 (FPF, ILL, WTU).

23c. ARCEUTHOBIUM VAGINATUM
subsp. DURANGENSE

Specimens Examined:

MEXICO

DURANGO: 36 mi. W of El Salto on Rte. 40, on *Pinus durangensis*, *H & W 353** and *527** in 1963 (COLO, FPF); 45 mi. W of El Salto on Rte. 40, on *P. montezumae*, *H & W 354** in 1963 (COLO, FPF) and *H & W 1237* in 1969 (FPF). Km. 1148, 50 mi. E of Rte. 15 on Rte. 40, on *P. herrerai*, *H & W 1249* in 1969 (FPF). SINALOA: Km. 1179, 46 mi. E of Rte. 15 on Rte. 40, on *P. montezumae*, *H & W 1234* in 1969 (FPF).

24. ARCEUTHOBIUM VERTICILLIFLORUM

Specimens Examined:

MEXICO

DURANGO: 36 mi. E of El Salto on Rte. 40, on *P. engelmannii*, *H & W 331** and *517** in 1963 (COLO, FPF) and *1241* in 1969 (FPF); 24 mi. E of El Salto on Rte. 40, on *P. engelmannii*, *H & W 341** in 1963 (COLO, FPF); 7 mi. E of El Salto on Rte. 40, on *P. cooperi*, *H & W 342** in 1962 (COLO, FPF).

Old World Taxa

25. ARCEUTHOBIUM CHINENSE

Specimens Examined:

CHINA

YUNNAN: W of von Fumin, vicinity of Yanggai and Dsolin-ho, on *Keteleeria davidiana*, *Handel-Mazzetti 4999* in 1914 (US); around Hoji between Hoching and Sunygueh, on *Keteleeria* sp., *Schneider 2951* in 1914 (K, US); West flank of Tali Range, Lat. 25° 40′ N, on "conifers," *Forrest 15557* in 1917 (K). SZECHWAN: vicinity of Huei-li Hsien, on *Keteleeria* sp., *Yü 1558* in 1932 (GH).

26. ARCEUTHOBIUM MINUTISSIMUM

Specimens Examined: All on *Pinus griffithii*.

WEST PAKISTAN

SWAT: 25 mi. above Bahrein, E of Kalam, *Rodin 5695* in 1952 (K, UC, US); 4 mi. W of Utrot, Kalam Agency, *Thatcher* in 1962 (FPF); above Utrot, *Stewart & Rahman 25213* in 1953 (BM).

KASHMIR

Nanga Parbat, near Rama, *Webster & Nasir 6471* in 1955 (K, US); Baltal, *Stewart 7549* in 1922 (K, PH); Pahalagon, *Singh* in 1965 (FPF); Sonamarg, *Stewart* in 1921 (MO); Baltal to Sonamarg, *Stewart 21297* in 1940 (US); Kishenganga Valley, W. Gurais, col? in 1892 (BM, K); Gurais Valley, *Duthie 14182* in 1893 (BM); Sonamarg in Sind Valley, *Duthie 14181* in 1892 (K); Kali River, Nabi, *Duthie 24933* in 1900 (K); Guohai Valley, Astor District, *Duthie 12292* in 1892 (K); 0.5 mi. S of Sonamarg, 59 mi. NE of Srinigar, *W & W 4358* in 1968 (FPF, UT); 0.5 mi. above Tangmarg, 24 mi. W of Srinigar, *W & W 4359* in 1968 (FPF, UT); above Sumblili, *Duthie 11204* in 1892 (K).

INDIA

HIMACHAL PRADESH: Sangla-Rupin rd., *Parker* in 1928 (UC). UTTAR PRADESH: Gangotri, *Dudgeon & Kenoyer 132–2–1* in 1920 (PH). PRADESH UNCERTAIN: Gangrinini, *Dudgeon & Kenoyer 561* in 1920 (MO).

NEPAL

Nampa Gadh, Western Nepal, *Duthie 5947* in 1886 (BM, K); Kali Valley near Kangua, Western Nepal, *Duthie 3359* in 1886 (BM, K); Near Tinkar, *Parker 2085* in 1923 (K).

27. ARCEUTHOBIUM OXYCEDRI

No specimens are cited for this taxon because (1) it is poorly represented in North American herbaria and (2) its distribution is fairly well known (see p. 169).

28. ARCEUTHOBIUM PINI

Specimens Examined:

CHINA

YUNNAN: E flank of Lichiang Range, Lat. 27° 30′ N, on *Pinus*, *Forrest 6672* in 1900 (K); Mekong-Salwin divide; Lat. 28° 12′ N, on *Pinus*, *Forrest 14194* in 1917 (K). SZECHWAN: Between Molien and Tialou beyond des Yalung, on *Pinus tabulae-formis*, *Handel-Mazzetti 2629* in 1914 (US). TIBET. SE Tibet: Kongbo Prov. Charko-Lilung, Valley of Lilung Chu, Lat. 29° 08′ N, Long. 93° 54′ E, on *Pinus* sp., *Ludlow, Sherriff* and *Taylor 4465* in 1938 (BM); Tongyuk, on *Pinus* sp., *Kingdon-Ward 12089* in 1935 (BM).

The first number is the collector's number for the specimen followed by the taxon number (1 through 28) in parentheses indicating our determination of it.

Darrow, Phillips & Pultz *1173*(17).

Davidson & Gill *FP 89991*(3).

Davy *7064*(18).

Detting *4255*(8).

Diehl *878*(23b).

Doherty *FP 15240*(23b).

Drake *FP 15119*(23b), *FP 15122*(11).

Dudgeon & Kenoyer *561*(26), *132-2-1*(26).

Dudley *758*(8), *1395*(1b), *1978*(8).

Dudley & Lamb *4411*(18).

Duncan *90*(18).

Duthie *3359*(26), *5947*(26), *11204*(26), *12292*(26), *14181*(26), *14182*(26), *24933*(26).

Eastwood *12138*(8), *18836*(18).

Eaton *443*(19).

Edmonston *FP 51*(3), *FP 175*(23b), *FP 188*(3), *FP 199*(3), *FP 295*(11), *FP 561*(23b), *FP 1511*(23b).

Eggelston *1561*(19), *1562*(19), *7459*(3), *9718*(8), *10599*(3).

Ehlers *1120*(19), *5144*(19), *6127*(19).

Ekman *1313*(5), *12024*(5).

Ellis *FP 89331*(10), *FP 89337*(10), *FP 89411*(10), *FP 89426*(10), *FP 89430*(17), *FP 89431*(4), *FP 89502*(10) *FP 89503*(10), *FP 89504*(11).

Ellis & Gill *FP 89500*(12a).

Ellis, Hackleman & Gill *FP 89491*(11).

Elmer *1246*(8), *4031*(18).

Englerth *FP 91031*(1a).

Erdman *120*(10).

Erlanson *484*(19).

Etheridge *BFDS 26*(13).

Evans *FP 17832*(3), *FP 17843*(3).

Ewan *3564*(7), *9924*(8), *9941*(10), *10110*(7), *10111*(8), *12721*(23b), *15154*(9).

Fassett *2185*(19), *2345*(19), *2527*(19), *3923*(19), *8996*(19), *10093*(19), *13767*(19), *14308*(19), *22395*(19).

Fassett & Sieker *14703*(19).

Fassett, Hoffman & Staffeld *18265*(19).

Faull, Childs & Hansbrough *FP 68266*(22).

Fendler *283*(23b), *312*(10).

Fernald *1741*(19), *23322*(19).

Fernald & Collins *218*(19).

Fernald & Long *13521*(19), *23788*(19).

Fernald & Pease *21041*(19), *21043*(19), *23878*(19), *25031*(19).

Fernald & St. John *10830*(19).

Fernald et al. *1655*(19), *1656*(19), *7327*(19), *21044*(19), *21045*(19).

Ferris *3649*(18), *7828*(1a), *9953*(23b), *10183*(10), *12158*(18).

Ferris & Duthie *422*(8), *467*(3), *857*(8).

Fiker *695*(8).

Fisher & Steyermark *38183*(23b).

Forrest *6672*(28), *10169*(28), *14194*(28), *15557*(25).

Frolich *61*(19).

Frye & Frye *2590*(13).

Fuertes *1923*(5).

Gaetz *FP 182*(23b).

Galbreath *FP 1691*(3).

Garrett *FP 15833*(9), *FP 38106*(9), *FP 38107*(9), *FP 38174*(9).

Gates *11116*(19), *14886*(19).

Gates & Gates *10682*(19).

Gayman *FP 26295*(3), *FP 26521*(11).

Gentry *587 M*(13).

Geyer *577*(8).

Gilbert *112*(17).

Gill *FP 68036*(12a), *FP 68037*(11), *FP 68038*(23b), *FP 68046*(3), *FP 68047*(23b), *FP 68056*(11), *FP 68060*(1a), *FP 68063*(3), *FP 68076*(18), *FP 68078*(18), *FP 68079*(18), *FP 68080*(18), *FP 68087*(8), *FP 68089*(18), *FP 68093*(18), *FP 68097*(8), *FP 68099*(18), *FP 68103*(18), *FP 68127*(11), *FP 68128*(4), *FP 68129*(23b), *FP 68130*(4), *FP 68131*(23b), *FP 68132*(10), *FP 68134*(11), *FP 68138*(23b), *FP 68139*(11), *FP 68140*(3), *FP 68141*(11), *FP 68143*(9), *FP 68144*(9), *FP 68145*(18), *FP 68182*(22), *FP 68183*(22), *FP 68184*(22), *FP 68185*(3), *FP 68186*(1a), *FP 68187*(22), *FP 68188*(22), *FP 68189*(16), *FP 68190*(3), *FP 68191*(8), *FP 68192*(11), *FP 68193*(22), *FP 68195*(22), *FP 68196*(22), *FP 68198*(22), *FP 68200*(3), *FP 68202*(16), *FP 68203*(8), *FP 68205*(3), *FP 68206*(11), *FP 68207*(11), *FP 68208*(19), *FP 68209*(19), *FP 68223*(1b), *FP 68224*(1a), *FP 68227*(3), *FP 68229*(3), *FP 68230*(10), *FP 68232*(10), *FP 68233*(10), *FP 68234*(10), *FP 68235*(9), *FP 68237*(8), *FP 68243*(8), *FP 68244*(23b), *FP 68246*(23b), *FP 68247*(23b), *FP 68248*(23b), *FP 68249*(23b), *FP 68251*(23b), *FP 68252*(23b), *FP 68253*(18), *FP 68255*(18), *FP 68256*(11), *FP 68262*(11), *FP 68263*(11), *FP 68290*(17), *FP 68291*(16), *FP 68295*(23b), *FP 68296*(23b), *FP 68297*(1a), *FP 68298*(17), *FP 68300*(10), *FP 68301*(10), *FP 68302*(17), *FP 68303*(11), *FP 68304*(23b), *FP 68305*(17), *FP 68306*(4), *FP 68307*(11), *FP 68308*(23b), *FP 68309*(23b), *FP 68310*(17), *FP 68313*(19), *FP 89313*(4), *FP 89420*(10), *FP 89984*(3).

Gill & Andrews *FP 87301*(17).

Gill & Ellis *FP 89496*(12a), *FP 89497*(11).

Gill, Ellis & Hackleman *FP 89492*(4), *FP 89490*(4), *FP 89492*(4).

Gill, Ellis & Sowell *FP 89498*(23b), *FP 89499*(23b).

Gill & Hindo *FP 89981*(3).

Gill & Lightle *63-51*(23b).

Gill & Long *FP 68136*(11), *FP 68137*(10), *FP 68250*(23b), *FP 68258*(23b).

Gill & Sargent *FP 68179*(11), *FP 68180*(22), *FP 68181*(1b).

Gill & Wagener *FP 68039*(8), *FP 68040*(8), *FP 68041*(7).

Gill & Warren *FP 68197*(22), *FP 68199*(22).

Gill & Wright *FP 68061*(10), *FP 68064*(10), *FP 68066*(18), *FP 68072*(8), *FP 68160*(7), *FP 68161*(1a), *FP 68162*(8), *FP 68225*(1a), *FP 68238*(10), *FP 68239*(10), *FP 68240*(8).

Gill et al. *FP 68284*(19), *FP 68285*(19).

Gillis *3007*(19).

Glowenke *2468*(19).

Goldman *177*(23a), *184*(12a).

Gonzales *1717*(20).

Goodding *17*(23b), *309*(6), *2088*(11), *FP 26737*(11), *FP 33284*(11), *FP 33285*(23b).

Goodman & Payson *2927*(23b).

Gorman *576*(3), *1753*(9).

Gould *1010*(18).

Grant *1113*(8), *3197*(19).

Green *9*(19).

Greene & Richter *112*(3), *113*(3), *114*(3), *115*(3), *116*(3), *118*(3), *119*(3), *121*(3), *122*(3), *123*(3), *124*(3), *125*(3), *126*(3).

Greeman & Greeman *4650*(3).

Greenman *2492*(19).

Griffith & Morris *803*(8).

Guppy *FP 96959*(18).

Haberer *188*(19).

Hall *6642*(8).

Hall & Babcock *4078*(11).

Hall & Chandler *426*(3).

Hall & Harbour *574*(3).

Handel-Mazzettii *2629*(28), *4999*(25).

Hansbrough *FP 68270*(3).

Hansbrough & Spaulding *FP 68210*(19).

Hansbrough, Mielke & Joy *FP 68273*(8).

Hanson *718*(18).

Hanzlik *FP 68257*(11).

Harger *45859*(19).

Harrington *4392*(23b).

Harris *C 2770B*(11), *C 16354B*(12a), *C 2912813*(23b), *FP 68283*(8).

Harrison *7868*(23b), *11184*(10).

Harrison & Larson *7859*(3).

Harrison, Kearney & Fulton *5979*(23b).

Hartley *3991*(19), *FP 1613*(23b), *FP 1774*(9), *FP 17865*(11), *FP 89795*(23a).

Hartman *340*(13), *364*(12a).

Harvey *FP 4159*(8).

Hawksworth *9*(7), *15*(11), *21*(23b), *23*(11), *24*(23b), *26*(11), *30*(1a), *35*(10), *36*(10), *39*(11), *44*(11), *49*(13), *51*(13), *56*(11), *81*(3), *82*(9), *84*(9), *85*(9), *87*(23b), *89*(3), *189*(3), *190*(3), *191*(3), *192*(3), *193*(3), *196*(9), *199*(23b), *200*(23b), *201*(23b), *203*(23b), *204*(23b), *205*(3), *206*(11), *246*(10), *252*(1a), *253*(17), *254*(1a), *255*(9), *256*(9), *257*(23b), *258*(3), *260*(11), *261*(3), *262*(23b), *263*(3), *264*(3), *265*(3), *266*(3), *267*(3), *268*(3), *269*(3), *270*(3), *271*(3), *272*(3), *273*(3), *274*(3), *275*(3), *276*(3), *277*(9), *278*(3), *282*(23b), *284*(9), *285*(3), *286*(3), *406*(3), *407*(3), *408*(3), *409*(3), *410*(23b), *411*(3), *412*(3), *413*(3), *414*(3), *415*(3), *416*(3), *417*(9), *418*(3), *419*(23b), *420*(23b), *421*(23b), *424*(23b), *427*(23b), *429*(11), *430*(11), *431*(23b), *432*(11), *433*(23b), *434*(11), *435*(23b), *436*(23b), *437*(23b), *438*(23b), *439*(23b), *440*(11), *444*(11), *445*(3), *446*(11), *447*(3), *448*(3), *449*(3), *450*(3), *451*(3), *452*(3), *453*(23b), *538*(11), *539*(23b), *540*(9), *541*(11), *542*(23b), *543*(23b), *544*(23b), *545*(3), *546*(3), *547*(3), *548*(3), *549*(3), *550*(3), *551*(3), *552*(23b), *553*(3), *554*(3), *555*(3), *559*(3), *561*(3), *562*(9), *563*(3), *566*(3), *567*(11), *568*(3), *569*(3), *570*(11), *571*(9), *572*(11), *574*(11), *658*(18), *659*(8), *660*(7), *678*(11), *679*(9), *680*(9), *681*(11), *682*(10), *684*(23b), *685*(11), *686*(11), *687*(19), *688*(19), *689*(9), *709*(23b), *710*(23b), *711*(3), *712*(3), *713*(10), *715*(23b), *728*(8), *730*(7), *731*(8), *733*(10), *734*(8), *735*(8), *736*(8), *738*(8), *739*(8), *740*(7), *742*(8), *745*(8), *751*(8), *752*(8), *795*(23b), *796*(6), *797*(23b), *808*(23b), *817*(10), *819*(17), *820*(11), *821*(23b), *827*(9), *828*(3), *829*(9), *830*(3), *843*(18), *844*(18), *847*(18), *848*(8), *876*(11), *877*(23b), *934*(3), *935*(18), *936*(18), *937*(1a), *938*(1b), *939*(3), *945*(3), *946*(11), *947*(3), *967*(11), *968*(11), *969*(16), *970*(8), *971*(11), *972*(3), *973*(16), *974*(16), *975*(11), *976*(3), *977*(11), *978*(8), *979*(3), *980*(11), *981*(16), *982*(11), *983*(8), *984*(11), *985*(16), *986*(11), *988*(3), *989*(8), *1011*(10), *1052*(10), *1055*(9), *1056*(23b), *1057*(9), *1058*(9), *1080*(11), *1082*(17), *1087*(10), *1089*(10), *1096*(23b), *1097*(23b), *1140*(22), *1141*(22), *1142*(22), *1143*(3), *1144*(18), *1188*(3), *1250*(22), *FP 98857*(11), *FP 89958*(11), *FP 89992*(11), *FP 98511*(23b).

Hawksworth & Bailey *1008*(9), *1009*(3), *1010*(3).

Hawksworth & Baranyay *90*(3), *91*(3), *92*(3).

Hawksworth & Gilbertson *1083*(17).

Hawksworth & Gill *194*(9), *195*(9), *198*(9).

Hawksworth & Hawksworth *1146*(7), *1147*(7).

Hawksworth & Hinds *197*(9), *422*(23b), *423*(23b), *425*(11), *426*(23b), *990*(1a), *991*(22), *992*(22), *993*(3), *994*(7), *996*(8), *995*(8), *997*(11), *998*(1a), *999*(1a), *1000*(1b), *1001*(8), *1002*(1a), *1004*(3), *1005*(3), *1007*(3), *1077*(10), *1118*(3), *1119*(3), *1120*(3), *1121*(3), *1122*(11), *1123*(11), *1124*(3).

Hawksworth & Landgraf *279*(9).

Hawksworth & Laut *1161*(11), *1164*(10), *1179*(23b), *1180*(23b).

Hawksworth & Lightle *101*(10), *103*(23b), *104*(23b), *105*(4), *107*(4), *109*(4), *106*(11), *108*(23b), *113*(23b), *119*(23b), *120*(11), *121*(4), *125*(10), *126*(23b), *127*(11), *131*(11), *132*(23b), *133*(10), *136*(23b), *140a*(23b), *140b*(23b), *142*(11), *146*(23b), *152*(11), *153*(12a), *154*(23b), *155*(23b), *156*(4), *157*(12a), *159*(12a), *161*(12a), *164*(12a), *165*(23b), *166*(11), *167*(4), *168*(23b), *169*(23b), *171*(23b), *172*(23b), *177*(23b), *183*(11), *184*(1a), *185*(23b), *187*(10), *188*(23b, *207*(17), *208*(10), *209*(11), *210*(4), *211*(23b), *212*(4), *213*(11), *216*(11), *217*(11), *218*(11), *219*(17), *220*(4), *221*(23b), *224*(17), *225*(17), *226*(11), *227*(23b), *228*(4), *233*(23b), *235*(6), *236*(12a), *239*(11), *243*(23b), *245*(10), *247*(9), *249*(17), *250*(11), *251*(11), *442*(11), *878*(11), *879*(23b), *880*(11), *884*(23b), *885*(23b), *886*(11), *889*(10), *890*(23b), *891*(4), *893*(23b), *894*(23b), *895*(23b), *896*(23b), *897*(17), *898*(11), *899*(10), *900*(17), *901*(23b), *902*(11), *903*(23b), *904*(10), *905*(10), *906*(10), *912*(23b), *913*(11), *914*(23b), *915*(10), *916*(10), *917*(23b), *918*(11), *919*(23b), *920*(11), *921*(23b), *922*(10), *923*(23b), *924*(11), *925*(17), *926*(10), *927*(10), *929*(4), *930*(23b), *1051*(23b), *1078*(10), *1079*(11), *1084*(10), *1098*(4), *1099*(11), *1102*(4), *1103*(23b), *1105*(4), *1107*(4), *1109*(6), *1111*(12a), *1114*(10), *1115*(23b), *1116* (23b), *1117*(4), *1168*(10).

Hawksworth & Scharpf *661*(8), *662*(1a), *663*(1b), *664*(3), *665*(22), *666*(22), *667*(1a), *668*(8), *670*(3), *671*(9), *672*(10), *674*(1a), *675*(8), *676*(1a), *690*(23b), *691*(10), *692*(10), *694*(11), *695*(23b), *696*(4), *697*(11), *698*(23b), *699*(11), *700*(17), *701*(10), *702*(1a), *703*(10), *705*(12a), *765*(8), *767*(8), *783*(8), *786*(10), *789*(8), *849*(18), *850*(22), *854*(18), *855*(1a), *856*(18), *857*(18), *1148*(18), *1149*(18), *1150*(18), *1151*(18), *1152*(18), *1153*(18), *1158*(18), *1159*(18), *1252*(22), *1255*(22), *1256*(22), *1257*(1a), *1261*(3), *1262*(16), *1264*(11), *1265*(8), *1268*(11), *1269*(3), *1270*(16), *1271*(8), *1272*(11), *1273*(16).

Hawksworth & Staley *280*(23b), *287*(23b), *288*(9).

Hawksworth & Stewart *832*(23b).

Hawksworth & Wicker *949*(3), *950*(3), *951*(3), *952*(3), *953*(11), *954*(3), *955*(16), *956*(16), *957*(16), *958*(16), *959*(16), *960*(16), *961*(16), *962*(16), *963*(16), *964*(16), *965*(16), *966*(8), *1126*(3), *1127*(3).

Hawksworth & Wiens *283*(3), *292*(12a), *293*(12a), *294*(12a), *295*(23a), *296*(6), *297*(12a), *298*(22a), *307*(12a), *308*(23a), *310*(23a), *311*(23a), *313*(23a), *314*(6), *329*(21), *331*(24), *334*(12b), *336*(12b), *337*(12b), *338*(20), *339*(20), *340*(20), *341*(24), *342*(24), *343*(12b), *345*(20), *346*(20), *348*(23a), *349*(13), *350*(6), *351*(13), *353*(23c), *354*(23c), *361*(13), *367*(13), *368*(13), *369*(13), *370*(23a), *371*(13), *374*(23a), *378*(23a), *380*(23a), *382*(12b), *385*(12b), *386*(12b), *391*(23a), *392*(6), *393*(23a), *394*(2), *395*(11), *396*(2), *397*(23a), *398*(23a), *454*(23b), *460*(12a), *461*(23b), *462*(23b), *464*(23b), *466*(13), *471*(23b), *474*(12a), *475*(6), *476*(23b), *479*(23b), *480*(23b), *481*(12a), *484*(12a), *483*(12a), *485*(23b), *486*(23a), *487*(12a), *491*(23a), *492*(23b), *493*(6), *494*(23a), *497*(12a), *499*(12a), *500*(21), *505*(21), *506*(21), *507*(23a), *508*(12b), *509*(12b), *510*(12b), *511*(20), *512*(20), *513*(20), *514*(11), *515*(23a), *516*(6), *517*(24), *518*(21), *519*(12b), *520*(12b), *521*(20), *524*(13), *525*(12b), *526*(13), *527*(23c), *530*(6),

Hawksworth & Wiens (continued)
531(23a), *533*(12b), *534*(12b), *535*(12b), *536*(6), *565*(9), *575*(9), *576*(11), *577*(8), *578*(16), *579*(16), *580*(8), *581*(3), *582*(16), *583*(8), *584*(11), *585*(16), *586*(3), *587*(11), *588*(16), *589*(16), *590*(11), *591*(3), *592*(1a), *593*(11), *594*(8), *595*(8), *596*(11), *597*(16), *598*(16), *599*(3), *600*(16), *601*(22), *602*(22), *603*(16), *604*(22), *605*(22), *606*(22), *607*(22), *608*(22), *609*(16), *610*(11), *611*(8), *612*(3), *613*(1a), *614*(3), *615*(1a), *616*(11), *617*(8), *618*(3), *619*(8), *620*(3), *621*(22), *622*(22), *623*(3), *624*(22), *625*(22), *626*(1a), *627*(8), *628*(11), *629*(1a), *631*(1a), *632*(1a), *633*(8), *634*(11), *635*(1a), *636*(11), *637*(1a), *639*(11), *641*(1a), *642*(9), *643*(1a), *644*(7), *645*(11), *646*(8), *648*(1a), *649*(8), *650*(1b), *651*(3), *652*(22), *654*(7), *655*(8), *656*(8), *657*(3), *833*(10), *835*(10), *836*(8), *838*(3), *839*(3), *840*(8), *841*(18), *842*(8), *858*(8), *859*(18), *860*(8), *861*(8), *862*(7), *863*(8), *865*(8), *866*(8), *867*(8), *868*(11), *869*(8), *870*(11), *871*(3), *872*(8), *873*(8), *874*(1a), *875*(8), *1193*(5), *1199*(5), *1209*(15), *1219*(13), *1221*(14), *1222*(14), *1223*(13), *1226*(14), *1229*(2), *1234*(23c), *1237*(23c), *1242*(21), *1244*(12b), *1245*(23a), *1246*(13), *1248*(20), *3339*(2), *3359*(2), *3404*(12b), *3414*(13), *3465*(21), *3490*(20), *3507*(23c).

Hawksworth, Andrews & Buchanan *80*(3).

Hawksworth, Hinds & Staley *281*(23b).

Hawksworth, Lightle & Gilbertson *1110*(4).

Hawksworth, Lightle & Lampi *1046*(23b), *1050*(10).

Hawksworth, Lightle & Laut *1165*(10), *1171*(10), *1174*(10).

Hawksworth, Lightle & Muñoz *1023*(23b), *1024*(23b), *1026*(23b), *1027*(11), *1032*(4).

Hawksworth, Stewart & Thompson *1128*(3), *1129*(16), *1130*(16), *1131*(3), *1132*(11), *1133*(16), *1134*(16), *1135*(11), *1136*(11), *1137*(11), *1138*(22), *1139*(22).

Hawksworth, Wiens & Molina *1203*(15).

Hedgcock FP *172*(11), FP *185*(11), FP *624*(3), FP *635*(9), FP *650*(11), FP *670*(23b), FP *813*(23b), FP *879*(3), FP *888*(3), FP *903*(23b), FP *905*(11), FP *988*(11), FP *997*(16), FP *998*(8), FP *1538*(11), FP *1539*(11), FP *1614*(9), FP *1649*(3), FP *1858*(1a), FP *1873*(8), FP *1897*(8), FP *1908*(3), FP *1909*(8), FP *4338*(3), FP *4457*(11), FP *4556*(11), FP *4765*(22), FP *4835*(8), FP *4837*(18), FP *4854*(23b), FP *4855*(23b), FP *4871*(11), FP *4907*(10), FP *4917*(10), FP *8126*(11), FP *8135*(10), FP *8139*(10), FP *8142*(10), FP *8640*(19), FP *9174*(23b), FP *9175*(23b), FP *9299*(10), FP *9339*(3), FP *9519*(11), FP *9526*(16), FP *9782*(4), FP *9899*(11), FP *11147*(9), FP *15834*(3), FP *15848*(3), FP *15849*(3), FP *15898*(23b), FP *15900*(11), FP *15909*(9), FP *15915*(11), FP *15965*(3), FP *19185*(9), FP *22549*(3), FP *22550*(23b), FP *22571*(23b), FP *22592*(3), FP *22598*(3), FP *22599*(23b), FP *22704*(23b), FP *22705*(23b), FP *22706*(9), FP *22707*(9), FP *22710*(23b), FP *22711*(23b), FP *22718*(3), FP *22719*(3), FP *24909*(23b), FP *47157*(3), FP *47529*(3), FP *47756*(3), FP *48627*(8), FP *49442*(8), FP *49544*(3), FP *54116*(3), FP *54990*(8), FP *54991*(8), FP *59245*(3), FP *67206*(3), FP *68059*(8), FP *93222*(11).

Hedgcock & Bethel FP *24413*(23b), FP *24639*(11), FP *24654*(11), FP *24656*(23b), FP *24688*(23b), FP *24689*(11), FP *24712*(23b), FP *24730*(10), FP *29454*(23b).

Hedgcock & Freeman FP *4145*(19).

Hedgcock & Johnston FP *24944*(23b), FP *24945*(11), FP *26406*(23b), FP *26425*(3), FP *26068*(3), FP *26433*(3).

Hedgcock & Long FP *9759*(23b), FP *9781*(23b), FP *9835*(23b), FP *9847*(11), FP *9936*(10).

Hedgcock & Meinecke FP *4788*(8), FP *4789*(8), FP *4822*(7), FP *4823*(1a), FP *4827*(7), FP *4833*(7), FP *4834*(1a), FP *4836*(8), FP *4838*(7).

Hedgcock & Pierce FP *15951*(23b).

Hedgcock & Thompson FP *24809*(23b).

Hedgcock & Weir FP *9442*(16), FP *9443*(3), FP *9444*(16), FP *9489*(3).

Hedgcock, Meinecke & Long FP *9668*(8), FP *9669*(11).

Hedgcock, Payson & Johnston FP *24852*(9).

Hedgcock, Thompson & Gayman FP *24755*(23b), FP *24901*(11), FP *24902*(23b).

Hedgcock, Thompson & Johnson FP *24828*(23b).

Hedrick FP *41*(10), FP *286*(10).

Heiser *848*(23b).

Heller *925*(8), *3608*(23b), *6776*(18), *10660*(8), *11060*(1a), *11144*(18).

Heller & Heller *3527*(11), *3533*(10).

Henderson *527*(8), *2535*(16), *2539*(3), *3581*(3), *11501*(3), *14130*(8).

Hendrix *616*(9).

Henry *1822*(22), *1881*(22).

Hicks *110*(18).

Hill FP *68236*(3), FP *68276*(9), FP *68277*(23b), FP *68278*(23b), FP *68279*(3), FP *68280*(11).

Hinckley *2650*(23b), *3163*(10).

Hinds *63-2*(11), *63-3*(23b), *63-4*(11), *63-5*(23b), *63-6*(11), *63-8*(23b), *63-10*(10), *63-11*(23b), *63-12*(11), *63-13*(3), *63-14*(10), *63-15*(11), *63-16*(23b), *63-17*(10), *63-19*(23b), *63-21*(3).

Hinton *3278*(2), *8901*(13).

Hitchcock *25*(10), *559*(1a).

Hitchcock & Martin *7423*(3).

Holdrige *1328*(5).

Holmgren *3748*(10).

Hoover *3610*(18), *6448*(18).

Hopkins *426*(3).

Hopping *391*(8), FP *97939*(22).

House *7186*(19).

Howard & Howard *8129*(5), *9125*(5).

Howe & Lang *1141*(19).

Howell *386A*(8), *929*(8), *2459*(1a), *5618*(18), *8135*(18), *15674*(1a), *19686*(18), *22902*(1b), *24505*(10), *27038*(3), *30162*(18), *33147*(18), *34093*(8), *34204*(8), *37436*(18), *38710*(18), *38805*(7), *38824*(8), *38844*(1b), *41197*(18).

Howell & Barneby *29387*(18).

Howell & Eastwood *7204*(9).

Hubert FP *91292*(8).

Hunt *286*(13), FP *25071*(8), FP *97958*(18).

Hunt & Bethel FP *24428*(10), FP *24429*(11).

Hurtt FP *20583*(11).

Iltis *17558*(19).

Iltis, Iltis & Flores *1701*(13).

Iltis, Iltis & Turner *22225*(19).

Jack *3225*(19), *3468*(19), *3473*(19), *3759*(19).

Jaenicke FP *21285*(1a).

Jiminez *1069*(5).

Johnson *1420*(18), FP *15106*(10), FP *18638*(23b).

Johnston *1688*(7), *1720*(8), *1777*(13), *3185*(23b).

Johnston & Mueller *591*(23b).

Johnston & Thompson FP *24881*(3), FP *24883*(9).

Jones *487*(23a), *801*(23b), *3439*(22), *3973*(10), *4299*(22), *5076*(3), *5372*(3), *5395*(11), *5911c*(11), *9307*(11), *9309*(16), *9312*(16), *9313*(16), *9380*(11), *23161*(23b).

Kearney & Peebles *9971*(17), *12724*(23b), *13761*(10), *14135*(17).
Kiener *5686*(3).
Kildare *2634*(1a), *8785*(8), *10484*(8).
Killip *7816*(19).
King & Soderstrom *5174*(13).
Kirby *FP 12673*(23b).
Kirby & Long *FP 18735*(23b).
Knowlton *40*(11), *295*(10), *23525*(19).
Korstian *FP 19276*(11).
Krebill *126*(11), *127*(3), *133*(16), *136*(16), *147*(16), *154*(8), *159*(11), *235*(23b), *244*(8), *247*(7), *453*(11), *288*(11), *453*(11), *454*(9), *538*(3).
Krebill & Nelson *467*(10), *468*(3).
Kuijt *528*(3), *535*(3), *536*(3), *544*(16), *546*(16), *547*(16), *553*(16), *556*(16), *563*(16), *566*(16), *581*(11), *588*(11), *589*(3), *591*(3), *592*(3), *598*(3), *602*(22), *618*(22), *650*(11), *1208*(18), *1213*(18), *1214*(18), *1215*(18), *1216*(1a), *1253*(18), *1254*(18), *1257*(18), *1272*(1a), *1274*(18), *1277*(8), *1300*(18), *1310*(18), *1313*(18), *1330*(3), *1331*(3), *1332*(3), *1333*(8), *1335*(3), *1337*(8), *1339*(8), *1340*(1a), *1341*(1a), *1343*(3), *1344*(3), *1345*(8), *1346*(8), *1347*(8), *1348*(8), *1350*(3), *1352*(3), *1354*(3), *1355*(3), *1356*(8), *1357*(8), *1358*(3), *1361*(18), *1362*(18), *1365*(1a), *1366*(19), *1367*(11), *1369*(1a), *1374*(18), *1389*(10), *1390*(3), *1393*(1a), *1394*(7), *1401*(18), *1407*(8), *1410*(18), *1411*(3), *1412*(3), *1413*(10), *1415*(9), *1423*(8), *1425a*(18), *1427*(18), *1428*(8), *1431*(1a), *1432*(8), *1437*(18), *1444*(18), *1471*(8), *1497*(8), *1501*(3), *1502*(7), *1503*(1a), *1506*(18), *1513*(3).
Lachmund & Childs *FP 68269*(22).
Lakela *4503*(19), *7912*(19), *18527*(19).
Langman *3713*(13).
Leavenworth *710*(13).
Leavenworth & Hoogstraal *1126*(13).
Lee & Mason *9153*(18).
Leiberg *520*(3), *5884*(9).
Leonard *4690*(5).
Lieberg *1672*(16), *3312*(10), *5363*(22).
Lightle *63-1*(23b), *63-2*(11), *63-4*(23b), *63-6*(10), *63-7*(11), *63-8*(11), *63-9*(23b), *63-11*(10), *63-13a*(23b), *63-13b*(10), *63-16*(10), *63-18*(10), *63-21*(23b), *63-22*(11), *63-23*(11), *63-24*(11), *63-25*(23b), *63-27*(23b), *63-29*(10), *63-31*(11), *63-32*(23b), *63-34*(11), *63-36*(10), *63-37*(23b), *63-38*(23b), *63-39*(11), *63-41*(10), *63-45*(23b), *63-54*(23b), *63-55*(11), *64-1*(11), *64-2*(23b), *64-7*(23b) *64-8*(23b), *64-9*(10), *64-11*(10), *64-12*(10), *64-13*(23b), *64-14*(11), *64-15*(23b), *64-16*(11), 64-17(23b), 64-19(10), 64-20(17), 64-21(4), 64-22(23b), *64-30*(10), *64-31*(23b), *64-32*(23b), *65-1*(10), *65-4*(10), *65-5*(10), *65-6*(10), *65-7*(11), *65-20*(10), *65-21*(11), *65-22*(23b), *65-23*(11), *65-26*(12a), *65-28*(11), *65-30*(10), *65-31*(11), *65-32*(23b) *65-33*(10), *65-34*(11), *65-35*(23b), *65-36*(4), *65-37*(23b), *65-38*(10), *65-39*(11), *65-40*(4), *65-41*(10), *65-42*(23b), *65-43*(11), *65-44*(10), *65-45*(10), *65-46*(11), *65-47*(23b) *65-48*(11), *65-49*(11), *65-50*(10), *65-51*(23b), *65-53*(23b), *65-55*(23b), *66-19*(4), *66-20*(11), *66-21*(23b), *66-22*(10).
Lightle & Gill *64-34*(10), *64-35*(8), *65-24*(11), *65-25*(11).
Lightle & Lampi *64-15*(11), *65-14*(23b), *65-16*(23b).
Lightle & Riffle *63-42*(23b), *63-43*(11), *63-56*(23b).
Lightle & Schacht *63-26*(11).
Lightle & Weiss *66-41*(10), *66-42*(23b), *66-43*(11), *66-44*(23b), *66-45*(10), *66-47*(10), *66-48*(11), *66-49*(23b), *66-50*(11), *66-51*(23b), *66-52*(10), *69-4*(10).

Lightle, Ela & Lampi *65-54*(10).
Linsdale & Linsdale *264*(10).
Little & Correll *19033*(10).
Loll *FP 11832*(9).
Loomis, Peebles & Harrison *2179*(23b).
Long *FP 318*(12a), *FP 19340*(11), *FP 19634*(10), *FP 19724*(23b), *FP 21126*(11), *FP 21128*(4), *FP 21671*(17).
Long & Fernald *21042*(19).
Long and Seay *FP 21275*(11).
Lory *FP 97940*(22).
Loughridge *273*(23b).
Löve & Löve *5740*(3).
Ludlow, Sherriff & Taylor *4465*(28).
Macbride *2677*(9).
Macbride & Payson *3270*(3), *3654*(3).
MacDougal *23*(23b), *190*(10).
McKelvey *1464*(10).
Mackenzie *78*(3).
McMillan *197*(10).
Macoun *79522*(11).
McVaugh *8156*(23b), *9781*(19), *9952*(13), *10071*(23a), *11518*(13), *12916*(23a).
McVaugh & Wilber *10130*(2).
Maguire *12138*(23b).
Maguire & Becraft *2535a*(10).
Maguire & Maguire *20377*(9), *20378*(9).
Malte *731/29*(19).
Marie-Victorin *28456*(19).
Marshall *809*(19).
Martin *883*(23b), *902*(4).
Mason *525*(18), *1079*(3), *2590*(8), *3987*(18), *4285*(18), *4748*(10), *5515*(18), *5639*(18), *5888*(18), *7168*(18).
Mason, Mason & Phillips *2422*(23b), *2422a*(23b).
Mathias *652*(10).
Matthews *2663*(19).
Matuda *4408*(13), *4601*(13), *4630*(13).
Maysilles *7260*(13), *7977*(13).
Mearns *4513*(3).
Meinecke *FP 9059*(18), *FP 10754*(1a), *FP 17026*(18), *FP 17053*(3), *FP 17062*(7), *FP 17100*(8), *FP 20151*(7), *FP 20152*(8), *FP 97934*(3), *FP 97938*(22), *FP 97941*(22), *FP 97947*(18), *FP 97948*(8).
Meinecke & Boyce *FP 17193*(1a), *FP 17194*(1a), *FP 17196*(8).
Metcalfe *288*(10), *493*(17), *964*(23b), *1173*(4).
Meyer *688*(8), *1685*(22).
Meyer & Rogers *2932*(23a).
Mielke *FP 40694*(22), *FP 58275*(22).
Mielke & Ellis *FP 89694*(11).
Mielke & Zentemyer *FP 89238*(9).
Milburge *253*(8), *1328*(8).
Miles *FP 15108*(8).
Miller *FP 68024*(10), *FP 97956*(1b), *FP 98023*(9), *FP 98034*(7), *FP 98112*(1b).
Milner *7250a*(23b).
Miranda *114*(23a), *872*(13).
Mitchell *FP 68212*(8).
Moberg & Gill *FP 68299*(11).
Molina, Burgur & Wallenta *16483*(13).
Moore *143*(19), *634*(19).
Moore & Steyermark *3470*(23b).
Morf *64-86*(3).
Morton *2063*(19).
Mueller & Mueller *1013*(23a).

Muenscher *10431*(22).

Muenscher & Muenscher *14562*(23b).

Muir *64-327*(3).

Munns *FP 9440*(8).

Munro *FP 15114*(23b).

Munz *4423*(18), *6260*(8), *8350*(8), *10566*(8), *10771*(10), *15220*(3), *21347*(8).

Munz & Johnston *8576*(1a), *8705*(8).

Murdoch *2010*(19), *5301*(19).

Nelson *845*(3), *866*(8), *3205*(23b), *3320*(9), *4887*(12a), *4959*(9), *6077*(23a), *6730*(23a), *8247*(9).

Nelson & Nelson *2697*(10), *5515*(3), *6833*(3).

Newcomb *156*(1a), *165*(8).

Newlon *856*(23b).

Ninman & Thompson *FP 38713*(19).

O'Bryne & Long *FP 18678*(10).

Offord *FP 98091*(18).

Olday *240*(19).

Oleson *328*(3).

Osterhout *2523*(3).

Otis *1011*(8), *1021*(8), *1036*(22).

Overbay *FP 68281*(8), *FP 68282*(3).

Owenby *875*(3).

Owenby & Brown *2428*(8).

Owenbey & Owenbey *2032*(3).

Palmer *2*(10), *774*(21), *33429*(23b).

Parish & Parish *966*(8), *1442*(10).

Parker *2085*(26).

Parker & McClintock *7587*(11).

Parks *FP 18385*(23b).

Parks & Long *FP 18383*(23b).

Parks & Parks *24063*(8).

Parks & Tracy *11533*(1b).

Parry *86*(11), *574*(3), *10659*(11).

Patterson *297*(3).

Payson *396*(23b), *FP 26016*(10), *FP 26022*(23b), *FP 26026*(11).

Payson & Armstrong *3406*(9).

Pease *400*(19), *3258*(19), *19055*(19), *20948*(19), *32509*(19).

Peck *9525*(1b), *9594*(3), *14322*(3), *21639*(3).

Peebles *12981*(23b).

Peebles & Smith *13264*(23b).

Peebles, Harrison & Peebles *2565*(12a).

Peirson *1720*(3), *1721*(8), *2322*(8), *2818*(7), *3251*(10), *4302*(18). *10136*(3).

Peterson *19-61*(23b), *30-61*(10), *37-61*(1a), *39-61*(1a), *43-61*(17), *45-61*(11), *49-61*(23b), *51-61*(11), *52-61*(9), *125-61*(3), *62-4*(3), *62-5*(3), *62-10*(3), *62-11*(11), *62-12*(11), *62-14*(3), *62-16*(11), *62-17*(3), *62-18*(3), *62-28*(11), *62-47*(3), *62-49*(8), *62-50*(11), *62-51*(3), *62-53*(9), *62-60*(3), *62-64*(11), *62-67*(11), *62-75*(9), *62-107*(10), *62-111*(11), *62-145*(4), *62-148*(12a), *62-165*(17), *63-87*(11), *63-129*(3), *63-131*(10), *63-134*(3), *63-136*(18), *63-139*(1a), *63-149*(3), *63-156*(18), *63-166*(8), *63-224*(8), *63-225*(8), *63-236*(16), *63-295*(5), *63-315*(8), *63-327*(10), *63-329*(10), *63-337*(11), *63-338*(10), *63-361*(3), *63-364*(11), *64-63*(11), *64-64*(11), *64-72*(23b), *64-83*(11), *64-87*(10), *64-92*(11), *64-93*(23b), *64-96*(23b), *64-100*(8), *64-144*(8), *64-217*(11), *65-69*(10), *65-74*(23b), *65-76*(11), *65-83*(23b), *65-88*(3), *65-89*(3), *65-90*(3), *65-116*(18), *65-339*(9), *65-370*(9), *65-395*(8), *65-403*(8), *68-91*(2), *68-105*(13), *68-106*(23a).

Petty *64-568*(3).

Pickle *57-15*(8).

Piper *663*(22), *1882*(16), *3701*(3).

Pohl *1145*(19).

Pond *FP 193*(8).

Pool *FP 20552*(23b).

Porter *8756*(3).

Pringle *4368*(23a), *4727*(13), *13876*(12a).

Proctor *10771*(5), *10772*(5).

Purpus *1778*(13), *3836*(23a), *6491*(2).

Putnam *FP 98054*(10).

Quibell *280*(8), *1658a*(18).

Quibell & Quibell *2641*(3).

Quick *53-27*(1a), *53-32*(7), *53-141*(18), *54-87*(1b), *60-21*(1a).

Ramaley *824*(23b), *1333*(23b), *3754*(3).

Ramaley & Robbins *1784*(23b).

Raue *50*(23b).

Raven *3678*(3), *3928*(18), *8349*(3), *10456*(3), *16874*(8).

Ray *1565*(18).

Reed *1831*(3)

Reed & Barkley *4381*(23b).

Riley *47-208*(3).

Robbins *1403*(18).

Rodin *877*(3), *5695*(26).

Rogers *6089*(23b).

Rolland-Germain *220*(19), *361*(19), *3061*(19), *7512*(19).

Roos *1028*(10), *1240*(8).

Ross *1917*(1a).

Root & Goodding *FP 68274*(1b), *FP 68275*(9).

Rose *3460*(23a), *3535*(23a), *60113*(8).

Rose & Fitch *17765*(10).

Rosendahl *826*(22), *1958*(22), *4450*(19).

Rosendahl & Brandegee *136*(22).

Rosendahl & Butters *1092*(22).

Rossback *236*(18), *237*(8).

Rothrock *69*(11), *213*(8), *429*(18).

Rouleau *612*(19).

Rydberg & Bessey *3938*(3).

Rydberg & Carlton *7371*(10).

Rydberg & Garrett *8542*(10), *9328*(23b), *9864*(11).

St. John *3051*(8), *6359*(16), *6936*(11).

St. John & Nichols *2281*(19).

Sandberg, MacDougal & Heller *744*(11), *787*(16), *892*(3).

Sampson & Pearson *21*(3), *168*(16).

Sandberg *925*(8), *9358*(3).

Sandberg & Leiberg *593*(8), *4443*(11).

Scharpf *FP 38026*(8), *FP 38027*(22), *FP 98107*(1b), *FP 98114*(8).

Schlising *124*(19).

Schmoll *498*(3).

Schneider *2951*(25).

Schoenfeldt *3600*(8).

Schreiber *776*(3), *853*(18), *891*(1a), *1017*(10), *1948*(3).

Schwartz *FP 68288*(19).

Seay *FP 33403*(3).

Seemann *2138*(24).

Seler *2190*(13).

Seymour *11906*(19), *14645*(19), *15104*(19).

Sharsmith *1406a & b*(18), *3848b*(18).

Shear *3764*(3).

Shear & Bessey *5317*(3).

Sheldon *439*(19), *8845*(8).

Shreve *5239*(23b).

Sloan *FP 97943*(8).

Smith *955*(18).

Snell *1047*(9).

Solbrig *2420*(3).

Spaulding *FP 303*(10), *FP 15107*(11), *FP 34543*(19), *FP 41633*(22).

Spaulding & Eno *FP 68312*(19).

Spenser *1018*(8).

Standley *4173*(23b), *7664*(11), *7810*(10), *7979*(10), *16335*(3), *81637*(13), *81642*(13), *81683*(13).

Stanford *629*(3).

Stanford, Tauber & Taylor *2495*(23a).

Steward *6605*(3).

Steward & Jackman *6499*(11).

Steward & Sowder *6803*(8).

Steward & Steward *7328*(16), *7471*(3).

Stewart *7549*(26), *21297*(26).

Stewart & Rahman *25213*(26).

Stewart & Stewart *7329*(11).

Steyermark *29788*(13), *36940*(13), *42524*(13), *49044*(13), *50130*(13).

Stone *201*(12a).

Stouffer *FP 68239*(11).

Stouffer & Gill *FP 68291*(17), *FP 68292*(4), *FP 68293*(4).

Stoutamire *3013*(19).

Straw & Forman *1777*(20).

Sueur *599*(12a).

Suksdorf *1364*(8), *2246*(1a).

Summers *926*(18).

Taylor *182*(23a), *FP 18641*(23b).

Thomas *5519*(18), *10262*(8).

Thompson *L-1128*(19), *9422*(22), *13844*(11), *15105*(3).

Thomson *FP 26558*(23b).

Thornber & Hockdoerffer *2944*(11).

Thorne *19860*(19).

Tidestrom *1300*(10).

Toko & Pinnay *65-34*(16).

Toumey *8*(23b), *292*(23b).

Tracy *1060*(1a), *2355*(8), *6912*(18), *8950*(1b), *10571*(1b), *16464*(8).

Tracy, Earle & Baker *388*(10).

Train *2150*(9), *2154*(1a), *2521*(10).

Tucker *2563*(23b), *3444*(18).

Tweedy *449*(3), *595*(10), *4973*(23b).

Twisselmann *8681*(8), *8832*(18).

Umbach *594*(3).

Valdivia & Soloranzo *633*(13), *634*(13), *637*(13), *646*(13), *648*(13), *649*(13), *650*(13).

Vickery *616*(23b).

von Turckheim *II 1815*(13), *3241*(5).

Voss *1048*(19), *1539*(19), *2660*(19), *3935*(19), *4581*(19), *6986*(19), *7009*(19), *7854*(19), *8602*(19), *11870*(19), *12076*(19), *12239*(19), *12467*(19), *12696*(19), *12712*(19).

Wadmond *1271*(19).

Wagener *FP 89603*(10), *FP 89604*(10), *FP 97951*(18).

Walpole *234*(3), *323*(3), *417*(8).

Ward *51*(18), *595*(8).

Warnock & McVaugh *5452*(23b).

Waters *242*(3).

Watson *6762*(19).

Weatherby *1667*(7), *1674*(1b), *3906*(19).

Weatherby & Weatherby *5770*(19), *6685*(19).

Weber *1957*(3), *6065*(10), *6093*(3), *6725*(3).

Webster & Nasir *6471*(26).

Weir *659*(16), *2374*(3), *2376*(3), *2379*(3), *2382*(3), *2384*(3), *2387*(3), *2394*(19), *2400*(11), *2412*(11), *2415*(11), *2416*(11),

Weir(continued)
2418(11), *2419*(11), *2421*(16), *2423*(1a), *2425*(16), *2426*(1b), *2427*(1b), *2429*(1a), *2449*(22), *2452*(22), *2456*(22), *3185*(8), *3187*(8), *3189*(8), *3191*(7), *3193*(8), *3194*(8), *3200*(8), *3202*(8), *3206*(8), *3216*(9), *3218*(9), *3239*(7), *3240*(7), *3242*(22), *3246*(9), *3250*(16), *3252*(16), *3258*(16), *3267*(16), *3271*(16), *3288*(7), *6162*(11), *6163*(23b), *6838*(22), *7196*(16), *7426*(11), *7473*(3), *8243*(8), *8252*(8), *8254*(9), *8334*(16), *8336*(16), *8337*(16), *8345*(9), *8362*(16), *8363*(16), *8364*(16), *8365*(16), *8366*(16), *8371*(16), *8373*(16), *8374*(16), *8384*(16), *8385*(16), *8389*(3), *8390*(16), *8391*(16), *8392*(16), *8440*(3), *8442*(3), *8444*(3), *8456*(3), *8475*(8), *8958*(23b), *9780*(3), *9829*(3), *9868*(8), *9872*(9), *9874*(3), *9875*(3), *9986*(11), *9995*(11), *FP 17047*(8), *FP 17048*(16), *FP 29660*(8), *FP 91207*(11), *FP 91249*(9).

Wetherill *919/3149*(10).

Wheeler *242*(8), *330*(3), *1115*(8), *2783*(11), *3005*(1a), *4428*(18), *4452*(18).

Whited *3171*(3).

Whiting *854/2825*(10), *1053/5338*(11).

Whitney *1703*(1a), *1717*(3).

Wibbe *11532*(19).

Wickens *2199*(23b), *2403*(23b).

Wiegland *6344*(19).

Wiens *2335*(18), *2444*(8), *2574*(12b), *2705*(23b), *2728*(18), *2740*(10), *2741*(8), *2802*(23b), *2808*(7), *2926*(9), *2966*(3), *2983*(23b), *2984*(11), *2986*(23b), *2988*(23b), *2994*(11), *3029*(23b), *3032*(8), *3033*(1a), *3034*(9), *3035*(23b), *3036*(11), *3168*(10), *3171*(10), *3178*(9), *3179*(10), *3180*(1a), *3183*(17), *3185*(10), *3204*(1a), *3205*(8), *3207*(10), *3210*(1a), *3211*(8), *3212*(8), *3217*(10), *3218*(18), *3219*(18), *3220*(18), *3221*(18), *3222*(8), *3223*(1a), *3224*(18), *3226*(3), *3227*(8), *3228*(1a), *3229*(8), *3230*(7), *3231*(8), *3232*(1a), *3233*(1a), *3235*(22), *3236*(8), *3238*(7), *3239*(8), *3240*(22), *3241*(22), *3242*(22), *3243*(22), *3244*(1a), *3245*(8), *3246*(9), *3247*(22), *3248*(22), *3249*(22), *3251*(22), *3252*(22), *3253*(8), *3254*(22), *3255*(16), *3256*(16), *3257*(9), *3258*(9), *3260*(3), *3605*(18), *3606*(8), *3607*(8), *3609*(7), *3610*(1a), *3611*(7), *3612*(8), *3613*(1a), *3614*(3), *3615*(1b), *3616*(8), *3617*(9), *3618*(11), *3865*(9), *3865B*(11), *3913*(10), *4120*(11), *4121*(11), *4122*(1a), *4123*(23b), *4124*(9), *4125*(9), *4127*(9), *4127a*(11), *4127b*(8), *4128*(11), *4129*(11), *4168*(10).

Wiens & Wiens *4358*(26), *4359*(26).

Wiggins *2106*(8), *2725*(8), *2817*(8), *9322*(8).

Wiggins & Demoree *5018*(8).

Wight *47*(18).

Wilbur & Wilbur *1837*(13), *1982*(13).

Williams *897*(16), *2402*(3), *15964*(15).

Wilson & Wilson *3067*(19).

Wittrock *5097*(22).

Wolf *1342*(18), *2880*(23b).

Wolf & Rothrock *70*(3).

Wood, Clover & Voss *8118*(19).

Woodrow & Long *FP 18399*(23b).

Woolsey *FP 12566*(17).

Wootson *23*(3).

Wright *FP 68048*(3), *68050*(1b), *FP 68052*(1a), *FP 68054*(18), *FP 68107*(3), *FP 68109*(8), *FP 68111*(8), *FP 68114*(3), *FP 68115*(1a), *FP 68116*(1a), *FP 68117*(8), *FP 68119*(18), *FP 68123*(1b), *FP 91563*(8).

Wyman *FP 1838*(10), *FP 12815*(23b).

Young *63*(10).

Yu *1558*(25).

Zeller & Zeller *1194*(22).

☆ U.S. GOVERNMENT PRINTING OFFICE: 1972 O—412-429